MORE
Good
Boats

MORE Good Boats

ROGER C. TAYLOR

INTERNATIONAL MARINE PUBLISHING COMPANY
CAMDEN, MAINE

Copyright © 1979
by International Marine Publishing Company
Library of Congress Catalog Card Number 78-75111
International Standard Book Number 0-87742-111-0
Typeset by A & B Typesetters, Inc., Concord, New Hampshire
Printed and bound by The Alpine Press, South Braintree, Massachusetts

DEDICATION

To Good Shipmates
Especially to Priscilla,
Rog, Dean, Becca, and Stephen

Contents

Preface

As the title of this book indicates, its contents are similar to those of one called *Good Boats*. *Good Boats* appeared in 1977 and is, I am happy to say, still in print and "available at your local bookseller's." (You see what happens when authorship gets mixed up with publishership.)

At any rate, much of what I wrote in the Preface to *Good Boats* naturally would be appropriate to the Preface of *More Good Boats*, but I do have some other things that I want to say here too.

The purpose of this book is to share with you plans showing the designs for more good boats. I hope you will have as much fun studying them as I have. The 36 designs on these pages were published in the *National Fisherman* from mid-1975 through mid-1978.

Thank you, Dave Getchell and Steve Saft, for your willingness to continue this rather long series of design presentations in the *National Fisherman* and for your expert handling of the raw materials with which you have been presented. Thank you, Kathy Brandes, Bruce White, and Nan Kulikauskas, for putting the book together. And thank you, Pat Feener, for transforming dictation having an unduly high percentage of weird words into exceedingly clean typescript.

Thank you to the late David Q. Scott, friend and working companion of twenty years, for designing this book and jacket. David, an expert sailor and aviator, as well as a fine artist, was killed in the crash of a commercial aircraft in which he was a passenger, coming to Maine with this jacket design. His artwork survived, but the great talent that created it was snuffed out. David Scott crammed more accomplishment and fun into his 51 years than most of us will if we live to be a hundred. He left much by which to remember him. I miss him.

Thank you, all the designers whose work graces these pages. When you think of the seamanship, knowledge of boatbuilding, knowledge of hydrodynamics and aerodynamics, common sense, and artistry necessary for a man to have if he is to produce the design for a good boat—let alone the effort and perseverance required—it is a wonder that so very many designs for good boats exist. Perhaps sailors can repay their huge debt to the designers of good boats by sailing good boats. Be that as it may, I feel a great sense of gratitude toward the men who conceived and drew these designs.

It has never ceased to amaze me that there is actually a way in which I can share my dreams about boats with others, apparently of like mind. I have spent a lot of hours daydreaming over boat plans with no inkling that such expenditure of time was anything but solitary pleasure. That the tentative sharing of such reveries met with sufficient response to warrant a continuation of that sharing and even its inclusion between book covers still seems to me to be too good to be true. Thank you, dreamers about boats.

And thank you, knowledgeable readers, you who have commented about many of these designs and whose comments I have incorporated into this book to make it better than it otherwise would have been.

Since this book is subjective, I think you deserve a few words about my prejudices. To me, there are only two kinds of boats, good ones and lousy ones. My definitions of the two kinds are quite simple: A good boat is handsome, able, and seakindly. A lousy boat isn't.

A good design doesn't result in a good boat, however, unless the craft is built to a high standard. By this I mean primarily that she should be built strongly and that she should be built to last a long time if cared for. She should also be joined and finished to a standard appropriate to her type, whether she be a jewel-like little daysailer or a big, rugged expedition schooner.

Most of the designs that appeal to me have been built to in wood because they come from an era before boatbuilding was popular in such materials as steel, aluminum, fiberglass, or ferrocement. It is my opinion, though, that a good boat can be built out of any of these materials—as long as she is built to a high standard, and, of course, to a good design.

It is also my opinion that each of these boatbuilding materials has its own aesthetic attractions and distractions.

Let's compare these materials from the aesthetic point of view, assuming we are to build to a single good design in each material and that in each case we will use the same high standard of construction.

To me, fiberglass, steel, aluminum, ferrocement, and cold-molded wood share one set of broad aesthetic qualities, while plank-on-frame wood construction has a different set of aesthetic qualities.

For the sake of reasonable brevity, I am limiting this discussion to hulls only and won't get into decks, deckhouses, cockpits, interiors, or spars.

For the former group of materials, I would list on the positive side the following overriding aesthetic element: the hull is all of one piece. There is something about a perfectly smooth, seamless hull that has great appeal to me aesthetically. A sense of solidity, imperviousness, invulnerability, and watertightness all come through in the very look of such a hull.

On the minus side, these materials look lifeless and cold. Even wood, when it has been saturated with an abundance of material foreign to it, seems to me to be quite transformed, and if not made lifeless, it is at least seriously wounded.

For a hull built of wood in the old-fashioned manner, there is, it seems to me, one great aesthetic appeal: the boat has a natural, lifelike quality. The very fabric of her hull seems to give her personality, even soul. And there are aesthetically positive by-products. Her frames, where visible, help show off her handsome shape. And if she happens to be planked lapstrake, the outlines of the strakes are most pleasing to the eye.

There is another subtle aesthetic appeal to the plank-on-frame wooden boat, I think. It is that the skill evident in her construction can be easily admired and identified with. Somehow the spirit of her builder often seems to be on board.

On the negative aesthetic side of old-fashioned wood construction are the seams. In a well-built carvel hull, they will hardly be obvious, but they can usually be detected, one knows that they are there, and they are a vulnerability. They might leak. They detract, slightly, from visual perfection.

So I end up at an aesthetic stand-off as regards the material from which the hull of a good boat might be built. On the one hand, I lean toward the warm humanness of traditional wood; on the other hand, I lean toward the smooth, one-piece perfection of the modern materials.

I wasn't always so objective about boatbuilding materials. The overcoming of my boatbuilding prejudices, however, does not really worry me, for I know there is really no way that my prejudices with regard to boat design can be changed, much less done away with. I am not about to be convinced that an ugly, unseaworthy boat is a good boat.

Nowadays boat design is influenced by requirements associated with the mass production of boats. Boat factories need designs that will prove popular, that will sell well to a generation that for the most part is newly come to the water. This requirement means that today boat design must adhere to style, that mysterious element in the design of an object that has more to do with newness, advertisability, and fads than with utility, safety, and comfort.

It really wouldn't matter except that the new generation of sailors getting started on the water may never have sailed in a good boat and never have experienced the look and feel of a pretty boat with a steady helm, seamanlike sails and gear, and a pleasant motion. It is my fervent hope that publicizing good boats will help sailors, designers, and builders to see their merits and persuade them to create similar craft, or even vessels to the specific designs in this book.

Let's have more good boats.

Roger C. Taylor
Camden, Maine

Prologue

The Great Duck Island Cribbage Cruise

In the late summer of 1940, when I was almost nine, it was decreed by my father that I was old enough to be his only crew on a cruise in our 32-foot Crocker yawl, the *Brownie*. (This vessel was described in *Good Boats.*)

Pop decided to go to the westward from our home mooring in the Pawcatuck River.

We got underway betimes, and a leading southerly breeze took us down the River, across Little Narragansett Bay, through Fisher's Island Sound, and along past Bartlett's Reef and the mouth of the Connecticut River without undue delay. Pop said he thought a good place to anchor for the night on our way up Long Island Sound would be Duck Island.

It's a tiny little speck of real estate a half dozen miles west of the Connecticut River, plunked down a mile off a bight in the Connecticut shore. The body of water—if it can be called that—between Duck Island and the shore is grandly called Duck Island Roads.

A harbor of refuge is made at Duck Island by two breakwaters, one extending north from the island and the other extending west to form an *L* with its open hypotenuse facing the land.

We headed in and brought up to an anchor well inside the *L*. Pop didn't think much of the place. He turned up his nose at the tiny, uninteresting island and made one of his faces at the low Connecticut shore a mile away, probably thinking about the fetch a northwester would have from that shore to the drab anchorage. He promised better things when we went on to the westward during the next few days, places like the Thimble Islands ("just like the coast of Maine") and Huntington ("wait'll you see the boats in there").

I thought Duck Island was a great place. To me, it was like being in a harbor but like still being at sea. The simple bleakness of the place somehow appealed to me.

The next morning we awoke to the patter of steady rain hitting the deck. It was blowing fresh from the east. Pop said there wasn't much point in going out and getting soaked, so we stayed put all day at Duck Island.

It was a very good day. To begin with, in came a husky, big, plumb-bowed yawl of obvious European lineage. She turned out to be the *Stoertebeker,* a vessel that had recently sailed across the Atlantic. She anchored to leeward of us, and I spent quite a bit of time on the companionway ladder staring over at her, mentally transporting myself on board her in mid-ocean.

Next the white mast of a sloop loomed up outside the breakwater. When she came round the end so I could see her hull, I could hardly contain myself. Her hull was white all over and she was all white turtleback where her deck and trunk cabin were supposed to be. Pop used to laugh and tell about a boat like that called the *Moby Dick* that towed a dinghy always chasing after her called the *Captain Ahab*. I never could figure out whether he was laughing at the combination of names or at the crazy design of the boat.

"Is this the *Moby Dick?*" I cried from my perch at the hatch. Pop got up to look. "That's her," he said.

I had always felt very left out when everybody in the family joked about the poor old *Moby Dick*, because I was the only one who hadn't seen her. Now I could join in the fun too. She was something else. I used to have to tease Mother to tell me once again about the time somebody painted great big eyes on her bow in the middle of the night. Now here she was, and maybe somebody would do it again tonight!

Pop's log for the day reads, "Ship's work and cribbage."

The day must have been a lot more tedious for him than it was for me, for he decided he'd better teach me his favorite card game. He knew cribbage isn't something you learn in a day, but I guess he figured he had to start breaking me in sometime.

So the cards came off the starboard shelf back of his narrow seat at the oiled mahogany cabin table. I sat on my identical seat to port and Pop started in patiently to explain the game. It was some growing-up feeling for me to be doing the same thing Pop was doing. Playing cribbage with him would be different from carrying out his orders to help him sail the *Brownie*. It would be different from seeing the *Stoertebeker* and having Pop answer my questions about her. It would be different from catching up with his experience of seeing the *Moby Dick*. Playing cribbage with Pop meant the beginning of times that I would sit down with him on an equal basis. We would each have 121 holes to peg on the cribbage board; each be dealt six cards at a time, each have four to keep in our hands and two to discard into the crib, one time his crib, the next time mine. Once I learned the game, there would be times when I could go out on him. Such victories would probably never be frequent but would always be possible. It was this possibility that slowly dawned on me as we began to play cribbage in the little yawl's cabin to

the sound of wind and rain at Duck Island. I thought cruising to Duck Island was just elegant.

The big scoring in cribbage is when you count up your hands and the crib, but first you have to play out the cards in your hand one by one trying to make pairs, runs, or get the cards to add up to 15 or go on to 31, while at the same time keeping your opponent from doing any of those things. This is where the real skill comes in.

And didn't Pop love to peg. If I put down a six, down would slap his nine with a merry, "Fifteen for two."

Then maybe I'd play a Queen. "Twenty-five."

Down comes his six with a gleeful, "Thirty-one for two."

But Pop hated not to peg even more than he liked to peg. Say he'd play a King. I'd play a seven. "Seventeen," I'd say.

"Seventeen," he'd mimic, making a face. How he hated seventeen! Even if he had a seven, he wouldn't dare pair mine for fear I'd have another one and make it thirty-one for eight. "Seventeen," he'd complain. "Why did you have to make it seventeen?"

The next day cleared off but blew harder than ever out of the east. Pop was a great pessimist about the weather. He said we might as well give up on our plan to go on up the Sound and start home. The *Stoertebeker* left, and the *Moby Dick* went out too, without anyone having added any cetaceous decoration to her.

We got underway with main and staysail, went outside, and put her close-hauled on the port tack. It blew harder. She did fine, but it was very rough, the wind was right on the nose, and we would be a long time getting anywhere.

Pop didn't like it much, so he watched for a smooth spot and put her about, rattlety-bang. We ran her off, and she scooted back to her berth behind the Duck Island breakwaters.

In the afternoon, in came a big, black schooner, and that was the first time I saw the *Blackfish* (see Chapter 18). That fine vessel demanded considerable staring and dreaming.

Pop was a pretty conservative cribbage player. He seldom put much of any use in my crib, for he didn't like to take chances.

If it was my crib and he started to make faces at his hand, I knew he had a good hand but keeping it meant giving me something good in the crib. "Well,

I guess I'll have to bust it all up," he'd say, and it would turn out he'd destroyed a double run so he could give me his usual Queen and nine, or whatever.

Or, if he looked happy when it was my crib, I knew that his hand split well. Then he'd toss two cards into my crib with, "See what you can make out of those," knowing full well that I wouldn't be able to make much of anything out of them. He'd groan complainingly if I ever got more than four points in my crib.

The next day it continued to blow fresh from the east and there were rain showers. The *Blackfish* left. We stayed at Duck Island.

In between showers, I sailed the *Blackie.* She was a futuristic fin-keeler with a free-standing oval rudder, a tall Marconi rig, and a flush-deck. She got her name from her glossy black topsides.

I always sailed her close-hauled, on which point of sailing she would steer herself. Her tiller pointed aft instead of forward, and I rigged a rubber band from the end of it to the permanent backstay fitting. The main sheet belayed on the tiller, so that the harder it blew the more the sheet pulled the tiller to leeward, thus supplying weather helm as needed to keep her on course.

It was really fun rowing alongside her in the dinghy watching her go. With an overall length of about 14 inches, she had to face some big breaking seas if it was blowing fresh, even behind the Duck Island breakwater. Her motion at such times seemed quite violent, but she would keep going fast. Anyone on board her would have had to hang on for dear life.

"Cut me a Jack," Pop would say every once in a while when it was his crib. Usually I wouldn't oblige, of course, but on those rare occasions when he said it and I did it, he'd peg his two points briskly and say, "That's the stuff," just as if he knew I would.

Pop would usually get eight or ten points in his hand, sometimes a dozen, and he'd get five or six in his crib and peg three or four every time, so I had to be some lucky to ever beat him. When I counted first, he'd often say, "Count your few," and all too often it was all too true. Plenty of times he'd skunk me.

The next day it was calm and foggy. We motored all the way home. Pop's log ends, "This cruise very disappointing as to weather. Roger learned cribbage."

I really loved it, being up there at Duck Island.

1/ The Naval Academy's Luders Yawls

> Length on deck: 44 feet
> Length on waterline: 30 feet
> Beam: 11 feet
> Draft: 6 feet
> Sail area: 878 square feet
> Displacement: 11 tons
> Designer: Luders Marine Construction Co.

Sail training hardly needs another printed word of explanation or justification after the deluge of articles, pamphlets, and books that have rained down on the subject in the wake of Operation Sail in 1976. Surely there is hardly a soul in this country who isn't convinced of some aspect of the benefits of sending young people to sea under sail in the Atomic Age.

Of course sail training is not new, either in America or in Europe. In the Old World, both Naval and Merchant Marine cadets have trained under sail in many countries throughout the era of mechanical propulsion. In America, the Coast Guard has had its *Eagle* since World War II, and the Naval Academy at Annapolis has provided a steady diet of training under sail for its midshipmen.

Still, the taxpayer may well ask why the world's most modern navy bothers with sail training, a navy that is at the same time showing its future officers how nuclear propulsion works, what a ballistic missile submarine can do, what are the many strategic and tactical uses of a nuclear-powered aircraft carrier with her embarked squadrons of jet aircraft armed with nuclear weapons, and how best to manage hundreds of thousands of people and billions of dollars to keep a cost-effective

fleet ready to fight. What does reefing the mainsail have to do with it?

The reason sail training makes sense and probably will for a long time to come is that the sailing vessel has this remarkable characteristic: she demands the utmost of devotion and competence from her master and crew; given anything less, she will inevitably get them into trouble, perhaps mortal trouble. If a man can accept that he must be devoted to his ship and that he must know her needs, then he is setting the right course toward becoming a professional seaman, no matter how big and powerful may be his vessel. As a matter of fact, the bigger and more powerful the vessel, the more difficult it is to sense when she is in danger, and the more valuable it is for her people to have been close enough to wind, wave, and tide to have developed sensibilities to their effects. The sailing vessel develops such sensibilities best of all. (Well, almost best of all. The small rowing craft is the world's greatest training vessel, in my opinion, but that is another story.)

For years the Naval Academy followed the usual pattern of using square rig for sail training. When my father was a midshipman soon after the turn of the century, he learned the ropes in a fine, big,

A. E. Luders, Jr., whose firm, the Luders Marine Construction Company of Stamford, Connecticut, was responsible for the design and building of the Navy's training yawls. (A. E. Luders, Jr.)

single-topsail ship, the *Chesapeake*. He liked her well enough, but I do remember him complaining about the footropes on the royal yards. To achieve the best possible appearance, all the footropes were given exactly the same arc beneath the yards. This worked out well on the big lower yards, but up on the little royal yards, when you stood on the footropes the yard only came to your knees, which was a bit precarious.

When Pop came back to the Academy as an instructor just before World War I, part of the job was to go in the *Chesapeake*. She had no power, and they did things the old-fashioned way. One time when we were waiting for wind to get underway from New London, Connecticut, Pop recalled the same kind of a morning in the same place in the *Chesapeake*. They hadn't waited that day. They had kedged her out into the sound by rowing out anchors and pulling up to them, with two boat crews and two capstan crews working in tandem so

as to keep the vessel moving continuously out to one or the other of her anchors, using a procedure too old-fashioned to be included in the then-current edition of Lieutenant Commander Austin M. Knight's massive tome, *Modern Seamanship*.

The Naval Academy also exposed the midshipmen to the wonders of small boats in big rowing cutters and in a variety of small sailing craft. These boats plied the waters of the Severn River and the nearby Chesapeake Bay.

There was always competition among these small craft. Pop told of a watermelon race. A launch would take off from the starting line with a cargo of watermelons and would steam dead to windward dropping a watermelon overboard every 50 yards or so. The boat that brought home the most watermelons won. Of course it takes a little time to heave a low-floating, slippery, heavy watermelon over the lee rail, and one strategy was to pass up the first few melons, try to work out a lead to windward, and then try to pick up every remaining watermelon before anybody could catch you. I suppose the price of watermelons would preclude such skillful fun today, although they could certainly provide the participants a juicy feed after the race.

In 1939, the Navy decided that it would be well worthwhile for the midshipmen to have some really good boats in which to sail on the Bay and in which to learn by sailing against civilian yachtsmen in both local and long-distance races. The Bureau of Construction and Repair put out the word to naval architects that the Navy was interested in a design for a boat 30 feet long on the waterline that would take no penalty under the Cruising Club of America rating rule of 1937. If the midshipmen were to campaign on the racing circuits, the Navy wanted their boats to be competitive.

Several prominent design firms submitted plans for the proposed new training vessels. The winner was the Luders Marine Construction Company of Stamford, Connecticut, with a design for a handsome yawl. The Navy not only selected the Luders design, but also had the company build the first three boats. They were put overboard in 1939, and were so successful that nine more boats were built to the design by 1943.

The boats were so aptly named that their names are worth listing: *Frolic, Fearless, Restless, Alert,*

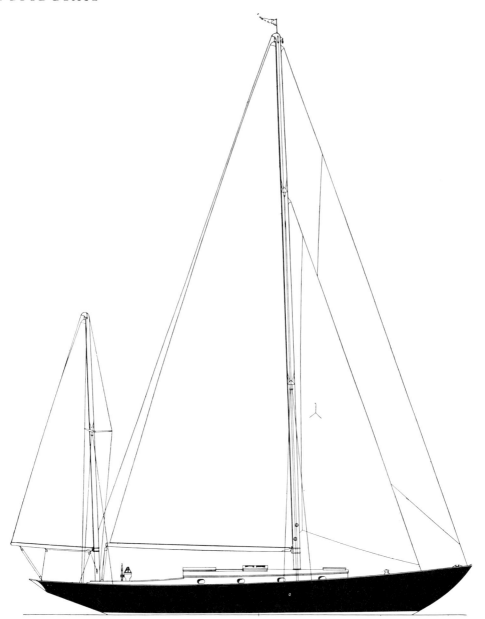

*The yawls have a tall rig and a graceful profile. (*Yachting, April, 1939)

Intrepid, Resolute, Active, Dandy, Flirt, Lively, Swift, and *Vigilant.*

At about this time, also, people began giving yachts to the Naval Academy for sail training. Some beautiful and famous vessels came to Annapolis, such as the wishbone ketch *Vamarie;* Frank Paine's big cutter, the *Highland Light;* the 89-foot Alden schooner *Freedom;* and the big yawl *Royono,* ex-*Mandoo II.*

These vessels and the 12 Luders yawls constituted the Naval Academy Sailing Squadron, and I was lucky enough to be able to be associated with the Squadron when I lived in Annapolis. It was great to sail in the big boats under the tutelage of such fine sailors as Frank Siatkowski and Alden Hefler (you could call them "Ski" and "Hap," and you'd better jump whatever they called you).

But most of my Squadron sailing was in one or

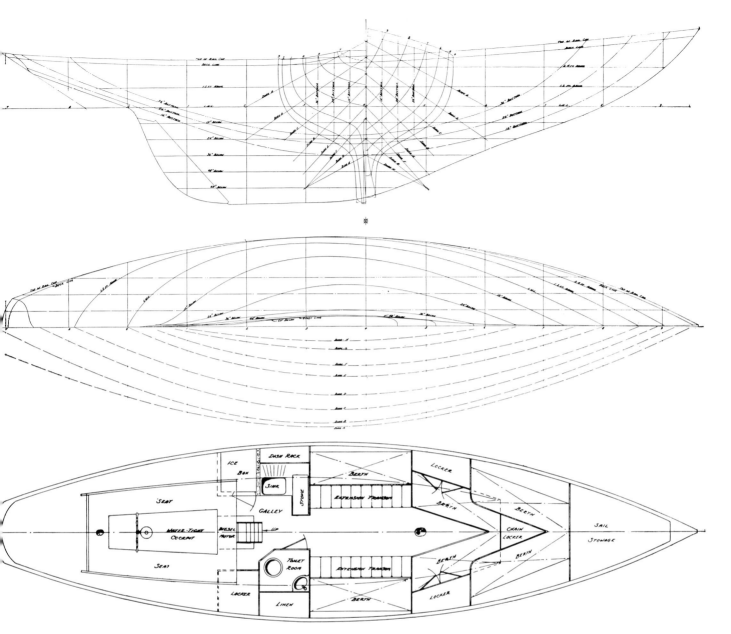

The lines of the Luders yawls are gentle and fair throughout. The bold, high bow is particularly good looking; the bilges may be a little slack. The layout is ingenious, with bunks for eight midshipmen. (Yachting, April, 1939)

the other of the Luders yawls, where there was ample opportunity to pass along the basics to new sailing instructors (junior officers fresh from the Fleet) and midshipmen.

The oldest of the yawls was 20 years old when I started sailing in them. The boats had been sailed just about every day from April 1 through November 1, and by the nature of their purpose, they had been sailed and maintained by people less experienced around small boats than the average private owner.

That they had survived so long and so well is a tribute to their design and construction by Luders.

During my time in the Squadron, the yawls were gradually replaced by fiberglass boats built to the same design. As the wooden yawls were retired, they were farmed out to various naval stations for recreational sailing.

Both wooden and fiberglass yawls have sailed in many local races on Chesapeake Bay, in ocean races along the eastern seaboard, and in the Ber-

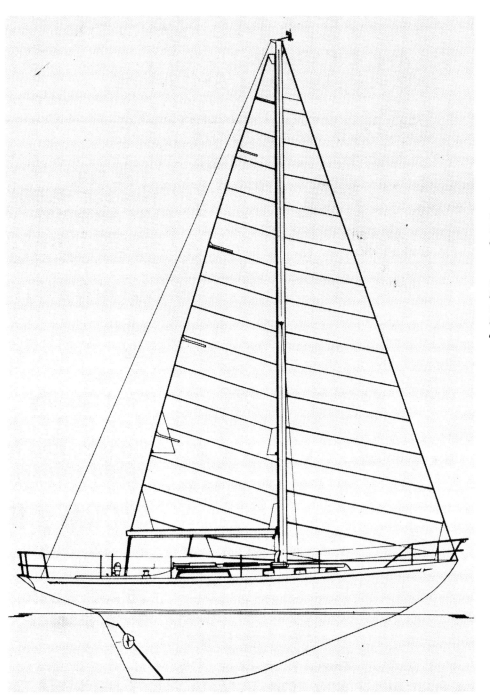

The Annapolis 44 is a current production boat based on the Luders yawls and built by Windsong Yachts, Inc., of Kirkland, Washington. The arrangement plan of the Annapolis 44 shows a conventional yacht layout with bunks for five instead of eight. (Sailing)

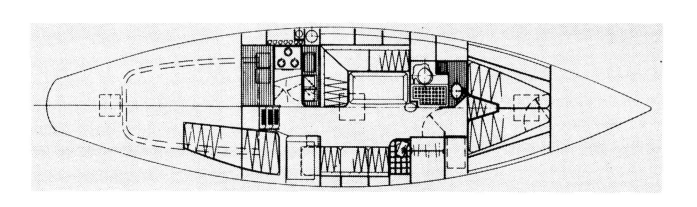

muda Race. In 1964, the Navy shipped the fiberglass Luders yawl *Fearless* to Buenos Aires, and she competed in the Buenos Aires to Rio de Janeiro Race under the command of Lieutenant Toby Tobin and was then shipped home. Two years later, Lieutenant Jock Williams raced the *Fearless* from Bermuda to Copenhagen.

The design is now being built as a stock boat, called the Annapolis 44, by Windsong Yachts, Inc., 135 Lake Street South, Kirkland, Washington. The hulls are built of fiberglass from the molds used by the Navy to build their fiberglass Luders yawls. The Annapolis 44 has been given a high-aspect-ratio sloop rig and a normal yacht's layout below.

With a waterline length of 30 feet, the Naval Academy Luders yawls are 44 feet long on deck, have a beam of 11 feet, and a draft of 6 feet. The working sail area is 878 square feet. Displacement is about 11 tons with 4½ tons of outside ballast on the keel. The Navy specified that the ballast-displacement ratio should be less than 43 percent, and it works out to just under 41 percent.

The construction of the boats is fairly heavy as indicated by their white oak frames sided 1⅞ inches, and molded 1⅝ inches at the head, increasing ¹/₁₆ inch per foot to the heel. Planking is 1⅛-inch Philippine mahogany. The boats have bronze hull straps and steel reinforcing knees. The masts are hollow, built up of Sitka spruce.

The Navy specified installation of its own 15-horsepower diesels turning feathering propellers. The yawls were said to be one of the few designs contracted for by the Navy with no specification for maximum speed under power.

The boats had no power during my time with them. (The fiberglass yawls have four-cylinder Westerbeke Model Four-107 diesels.) The only time an engine was missed was on those hot, windless days the Bay produced in mid-summer when you were trying to get back to Annapolis from some training trip.

The Luders yawls are big boats for their waterline length. The Navy specified that the ends be "moderate." They look fairly long by today's standards, especially the stern with its long, fine counter. The bow is especially pretty and is high enough to keep the foredeck reasonably dry.

The bow and buttock lines and waterlines are all fair and easy throughout. The boats' only fault, if

The **Dandy** *near the mouth of the Severn River. The boats seem a bit tender at times. (U.S. Naval Institute)*

it is a fault, is their slack bilges. It is interesting to compare the midsection of the Luders yawl with that of the Concordia yawl (described in the next chapter), a boat somewhat shorter on the waterline. The Concordia yawls have much harder bilges and certainly seem to stand up to their sail better. The Luders yawls seemed a bit tender at times. When not driven too hard they were always fast and handy. When pressed too much, however, they would just keep on knocking down. Perhaps that is an advantage in a training vessel.

When the Luders yawls were being driven fairly hard off the wind in a race, they were a bit hard to manage, especially if there was much sea running. They have recently been given new rudders, however, with more area at the bottom than at the top, produced by a profile with a concave trailing edge ending in a pointed corner. It is reported that this change has helped their steering.

Doubtless a contributing factor to the yawls' tenderness is their tall rig. The masthead stands 52 feet above the deck.

The Frolic *standing in to Annapolis under main and staysail. Hopefully, someone will soon furl up the mizzen and top its boom up at a nice jaunty angle. (*Sail and Power *by Richard Henderson with Bartlett S. Dunbar, courtesy Naval Institute Press.)*

Four Luders yawls working to windward under different reduced sail combinations. From left to right these are: number 2 Genoa, reefed main and mizzen; number 2 Genoa and mizzen; number 1 Genoa and trysail; and number 3 Genoa and full main. (U.S. Navy photo from Sail and Power *by Richard Henderson with Bartlett S. Dunbar, courtesy Naval Institute Press)*

When the boats were first delivered they had 13 sails: the four working sails, a spinnaker, a mizzen staysail, and seven additional headsails of various shapes and sizes. The mast is well aft, and to make these boats go you have to really pay attention to your headsails. When I was sailing them, we had three sizes of Genoa jib to choose from: a Number 1 of 640 square feet; Number 2, 540 square feet; and Number 3, 220 square feet. Of course by International Offshore Rule (IOR) standards, the mainsail looks huge and the headsails tiny (which just goes to show you how peculiar the IOR is).

The mizzen on the yawls has an area of only 94 square feet. This sail with its staysail was free sail area under the Cruising Club of America rule. The chief use of the mizzen is for balancing the forestaysail in one of the famous Chesapeake Bay squalls. It's too small to have much drive or really pay for the expense and windage of its gear.

The forestay comes down to a lever on deck and can be broken down out of the way when setting a big jib on the outer stay. The boats have running backstays (not shown in the sail plan) working in opposition to the forestay.

The yawls seldom sail without a big gang on board, and with their big cockpit, narrow house, and large deck area, they are well designed to handle a crowd.

The pedestal wheel is a joy to use. You can stand up to it or sit behind it either to windward or to leeward. The binnacle tends to keep the gang's legs out of the spokes.

Another nice feature is a really stout capstan on the foredeck. It is doubtless oversize, but if you want something for man or rope to hang onto that can't be missed and isn't going to carry away, there it is. It also makes a fine seat when running off the wind.

One of the Navy's requirements was for a large number of bunks in the boats. Luders got in no fewer than eight, counting the slide-out transoms in the saloon. The placement of the high and low bunks forward is ingenious.

It was always most interesting and instructive to

Bending sail on the Frolic. *The yawls are seldom undermanned. (U.S. Navy photo, courtesy U.S. Naval Institute)*

take out young officers or midshipmen in the yawls. We'd reef and shake out, anchor and get underway again, practice landings alongside the sea wall, run man-overboard drills, and tack ship with the rudder locked amidships. One time we picked up every mooring in the harbor.

A less satisfying duty in the yawls was acting as safety officer. You were there supposedly to prevent catastrophe. There were some trying moments, especially in hotly contended round-the-buoys racing on the Bay. You were supposed to

take over when collision was imminent and pull a miracle escape with some exotic maneuver at the last second. I have to confess to asking the midshipmen skippers an occasional pre-emergency question, such as, "What are you going to do about this guy to leeward?" or "Have you looked at the chart lately?" (This was my very favorite question when playing this role in the *Freedom,* taking her ten-foot draft around the Bay.)

Since many people with different backgrounds and experience in ways of doing things around the water were using the yawls, you never knew what you'd find when you stepped on board. A few brief excerpts from the log may be amusing:

November 3, 1962. Aboard *Alert* at 0800 for Skipper Race. Strong northeast wind with rain. Gale warnings up. Race cancelled. Boat making considerable water at mooring. Had no trouble clearing her with gasoline handy-billy pump we had brought aboard. Discovered packing gone on boat's installed bilge pump, water coming in through pump. Plugged it and went ashore at 1100.

July 26, 1964. . . . Shifted to the *Lively* for the third [Lloyd Phoenix] Race. Found her with water to the top of the floors. Pumped her out and found a steady leak forward, but able to keep up with it by giving her a dozen strokes or so every five or ten minutes.

August 22, 1967. . . . backstay foul of spinnaker lift block, so went aloft to clear it. Crew lost forestaysail halyard aloft, so went back up for that.

But all in all it was plenty of fun and certainly mighty good training. I know it was for me. Here is a day I still remember well:

April 12, 1965. On board the *Flirt* for an afternoon sail with eight relatively green Sailing Squadron members for training. Fresh breeze from northwest. Clear and bright, warm. Underway at 1615 with single-reefed mainsail. Ran down the channel setting fore-staysail. Rounded up off Greenbury Point, tacked and fell off to reach up to Hackett's Point can. Increased to strong breeze. Boat sailing with wind abeam, main luffing a little, rail down and under at times. Tacked and stood back for Greenbury Point on a close reach. Water up to the house in the gusts. She handled well in the smooth sea though. Beat up the river. Off the sea wall took in staysail. Tacked again with main alone. Picked up mooring at 1815. Wind howling, glad to be tied up.

2/ The *Java* and the Concordia Yawls

Length on deck: 39 feet 10 inches
Length on waterline: 28 feet 6 inches
Beam: 10 feet
Draft: 5 feet 8 inches
Sail area: 618 square feet
Displacement: 9 tons
Designer: C. Raymond Hunt

Some of us schoolboys groaned when we heard that the speaker for a meeting of our boating club was going to be some old geezer who had graduated from the school who knows how many decades back in history. We were pretty confident that we knew just about all that was worth knowing about boats, so we sauntered along to the gathering place fully prepared to be both patronized and bored. We were neither.

Llewellyn Howland hurried in from Padanaram, Massachusetts, face aglow and eyes atwinkle, and absolutely bowled us over with the wit, charm, and enthusiasm with which he yarned to us about boats and cruising. For a couple of us, the occasion marked the beginning of a precious friendship between old and young, shellback and greenhorn, a friendship that lasted ten years until that grand old man died. During those ten years, we were lucky enough to be the mirthful audience for his well-told tales by the fireside in the big terracotta house in Padanaram that is no more, to make a Buzzards Bay cruise with him in his lovely yawl, the *Java*, and to earn the right, in his eyes at least, to call him "Skipper."

In the summer of 1893, Llewellyn Howland, aged 16, needed to convalesce from typhoid fever. He had the same kind of a friendship with an old man, wise in the ways of the sea, whom he called "Skipper." It was to that Skipper's cottage, overlooking Buzzards Bay, that Llewellyn Howland went to rest.

The resting began and ended the first night he was there. On that night, his "Skipper" showed him a large, beautifully made model of the *St. Esprit du Conquet*. The model was of an 86-foot armed lugger, probably of the Chasse-Marée type—deep, powerful vessels with three lugsails stacked up high on fore and mainmasts and two more set on a small mizzen mast, balanced off with a long, low jib set on a running bowsprit. The fully rigged model was one of a pair ordered built by the Minister of Marine in Paris from lines and specifications furnished by "Monsieur le Capitaine Pierre Reynard." Capitaine Reynard had built the *St. Esprit* in his own yard at Le Conquet, a fishing village near Brest, in 1799 and had used her for running contraband in what was then for a Frenchman a very dangerous English Channel.

Llewellyn Howland
(Skipper,
April, 1957)

Waldo   Howland
(Skipper,
April, 1957)

The model of that lugger was totally romantic and beautiful to Llewellyn Howland, and he studied her every detail of form and fabric.

The next morning the Skipper put Llewellyn Howland to work. The task they shared was the intensive testing of a dozen three-foot sailing models, all with identical rig but different hull designs, six being moderate craft and six being extreme. The models were tested not only for speed, but also for how they sailed and behaved in rough water. When the objective analysis was completed, the model with the highest marks was one of the moderate ones, and it was not lost upon the experimenters that her lines were the fairest, most harmonious, and prettiest of the lot. Llewellyn Howland continued to study the model of the *St. Esprit* with her own fair, harmonious, and pretty lines, and he understood well why she had served her captain so successfully.

Skipper Howland was not one to lock away the knowledge and wisdom he acquired. He shared it via many friendships and via the excellent writing he did later in life. His story of the model of the *St. Esprit* is part of an article he wrote for the *Atlantic Monthly*, "A Boat is Born," reprinted, with a number of his other stories, in the book *The Middle Road*, published by the Concordia Company, South Dartmouth, Massachusetts, in 1961, four years after his passing. He wrote a grand series of articles for the *Rudder* in the mid-Forties,

gathered together in the book *Sou'west and By West of Cape Cod*, published by Harvard University Press in 1947. He published himself in 1953 a little book called *Triptych*, containing three of his writings out of his own experience in life, writings that mean much to those who knew him.

Llewellyn Howland ended the article, "A Boat is Born," with an acknowledgment of the debt he owed Capitaine Reynard and his *St. Esprit du Conquet* for the creation of his own excellent cruising yawl, the *Java*, in 1939.

The hurricane of September 21, 1938, left Skipper Howland boatless. He immediately began making plans with his son Waldo and Waldo's partner at the Concordia Company boatyard at Padanaram, C. Raymond Hunt, for the designing and building of the best small cruising vessel they could create. She was to be designed specifically for Buzzards Bay, where the sou'wester comes breezing on with great regularity and the seas are high and steep.

Llewellyn Howland wrote, "I freely called on the time and skill of many willing hands to help me carry out my plan for the creation of a 40-foot boat which, in essence, should sail on her bottom, not on her side, and, at that, approach the speed limit of her length under the widest range of weather conditions likely to be met with off or along shore on our Atlantic seaboard. All other details were subordinate to these cardinal qualifi-

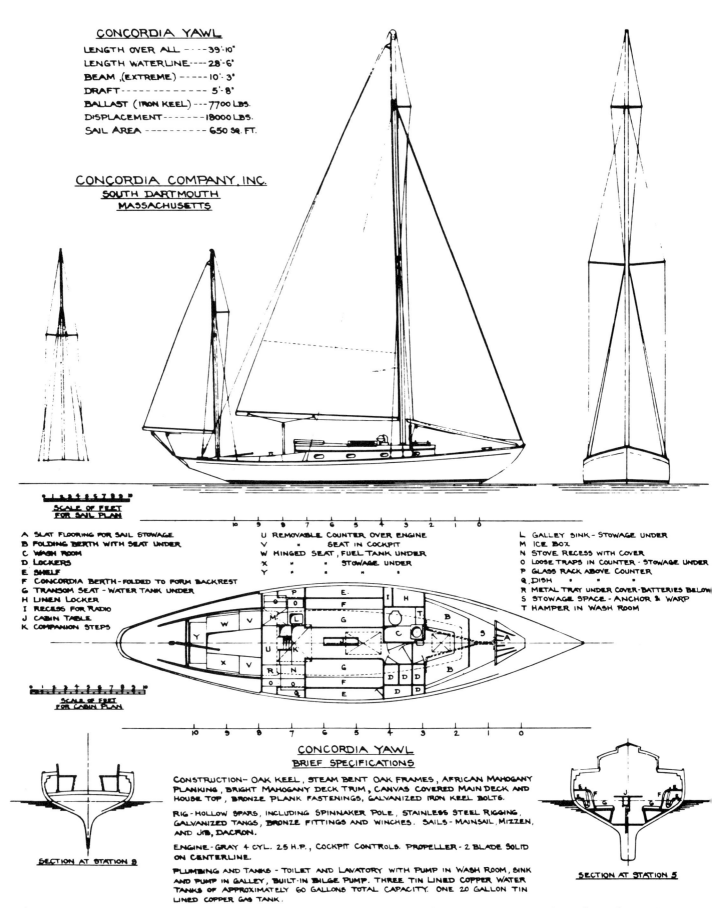

CONCORDIA YAWL

LENGTH OVER ALL	39'-10"
LENGTH WATERLINE	28'-6"
BEAM (EXTREME)	10'-3"
DRAFT	5'-8"
BALLAST (IRON KEEL)	7700 LBS.
DISPLACEMENT	18000 LBS.
SAIL AREA	650 SQ. FT.

CONCORDIA COMPANY, INC.
SOUTH DARTMOUTH
MASSACHUSETTS

SCALE OF FEET
FOR SAIL PLAN

A SLAT FLOORING FOR SAIL STOWAGE
B FOLDING BERTH WITH SEAT UNDER
C WASH ROOM
D LOCKERS
E SHELF
F CONCORDIA BERTH - FOLDED TO FORM BACKREST
G TRANSOM SEAT - WATER TANK UNDER
H LINEN LOCKER
I RECESS FOR RADIO
J CABIN TABLE
K COMPANION STEPS

U REMOVABLE COUNTER OVER ENGINE
V " SEAT IN COCKPIT
W HINGED SEAT, FUEL TANK UNDER
X " " STOWAGE UNDER
Y " " "

L GALLEY SINK - STOWAGE UNDER
M ICE BOX
N STOVE RECESS WITH COVER
O LOOSE TRAPS IN COUNTER - STOWAGE UNDER
P GLASS RACK ABOVE COUNTER
Q DISH " " "
R METAL TRAY UNDER COVER - BATTERIES BELOW
S STOWAGE SPACE - ANCHOR & WARP
T HAMPER IN WASH ROOM

SCALE OF FEET
FOR CABIN PLAN

CONCORDIA YAWL
BRIEF SPECIFICATIONS

CONSTRUCTION - OAK KEEL, STEAM BENT OAK FRAMES, AFRICAN MAHOGANY PLANKING, BRIGHT MAHOGANY DECK TRIM, CANVAS COVERED MAIN DECK AND HOUSE TOP, BRONZE PLANK FASTENINGS, GALVANIZED IRON KEEL BOLTS.

RIG - HOLLOW SPARS, INCLUDING SPINNAKER POLE, STAINLESS STEEL RIGGING, GALVANIZED TANGS, BRONZE FITTINGS AND WINCHES. SAILS - MAINSAIL, MIZZEN, AND JIB, DACRON.

ENGINE - GRAY 4 CYL. 25 H.P., COCKPIT CONTROLS. PROPELLER - 2 BLADE SOLID ON CENTERLINE.

PLUMBING AND TANKS - TOILET AND LAVATORY WITH PUMP IN WASH ROOM, SINK AND PUMP IN GALLEY, BUILT-IN BILGE PUMP. THREE TIN LINED COPPER WATER TANKS OF APPROXIMATELY 60 GALLONS TOTAL CAPACITY. ONE 20 GALLON TIN LINED COPPER GAS TANK.

SECTION AT STATION 8

SECTION AT STATION 5

CABIN EQUIPMENT - 2 SPECIAL FOLDING BERTHS FORWARD, 2 CONCORDIA BERTHS IN MAIN CABIN, TRANSOM CUSHIONS, KAPOC BERTH MATTRESSES, CABIN TABLE, ICE BOX OF 50 LBS. CAPACITY, ALCOHOL STOVE. 7 ELECTRIC LIGHTS, 1 KEROSENE LAMP, COCKPIT CUSHIONS.

OTHER EQUIPMENT - RUNNING AND RIDING LIGHTS, ANCHOR AND WARP, BOAT HOOK, FLAG STAFF, CANVAS BUCKET, MOP, FEW TOOLS, FENDERS, LIFE RING, DOCK LINES, COMPASS AND BINNACLE, LIFE LINES, PULPIT.

FINISH - SPARS BRIGHT, DECK TRIM AND HOUSE SIDES BRIGHT, DECK PAINTED BUFF, TOPSIDES WHITE, BOTTOM GREEN, COCKPIT FLOOR TEAK, BARE. INTERIOR: PINE BULKHEADS, HARDWOOD TRIM, ALL BRIGHT. UNDERSIDE OF HOUSE TOP WHITE, FLOOR PAINTED, TOILET ROOM WHITE EXCEPT FOR FLOOR.

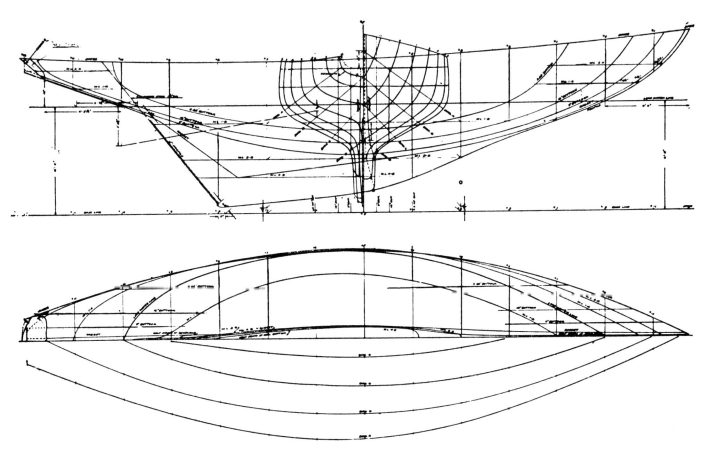

The Java's *lines show a fair, harmonious hull of great power, yet great beauty. (*Yachting, *April, 1952)*

cations." And, as Waldo Howland added recently, "Rules for racing did not determine anything, nor was big cabin space or great headroom a requirement."

Ray Hunt drew the lines of the new boat. William Harris did the construction plan and layout. Waldo Howland says he "fussed with the details like Concordia berths, cabin heaters, stoves, hatches, cockpit design, etc. But father knew what he wanted and was the one who conceived the basic ideas."

When Hunt drew the new boat's lines, he made them—as Llewellyn Howland was quick to appreciate—fair and harmonious to the eye. She was a very different vessel from the *St. Esprit,* but she shared a general inspiration of boldness of form with that fascinating vessel, an inspiration remembered for 45 years by Llewellyn Howland.

The general requirements and their resulting

characteristics of the new yawl were not unfamiliar to Ray Hunt, for he had designed a similar boat, the *Cinderella,* built in 1936. But there were differences that led the new design close to the perfection Skipper Howland sought.

The yawl has moderate overhangs, a fairly deep keel, but rather shallow bow and buttock lines. The waterlines are quite convex, but with very moderate deadrise in the midsection, the boat's lines are still quite fine. The remarkable thing about this design is her very hard bilges, combined with tumblehome, at the midsection. This shape gives the yawl great power to carry sail and makes her stiff and dry. This extraordinary power for her size is not gained, however, at the expense of heaviness or clumsiness.

The new design had a length on deck of 39 feet 10 inches, a waterline length of 28 feet 6 inches, beam of 10 feet 3 inches and a draft of 5 feet 8

The Java *outside Padanaram harbor making the most of the afternoon sou'wester. (Norman Fortier)*

inches. The displacement was 18,000 pounds, with 7,700 pounds of outside ballast in an iron keel. The sail area of her yawl rig with a working jib was 618 square feet.

The boat was built at Casey's yard in Fairhaven, Massachusetts, and was launched in 1939. She was christened the *Java,* after a lucky vessel among those owned by Llewellyn Howland's New Bedford ancestors. The *Java* was beautifully built and was always perfectly maintained. Every inch of her had the patina of a piece of polished furniture.

The *Java* was a most successful boat, attracted attention, and begat a long line of sisterships and near sisters that became known as the Concordia

The Cinderella, *designed by Ray Hunt two years before he drew the plans for the* Java. (Yachting, *June, 1936)*

The Polaris, *a sloop-rigged Concordia stretched out to 41 feet long on deck. (Roberts Parsons)*

H. A. Taylor, Jr.'s Sumatra *driving to windward. (Norman Fortier)*

Above: *Looking aft in the main cabin. (Norman Fortier).*
Below: *The stern on the yawls is quite narrow. Here are the cockpit back rests ready for use. (Norman Fortier)*

yawls.* The fifth Concordia yawl (the *Suva*, in which I was lucky enough to sail many times) was the first of the class to be built in Hamburg, Germany, by Abeking and Rasmussen. More than 100 Concordias have been built, many of them by Abeking and Rasmussen. Some of the boats were built to a design that was lengthened to about 41 feet. Some have been rigged as sloops, and some, especially the newer boats, have been given mast-head rigs.

The Concordia yawls have proven to be fine boats for cruising, daysailing and racing, and ocean racing. Some have made notable ocean cruises and some have won major races, such as the Marble-head-Halifax Race, the race between Newport and Annapolis, and the Bermuda Race. These honors gladdened Llewellyn Howland's heart, but they were mere by-products of the happiness he felt

*For a quite complete history and catalog of most of these boats, see *The Concordia Yawls: 1938-1978*, edited and published by Elizabeth Meyer.

Above: *Looking forward in the main cabin.* *(Norman Fortier).* Below: *Up forward in the Suva. (Norman Fortier)*

each time he sailed out into Buzzards Bay in his beloved *Java.*

The rig makes sense for the fresh and strong breezes of Buzzards Bay, but for other sailing areas where a higher percentage of light weather may be encountered, additional sail area might be desirable. For most folks nowadays this means setting a Genoa jib, but that's the hard way, in my opinion. A Concordia yawl based on the Chesapeake Bay, for example, might do very well with a bigger mizzen and a bowsprit, setting an extra jib. These sails are easier to handle than the big overlapping jibs; they would be stowed in a hard breeze, and the yawl would then become a jib-and-mainsail boat. A larger mizzen would also balance better when sailing under stem-head jib and mizzen than does the small mizzen, though the small mizzen does work in this regard. Notice that the mainmast is set quite far forward in this boat, a sensible arrangement to keep the rig simple by giving it a single headsail. My proposed double-head rig for light weather may seem unduly complicated to some folks, but I maintain it is a more sensible cruising rig than a big, deck-sweeping Genoa jib with its heavily straining, single-part sheet and its creation of a big blind sector forward.

There are some very nice details worked out on the Concordia yawls. The boats with the older seven-eighths rig have running backstays, and these terminate in a slide running on a heavy track along the deck. Lines lead forward and aft from this slide (the forward one leading through a block and then aft) so that the slide may be pulled forward or aft along the track from the cockpit. With this rig you can set up the backstay a lot harder and with less effort than with a purchase.

The yawls have a wide, flush covering board along the outboard edge of the deck with a toerail set inboard of it three or four inches. This arrangement looks very handsome, emphasizing, as it does, the tumblehome of the topsides amidships.

The two-part forward hatch is hinged on each side and has athwartships strongbacks that rest on deck when the hatch is open in such a way that the two halves of the hatch cover are level and become

fine little seats. At the after end of the cockpit seats, there are hinged backrests that fold down out of the way when they are not wanted. Note the setback of the seat risers in both cockpit and cabin to give more room for feet.

The arrangement below is the standard one for a four-person boat. It's really hard to improve on in a boat of this size.

The Concordia berths are most ingenious contraptions, making nicely curved wooden slat backrests when you are sitting on the transoms and folding down to make comfortable canvas berths for sleeping. When the berth is folded back, it can also be used to store bedding out of the way.

Llewellyn Howland's wonderful boat—born out of the destruction of the hurricane of 1938; inspired by a model of a French lugger of 1799; created by the Skipper himself, his son Waldo, Ray Hunt, William Harris, and those who built her; and sailed for many years by Skipper Howland and his friends—has well deserved the emulation of her many sister Concordia yawls. Long may these fine vessels continue to spread Llewellyn Howland's wisdom.

3/ The *Awa*

Length on deck: 43 feet
Length on waterline: 30 feet
Beam: 10 feet 9 inches
Draft: 6 feet 5 inches
Sail area: 857 square feet
Designer: Philip L. Rhodes

Symmetrical design is a nice thing in a boat. If a boat has a hatchway, interior compartment, or even deck fitting on one side there is somehow felt the need for that same structure, arrangement, or fitting to be on the other side so that the boat will not seem to change her sense of balance in any way when she changes tacks.

The realization that I have sensed this urge for symmetry afloat came to me when studying a design in which it seems to have been achieved to a remarkable degree. Symmetrical design was a key requirement laid onto Philip L. Rhodes by G.M. Bulkley when the latter went to the New York designer in 1929 for plans for a cruising cutter.

Rhodes met the requirement and produced a very pretty boat indeed. Mr. Bulkley named her the *Awa*. My dictionary gives three possible meanings for the word: Scottish for away; Hawaiian for milk fish; or, a shortened form of kava, that ancient intoxicating drink of the South Seas. Whatever it means, the name itself is symmetrical.

The boat is 43 feet long on deck, with a waterline length of 30 feet, a beam of 10 feet 9 inches, and a draft of 6 feet 5 inches. Her sail area is 857 square feet. She was built by William Haff at New Rochelle, New York.

The *Awa*'s sheer, though gentle, is certainly fair and beautiful. And her long ends give her a grace obtainable in no other way.

She has quite a deep keel; she'd be a good boat to windward. She'd also be stiff, for her ballast is very low. But for her tall mast, she might have quite a quick roll in a wrong-sized beam sea. (Her mast stands 55 feet above the water.)

She is prettier than the quite similar but narrower, lower-sided, and lighter New York Yacht Club 30-footers designed by Nathanael G. Herreshoff 25 years earlier, but she would not be quite as fast as they are. Yet with her fair diagonals, her efficient rig, and her fine-lined hull, she would hardly be a slow boat.

Her sail plan shows 610 square feet in the mainsail, 160 square feet in the staysail, and 187 square feet in the jib. That big mainsail would be a real driver on any point of sailing. You'd probably want a small one for out-of-season sailing or for day-and-night passagemaking along the coast, probably a sail with its head reaching to the forestay but a full-length foot. That would be just a little more sail than the big mainsail triple-reefed.

The forestaysail is long enough on the foot to set well, not a common characteristic of forestay-

Philip L. Rhodes, the designer of the Awa. *(Photo by Morris Rosenfeld, courtesy of Philip H. Rhodes)*

sails on clubs. You'd want that paragon of cruising light sails, the balloon forestaysail, for reaching in light weather and to pole out when running. There ought to be a big, flat-cut jib overlapping the mast cut with the clew well up off the deck. You'd tuck away a storm jib and main trysail for that hard chance.

Her running backstays are double, pulling against both forestay and topmast stay. The topping lift pulls against the jib stay. Thus the *Awa* has a degree of symmetry even in her standing and running rigging.

This cutter is not particularly well suited for shorthanded sailing. It would take two people to reef her mainsail comfortably and she has both jib sheets and running backstays to tend when tacking. She'd be some work to sail; you'd have to reef and shake out the large mainsail fairly often, though of course that is less work performed in a more docile part of the boat than is changing headsails.

Of course she could be sailed shorthanded, or singlehanded even, if necessary. Most any boat can be. A couple of us used to enjoy sitting around yarning about just how we would go about getting underway alone in the 89-foot Alden schooner

Freedom, a craft in which we had both sailed with much—sometimes too much—crew. We never got the chance to try it, but we are both still convinced we could have done it given half a day or so.

On deck, you could stow an eight-foot dinghy atop the trunk cabin either forward of or abaft the mast. She'd be stowed exactly on center, of course.

Doesn't she look nice without lifelines? I'd leave off the stanchions and wires and rig up heavy rope temporary lifelines when needed (just before somebody falls overboard). Which means always when underway, unless you're a 100 percent accurate prophet, in which case you're hardly likely to be wasting your time fooling around in boats anyway.

The *Awa* has a one-cylinder Bolinders diesel located on the centerline under her bridge deck and rated at 6-8 h.p. There are two 25-gallon fuel tanks under the cockpit seats, one on each side. She also has two 30-gallon water tanks under the forward berths amidships, again one on each side.

Her symmetrical arrangement below certainly looks neat and clean on paper and would be most attractive to live with. It's a practical layout with bunks tucked back out of the way and located nearly amidships where the motion is least.

The head and washroom are split starboard and port respectively; having these plumbing facilities in separate compartments is really a pragmatic rig when you think about it.

The galley is big and has a lot of storage space. And there is a huge amount of storage space up in the bow.

One thing that surprises me a little about this design is that Mr. Bulkley didn't specify that she have a canoe stern so that both ends would have been just about the same. Phil Rhodes achieved this particular kind of symmetry a couple of years after designing the *Awa* with his design for the 40-foot double-ender *Narwhal.* (See *Good Boats,* pages 83 and 84.)

Of course to really go all the way with this symmetry business, maybe the *Awa*'s mast should have been placed dead amidships and she should have been given one big masthead jib of the same shape and area as the mainsail, with the same sheeting arrangement and placement of reef points. At a glance, she then would have looked as if you could have sailed her backwards as well as forwards. But the only boat that seems able to do that is the proa, and, ironically, although these craft

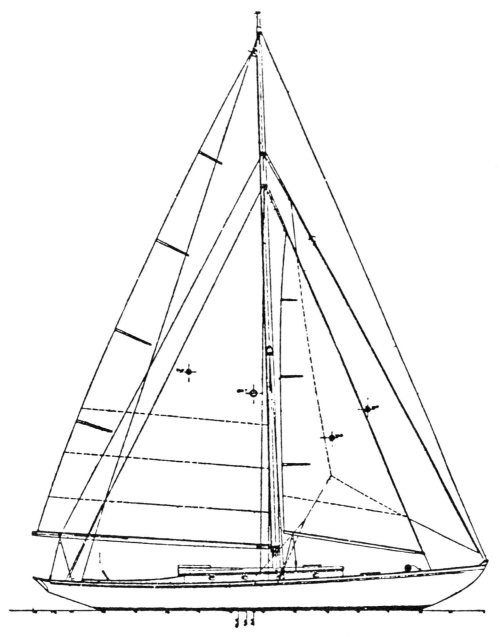

The Awa *is a handsome cutter designed nearly 50 years ago.* (The Rudder, *January, 1930)*

have much fore-and-aft symmetry, they are the essence of asymmetry athwartships. Actually a good name for a proa might be *Palindrome,* which means (one of the editors here tells me) a word that is spelled the same way forwards and backwards.

Of course this boat's name, *Awa,* is a palindrome. And, as a matter of fact, if block capitals are used, the name *AWA* is perfectly symmetrical, not only in terms of the order of its letters, but in terms of the designs of the letters themselves.

I referred earlier to that ability of the sailing craft to do exactly the same thing whichever tack she is on and thus by behaving symmetrically to seem to want to be symmetrical. Maybe it works backwards too. Pop and I always thought our yawl *Brownie* went better on the starboard tack than she did on the port, which was discouraging when beating up the beach for home in a typical sou'wester, because the short legs offshore were starboard boards and the long ones along the beach were port boards. If she really did go better on the starboard

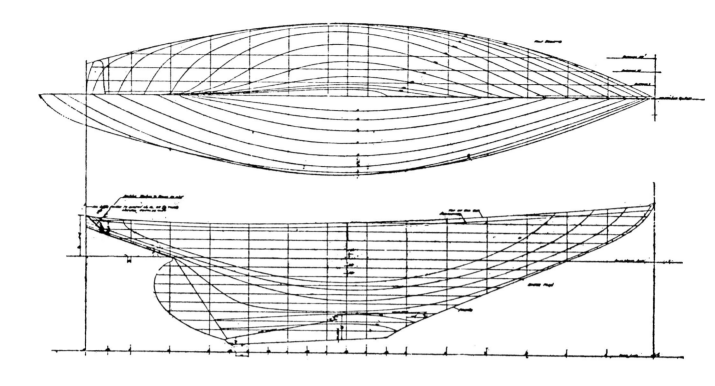

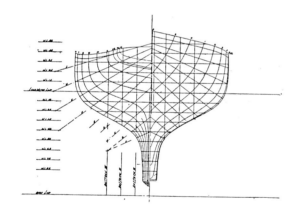

The Awa's lines show a fast and powerful hull, one that would have no great faults or foibles and that would sail well under a wide variety of conditions. The boat was built for Mr. G. M. Bulkley, and her interior layout demonstrates his fetish for symmetry. (The Rudder, *January, 1930*)

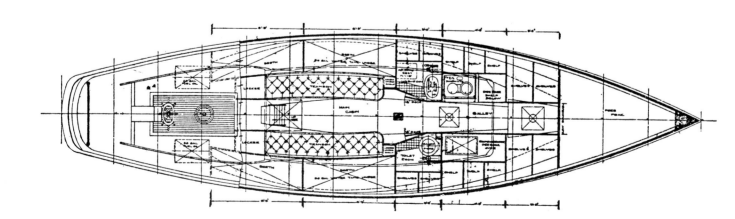

tack, maybe it was because her main companionway was a bit off center to port or that she had just one stovepipe, on the starboard side. If this theory is correct, then the *Awa*, of all boats, ought to sail the same way on one tack as she does on the other.

But all of this reverse logic aside (no, on second thought, let's heave it dead astern), the *Awa* would be a very fine boat for family daysailing or coastwise cruising. She would make some fast passages, because she would sail fast under a wide variety of conditions. She would have no bad point of sailing and there would be no force of breeze or state of sea—within reason—that she wouldn't like.

4/ The Ketch *Sunrise*

> Length on deck: 59 feet 3 inches
> Length on waterline: 48 feet 3 inches
> Beam: 14 feet 4 inches
> Draft: 8 feet
> Sail area: 1,826 square feet
> Displacement: 32½ tons
> Designer: Warren Sheppard

Years ago I chanced to have for awhile some bound volumes of *The Rudder* magazine for the years immediately following the turn of the century. I expected these treasures to be gold mines of good boat design and to yield up many nuggets worth careful scrutiny.

The books were disappointing. The average sailing craft of the day, whether 20 feet long or four times that, seemed to be a great, over-rigged, flat-hulled affair on which anything more than the subtlest hint of a nice sheerline was strictly taboo. Evidently the flapper era came to boating a couple of decades early.

Those old volumes are no longer in my possession, but one of the designs—that for a fine, big, able ketch—has been remembered well enough over the years so that her plans could be tracked down and reproduced with the able assistance of Carole Bowker at Mystic Seaport.

The plans of the ketch are beautifully drawn and show much detail. For instance, the inboard section at the forward end of the saloon shows an elaborately carved panel on the divider that crosses the cabin house. Carved into that panel is the name the designer intended for his great creation: *Sunrise.*

All I know about the *Sunrise* is that she was built in Seattle and that her owner "considered the boat to be satisfactory." Indeed. The ketch combines, in my opinion, a very able hull with a very beautiful one. It is not surprising that the *Sunrise* was designed by a marine artist: Warren Sheppard. He intended to have her built for his own use, but never did; it's good, though, that a boat was built to the design. Mr. Sheppard is probably best known for those of his paintings that hang in museums, such as his grand oil of the clipper ship *Flying Cloud* in the U. S. Naval Academy Museum at Annapolis. For my money, though, his best paintings were those he did of smaller craft. Sheppard paintings were used to illustrate two books by Thomas Fleming Day, the editor of *The Rudder* in that era, *Across the Atlantic in Sea Bird*, and *The Voyage of Detroit.* Day, out to prove that well-designed, fully found small boats were safe at sea, crossed the Atlantic in the 25-foot yawl *Sea Bird* in 1911, and the following year did it again in the 35-foot motorboat *Detroit.* Sheppard made paintings of these craft at sea, and they were reproduced in the books. The sense of a small boat offshore has never been better portrayed on a flat surface. The sensibility, knowledge, and ability to perform such a miracle shows up in this design by the artist.

The *Sunrise* is 59 feet 3 inches long on deck,

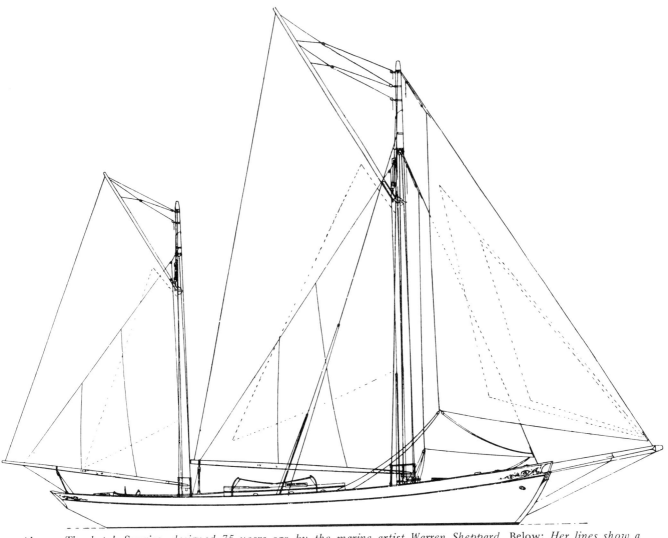

Above: *The ketch* Sunrise, *designed 75 years ago by the marine artist Warren Sheppard.* Below: *Her lines show a handsome hull with a nice sheerline and wineglass sections with plenty of tumblehome.* (The Rudder, *January, 1904)*

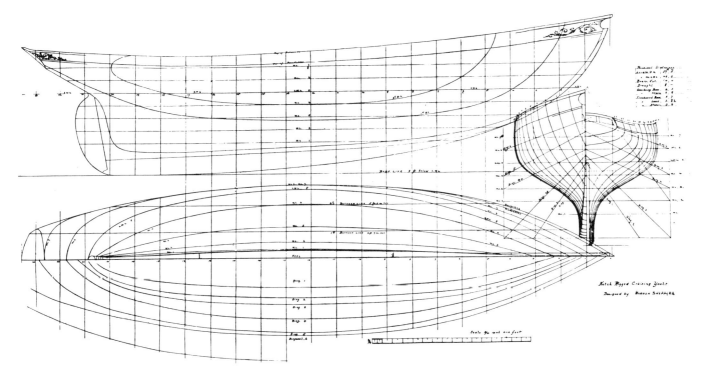

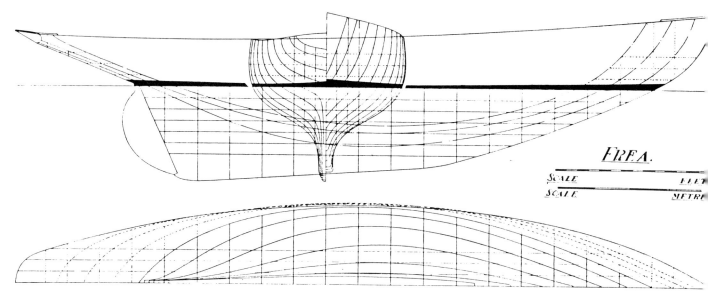

The lines of the Frea, *a ketch of about the same size as the* Sunrise, *designed by William Fife, make an interesting comparison with the* Sunrise. *(Uffa Fox's Second Book by Uffa Fox)*

with a waterline length of 48 feet 3 inches, a beam of 14 feet 4 inches, and a draft of 8 feet. She displaces 32½ tons. Her sail area is 1,826 square feet in the four working sails including the overlapping jib shown.

The ketch has a lovely set of lines. The sections show some beautiful wineglass curves with considerable tumblehome from amidships aft, firm bilges, and a nicely hollowed-out garboard.

It is too bad the artist-designer didn't draw another buttock line between the two shown. Does her run rise too steeply? Is it flat enough? She has a big-ship fullness to the stern that could make her a dull sailer, but I think Sheppard just gets away with it. The great Scottish designer William Fife always gave his boats a flatter, less-steep run than we see on the *Sunrise*, as for example in the *Frea*, a ketch 1 foot 3 inches shorter on the waterline than the *Sunrise*. The *Frea*'s stern would doubtless produce less drag than that of the *Sunrise*, but it would also contribute less righting moment to stability and would be a bit more easily surmounted by a steep following sea.

The *Sunrise* has a bold stem profile (her freeboard forward is 5 feet 7 inches) and a long, fairly deep keel. She should be reasonably dry in a head sea and should hang on well going to windward in rough water.

The ketch's waterlines forward are a good compromise; they are fine enough so that she shouldn't be slowed unduly when punching to windward, yet full enough so that she shouldn't bury her bow unduly when running off before a big following sea. Her rudder would be most efficient, being well aft and nearly vertical, like that of a big sailing ship.

The construction plan shows that the *Sunrise* is very strongly and quite heavily built. Note the generous size of the members in her backbone, of her sheer clamp, and of her two full-length stringers. She should stand long years of hard driving without hogging.

Although the deck beams are of ample scantling, she could benefit from a trick of Sam Crocker's that I always thought made great good sense. This was to make deck beams to which mast partners are bolted heavier than the others. (I never noticed this on our little Crocker yawl until I got old enough to berth forward where the deck beams in way of the mast were what you stared at when you were too excited to go to sleep.)

The ketch rig of the *Sunrise* is well balanced, good looking, and most versatile. Her mainsail has 804 square feet; the mizzen, 425; the forestaysail, 187; and the overlapping jib, 410. The main trysail has 270 square feet; the mizzen trysail, 119; and the storm jib, 118. Under main trysail, mizzen trysail, forestaysail, and storm jib, her working sail area of 1,826 square feet would be reduced to 694 square feet.

On a copy of the sail plan, I couldn't resist drawing in club topsails for both main and mizzen,

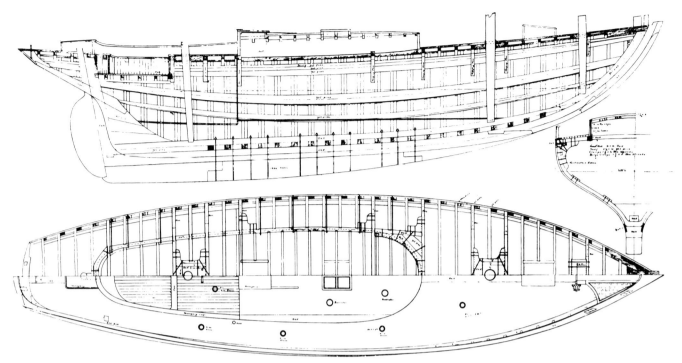

The construction plan of the Sunrise *shows she is strongly built with considerable attention paid to longitudinal stiffness.*
(The Rudder, *January, 1904)*

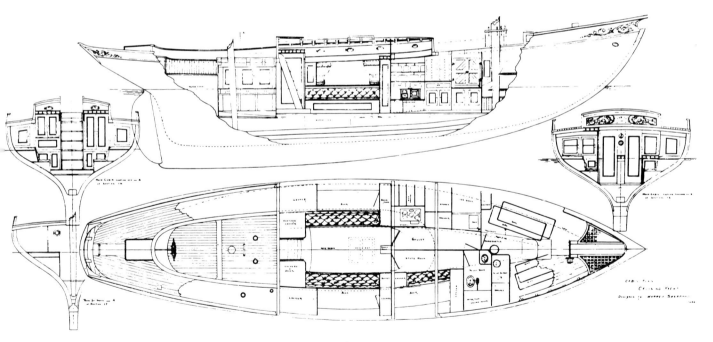

*The layout is spacious indeed. (*The Rudder, *January, 1904)*

the latter surely being a sail to hide below until the Fourth of July. I have spared the reader this addition to Sheppard's handsome sail plan, but in case anyone is interested, the topsails don't detract at all from the vessel's good looks, and they work out to 169 square feet for the main topsail, and 56 square feet for the toy set above the mizzen.

The big working jib shown in the sail plan would be a fine sail indeed. It has enough extra area to really help out in a light or gentle breeze, yet would not obstruct visibility forward or be difficult to handle when tacking. Note that the smaller working jib and the storm jib are set flying on their own halyard well below the masthead. You'd want a way to bring the tacks of these sails in to the stemhead when handing them, and this might involve a jackstay on top of the bowsprit, since the British-style ring around the bowsprit would fetch up on the inner bobstay. A balloon forestaysail would make a fine sail for this boat.

The mainsail would probably have three deep reefs and the mizzen two. Naturally, I'd rig my usual vang from the end of the main gaff to the mizzen trysails, forestaysail, and smallest jib, or reach or run in a real breeze under forestaysail and When they take me away, I'll probably be mumbling, "Just trim that main gaff in a little with that little rope belayed right there on the mizzen mast, won't you, doctor?")

There probably should be more spread to the backstay tackles to eliminate the possibility of a twist.

The ketch would balance well under mainsail and forestaysail or, off the wind, under mainsail alone. She'd also sail well in a strong breeze under headsails and mizzen and would then have set only sails that could be handled by just one person. Her trysails look most practical, with their short, single-halyard gaffs and high tacks. The vessel could get to windward in a hard chance with her main and mizzen trysails, forestaysail, and smallest jib, or reach or run in a real breeze under forestaysail and mizzen trysail.

On deck, her cabin house and cockpit coaming make a unified, nicely shaped oval. This is the kind of handsome detail that is overlooked by many designers. And see her curved bowsprit gratings.

There is enough deck space to carry a dinghy in davits swung in on deck, though she'd block the way forward on that side.

Although Mr. Sheppard never built the Sunrise *for himself as he intended to when he designed her, this vessel was built to her design at Seattle. Her cabin house seems to be longer in both directions than called for by the plans. (*The Rudder, *May, 1918)*

The steering seat could use a divider on the centerline to chock yourself off against when the boat is heeled. You seldom sit directly behind the wheel in a vessel like this. It might be good to have an extension shaft rigged on the steering wheel, like the one the great Irish sailor Conor O'Brien developed, enabling the wheel to be moved forward and higher so you could stand up to it comfortably. There is nothing like being able to shift your position if you're going to steer for awhile. And there would be plenty of times when it would be just as well to stand up to handle this vessel.

There is room for short, fore-and-aft seats in the cockpit just abaft the bridge deck, and such would add a bit of versatility to the cockpit arrangement.

For some reason, I have never liked the looks of an open-work transom. Especially on a pretty stern, it seems to spoil the shape. I suppose the reason for leaving it open is to let water rushing aft on deck keep right on going over the stern, but I guess I'd rather put up with what little water the closed transom trapped and threw back than cut into a stern's good looks.

There is no apparent entry into the steerage under the bridge deck. She could have a hatch on one side of this deck, clear of the short mainsheet horse and far enough off center so that when it was left open inadvertently somebody wouldn't rush up out of the companionway only to fall right back down into the boat again. In this era of going places at high speed, many folks, I am sure, could think up an obvious use for this nice, big, versatile steerage, but anybody who can mentally cut a propeller aperture out of this hull has far more fortitude than I have.

The ketch has seven bunks, just the right number for a big, offshore boat. You'd have a master and six watch-standers. In fair and settled weather, two people in a watch could have the luxury of standing one in three, while in hard weather watches of three each could stand port and starboard. Incidentally, on a long cruise, it's really better not to rotate the watches very often, but rather stand the same watches every day for a week or two. Even the midwatch isn't too bad after a few days of adjusting your metabolism to it.

This is the only Warren Sheppard design that I know of, and she is one of my favorite designs. A few years after designing the *Sunrise,* Sheppard wrote that she was still his own favorite dream ship.

Sometimes when studying this design, I find myself wishing that all great marine artists had designed boats. How about a nice schooner from the board of Gordon Grant? Or a handsome cutter designed by Montague Dawson? I guess we should be grateful that some marine artists, like Warren Sheppard, designed boats as well as painted pictures of them.

5/ The *Tern II*

Length on deck: 39 feet
Length on waterline: 30 feet
Beam: 9 feet
Draft: 6 feet
Sail area: 710 square feet
Designer: Stowe & Son

One of the most experienced and expert British yachtsmen of the early part of this century was Claud Worth. He owned a succession of boats, to each of which he made carefully worked-out modifications. His last two boats he designed himself.

Mr. Worth wrote articles on design, maintenance, and seamanship for the leading British boating magazines of his day. And he wrote two fine books on cruising, *Yacht Cruising* and *Yacht Navigation and Voyaging,* the former of which in particular became a highly respected text for his own and succeeding generations of small boat sailors. *Yacht Cruising* was published in 1910 and went through several printings, one quite recent.

While Claud Worth was designing the boat of his dreams, a big cutter with the best features of many of the boats in which he had cruised, he looked about for "a small yacht for temporary use." What he found was the *White Kitten,* a traditional English cutter with a tiny mizzen perched on her long, fine counter to make her, technically, a yawl. She had been designed and built by Stowe & Son of Shoreham on the south coast of England in 1899. Mr. Worth bought her in 1910. He ended up keeping her several years.

He had had a little cutter named the *Tern,* and he renamed the yawl the *Tern II,* in the belief that "one good *Tern* deserves another."

She has all the earmarks of the usual English plank-on-edge cutter, but she is not as extreme as many of them were.

You wouldn't think the combination of a plumb bow with no overhang at all would go well with its exact opposite, a stern with a very long overhang, but somehow it does. Perhaps it is the very strength of the contrast between bow and stern that makes these boats handsome. It may be that at the time when Mr. Worth was sailing the *Tern II* her looks were well accepted merely because they were so common. Yet I think this boat makes a very handsome design for today, though she would hardly be considered common in appearance.

One thing that helps her looks greatly is the clean sweep of her sheer unbroken by deck structures of any height.

This boat would certainly be weatherly and would have an easy motion in rough water. She would pitch some when working into a head sea, but her pitching would not slow her down unduly, for the verticality of the sections that would allow it makes for a very fine entrance that would tend to carry through a wave. Mr. Worth said she carried on well when going to windward in a chop, but that she could throw spray. Her freeboard forward is 4 feet 3 inches.

The *Tern II* is 39 feet long on deck, with a

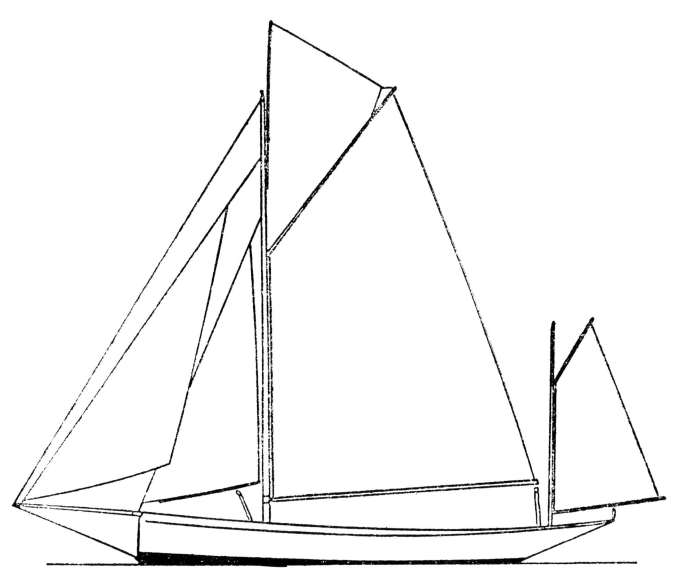

The Tern II *was, for a time, owned by the astute and experienced British yachtsman Claud Worth.* (Yacht Cruising *by Claud Worth*)

waterline length of 30 feet, a beam of 9 feet, and a draft of 6 feet. It is her beam and draft that are in moderate proportion by comparison with the more extreme plank-on-edge cutters, some of which were no broader than they were deep. The *Tern II* has the typical sections of the plank-on-edge boats, with straight topsides, little turn to the bilge, and little hollow to the garboard. Her bow and buttock lines are deep, but her waterlines are exceedingly fine.

All the yawl's ballast is outside, and Mr. Worth cautioned that in a hull like hers you had to concentrate the ballast pretty well amidships, otherwise her sharp bow would dive too deep.

The yawl's scantlings are fairly heavy. The stem and stern posts, of oak, are sided 7 inches. She has alternate double and single sawn frames, of oak, sided 3½ inches and molded 4½ inches at the heels and 3 inches at the heads, spaced on 15-inch centers. She has wrought-iron floors and steel hanging knees. The topside planking is of teak; the bottom planking is 1¼-inch pitch-pine. The deck is 1⅜-inch yellow pine.

The *Tern II*'s sail area is 710 square feet, with 400 in the mainsail, 75 in the staysail; jib 100, topsail 70, and mizzen only 65.

Her yawl rig looks like a caricature; the mizzen looks too tiny to be anything but a joke. Yet in a

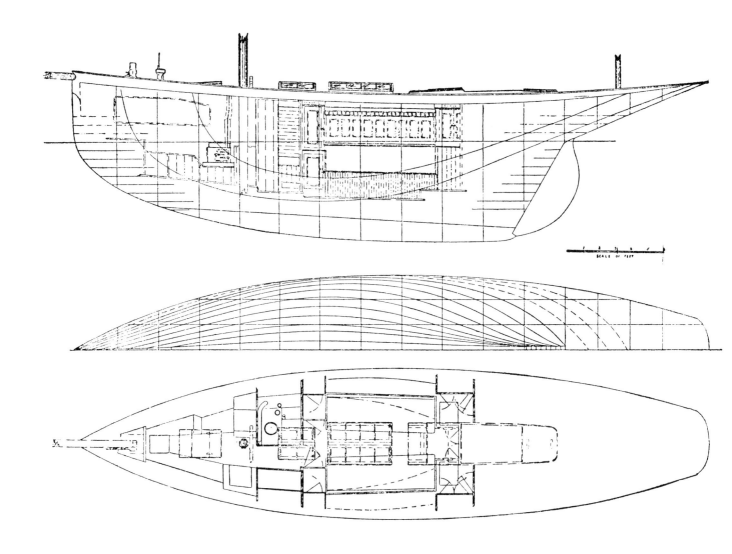

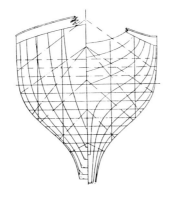

Her lines show her hull to be that of the typically English plank-on-edge cutter of her time, though she is not nearly as deep and narrow as were some of them. (Yacht Cruising by Claud Worth)

The Tern II *at anchor, showing the clean sweep of her sheer, sheered waterline forward, and nicely cocked-up mizzen boom. But the bowsprit, instead of carrying out these nice lines, droops down parallel to the horizon, a foolishness the British fortunately later outgrew. (*Yacht Cruising *by Claud Worth)*

squall with the mainsail down, the toy mizzen would help balance her. And besides, the thing would keep people from falling off her long, fine stern into the water.

To shorten her down, you'd probably want to start by reefing the mainsail—easy with Worth's own design for a roller reefing gear—and then take in the mizzen and go to a smaller jib. Then you could roll down some more mainsail and take in the small jib, leaving just the forestaysail (or foresail as the schoonerless English call it) standing forward.

Mr. Worth replaced the lower mast and long, housing topmast that were in the *White Kitten*

with a pole mast of shorter overall length. Then, to retain sail area, he set a jackyard topsail on the pole mast. It is Worth's modified sail plan that is shown. For light sails on this boat, you'd want a big, overlapping, high-cut jib and a balloon staysail.

Her bowsprit looks fine in the sail plan but terrible in the photograph. Fortunately, the English have broken their bad habit of spoiling nice sheerlines with droopy bowsprits, and doubtless they keep themselves and their jibs a bit drier in the bargain.

Claud Worth put a kerosene engine under the *Tern II*'s watertight, self-draining cockpit.

This cockpit is little more than a footwell, so the

*Her flush deck looks well with its low companionway and skylights. The husky dinghy is hoisted out against its fenders. The vessel's lady looks well protected against the ravages of the English sun. (*Yacht Cruising *by Claud Worth)*

spaciousness of the boat's flush deck would be particularly appreciated. She has 7½-inch bulwarks, and Mr. Worth added lifelines 20 inches high.

The dinghy stows upside down over the skylight and is hoisted out on the forestaysail halyard and a tackle rigged to a thimble seized to the running backstay about eight feet above the deck. In the photograph of the *Tern II* at anchor, you can see the dinghy hoisted to the rail—a better place for it at night in a tideway than bumping up under the counter—and kept off the topsides by two padded wooden fenders.

Going down her companionway you find nice lockers on both sides of it at the after end of the saloon. This is a handy place for lockers and they give a symmetrical, finished-off look to the saloon that most boats don't have.

In the profile drawing, you can see some elegant paneling along the sides of the saloon. This paneling hid two swing-down berths, one on each side, and Mr. Worth was particularly proud of the ingeniousness with which he designed them. I'll let him show them off to you:

> On each side of the saloon, above the padded sofa back, is a piece of wainscot containing nine little panels. The wainscot was set back about eight inches, leaving a shelf of this width, which was of no use except to collect odds and ends, and make the cabin look untidy. There is a little shelf above the wainscot about six inches below the deck. We brought the lower edge of the wainscot forward to the level of the sofa back, and the upper edge to the level of the upper shelf. Four strong hinges were then fixed on the lower edge of the wainscot, and the upper edge was secured by three concealed locks opened by a small railway key. We had made for each side a steel spring cot with tubular frame. The cot, instead of being hinged at the lower edge, is hung on a sort of trunnion at each end six inches from the edge. When the cot is turned down for use the lower edge turns up against oak chocks, so that supporting cords for the cot are not required. Six little brass chains, sliding on brass rods four inches long, pass from the upper

edge of the cot to the wainscot and support the latter when the berths are open. Before folding up the berths four pairs of webbing straps are tied to keep the horsehair mattress, blankets, and pillows in place.

> No visitor even suspects the presence of these berths until he is shown them. They are very comfortable and, being high up, are healthy and airy. The sofas, which were formerly used for sleeping upon, are still available for the purpose if one should ever wish to berth four people in the saloon.

In truth, the *Tern II*'s saloon, with its berths concealed behind handsome paneling, and its symmetrical lockers in each corner, must be one of the nicest in any boat of her size.

The boat's galley is in her fo'c's'le. I think I'd make the head and wardrobe opposite it into a full-width galley just forward of the saloon, and relegate the head to the fo'c's'le. It's a question of priorities.

Claud Worth and his family had some good cruising in the *Tern II*, including a six-week exploration of the coast of France in 1912 described in *Yacht Cruising*. Mr. Worth wrote of the boat: "*Tern II* is a fine sea-boat and easy in her motion. She is light to steer and very steady on her helm. With the wind anywhere forward of the beam she will sail herself with the helm lashed. With a good working breeze she will turn to windward in a narrow channel, shooting a great distance each time in stays. But in light winds, she will not come round on her heel and wriggle through a narrow ditch in the same way that *Maud* will."

[The *Maud* was Mr. Worth's 42-foot double-ended ketch designed by William Fife. See *Good Boats*, pages 24-27.]

The yawl—tiny though her mizzen may be—would be an admirable little vessel to sail in any reasonable weather. Sitting in her cockpit with her long tiller crooked under your arm, with an unobstructed view across her flush deck, watching her work her way through a seaway—well, that would be all right.

6/ The *Faith*

Length on deck: 55 feet
Length on waterline: 43 feet
Beam: 13 feet
Draft: 8 feet
Sail area: 1,275 square feet
Designer: Harold Clayton

We young fellers were some excited when, right after World War II, there showed up in the nearby harbor of Stonington, Connecticut, a real live Bristol Channel pilot cutter. We'd read all about their feats of derring-do in screaming gales in the books of such "authorities" as E. Keble Chatterton, and now here was one of them in our own home waters!

We rowed round and round her at close quarters drinking in her every feature, from the high, straight bow, with its planking painted a dull black, to the huge, round, main boom, to her rugged counter stern with the name *Frances* painted on it. She was a big, able craft, and the two white wicker deck chairs arranged on the stern seemed out of place.

This was the vessel in which Alec Morison, a retired Royal Navy Commander, had set out from England in 1937 with his two sons on a cruise around the world. They went south and crossed the Atlantic to the West Indies, riding out a 90-knot hurricane near Barbados with the help of two sea anchors and considerable fish oil. They sailed north to New England and were about to leave for Bermuda, the Panama Canal, and the South Seas, when the voyage was interrupted by the war.

The *Frances* spent most of the war years laid up in the Mystic River. Robert F. Tatro, of Mystic, wrote me that as a 15-year-old he helped Commander Morison overhaul her after the war in anticipation of continuing the round-the-world voyage. The needs of the vessel outran Commander Morison's resources, however, and he had to abandon his plans and sell her. A couple of young fellows bought her cheap and headed south in her. She went ashore on the New Jersey coast and was a total loss. But she sure gave us a thrill while she was in Stonington.

Chatterton needn't have waxed so dramatic about the deeds of the Bristol Channel pilot cutters. Just the bare facts, as presented by such later historians as Edgar J. March and, more recently, Peter J. Stuckey, make exciting enough reading.

The Bristol Channel is a 100-mile-long funnel with a 30-mile-wide mouth open to the west. Into the funnel sweeps a succession of North Atlantic gales. There are places in the Channel where the rise and fall of tide is 48 feet, and a current of three knots out in the open water of the Channel is perfectly normal. With a strong spring ebb pouring out to steepen the big mature seas of a westerly gale, the Channel was not conducive to the orderly goings and comings of merchant shipping that its several thriving ports, backed, in particular, by the

The 52-foot Bristol Channel pilot cutter Frances. *(Yachting, April, 1944)*

Welsh coalfields, demanded. It was up to the Bristol Channel pilots, in their stout cutters, to serve the needs of commerce despite the weather. In the process, they had to make a competitive living, seeking to board as many large, deeply laden vessels in a year as they could. The successful ones were hard working, smart, and well-nigh fearless. To take a big vessel out, drop off into your punt (dinghy), get back aboard your skiff (pilot cutter), and then pit your mind and body against the elements, the other pilots, and the not-always-predictable arrival of vessels in order to be the one to board a big, deep-water freighter running in for your port—well, that was an accomplishment!

The boats used by the pilots for this demanding service evolved from fishing craft. Over the years, the pilots gave their boats distinctive characteristics to meet their own special requirements.

Since he spent most of his life going, coming,

and seeking in his vessel, often in rough water, a pilot's prime requirement was for a boat with an easy motion, particularly an easy roll, and one steady enough on her helm not to need attention when hove to and not to object to her helm being lashed for a few minutes on nearly any point of sail. The boats had to be able to put the miles astern steadily, but real speed was not a consideration, and the Bristol Channel pilot cutters were not particularly fast, especially to windward. This is not to say that they were not weatherly, for they could make headway to windward against frightful conditions of wind and sea.

Perhaps the most famous Bristol Channel pilot cutter was the *Mischief* in which H.W. Tilman, the British mountaineer, sailed to climbing objectives all over the world. She was built at Cardiff in 1906 by Thomas Baker. She was 45 feet long on deck, with a beam of 13 feet, a draft of 7 feet 6 inches,

Commander Alec Morison on board his vessel. (Yachting, *April, 1944)*

and a displacement of 55 tons. In a case of a man being named after a boat, her first pilot-owner, William Morgan, was known as Billy the Mischief during the 13 years he had her. She went to yachting in 1927. Tilman bought her at Mallorca in 1954. He sailed the *Mischief* to Kerguelen Island, 2,700 miles southeast of Cape Town; to the South Shetland Islands, south of Cape Horn; to both coasts of Greenland; to Patagonia; and around Africa. He sailed her more than 100,000 miles. Two mountains and a cape were named after her. Tilman lost her in 1968 near the island of Jan Mayen in the Arctic Ocean.

Tilman next bought the Bristol Channel pilot cutter *Sea Breeze,* a 49-footer built in 1899 by J. Bowden at Porthleven. He sailed her over 15,000 miles to Greenland and Iceland and lost her in 1972 on the east coast of Greenland.

He then bought the *Baroque,* another Bristol Channel pilot cutter, built in 1902 by J. Hambly of Cardiff. I saw the *Baroque,* a 50-footer, hauled out at Lymington, England, for some repairs after a voyage to Spitsbergen. Looking at her big, able hull, and thinking about her indomitable master, it seemed perfectly natural that that's where she had just come from.

While these Bristol Channel pilot cutters are all most interesting craft, the most fascinating of all the breed to me is the *Faith,* for she shows the

thinking of an innovator familiar with the type applied to the traditional craft.

Her port was Barry, Wales. She was the first—and perhaps the only—pilot cutter built from plans instead of a model. She was designed by Harold Clayton, a yacht designer, and was built in 1904 at the Penarth (Wales) Yacht Building Company.

Before examining her in detail and comparing her to her immediate ancestors, let's look a bit more closely at these ancestors and at what they did. For much of the following discussion, I am indebted to the writings of the aforementioned Messrs. March and Stuckey in their respective books, *Inshore Craft of Britain in the Days of Sail and Oar,* Volume 2, and *The Sailing Pilots of the Bristol Channel.*

It cannot be said that the Bristol Channel pilot cutters were not seaworthy boats. Very few of them were lost through the years by foundering, though there were losses from being run down by vessels in poor visibility.

The boats were hove to generally under foresail and mainsail, both reefed as need be to suit the wind strength, with the foresail backed and the mainsail just luffing, the helm being lashed a little down. Balanced thus, a skiff would require no attention and would make just a little headway and a little to weather.

These craft achieved what was reputed to be a

Outbound vessels would sometimes oblige the pilot by taking his skiff in tow, so that when his work was done she would be handy. This is the bark Asta *outward bound in the Bristol Channel off Portishead. The pilot boat is from Cardiff. (National Maritime Museum, Greenwich, England)*

very easy motion partly from their hull shape and partly from the fact that all their ballast was inside. After World War I, power vessels took over the pilotage duties from the skiffs, and a number of the skiffs went to yachting. In converting the skiffs for pleasure use, yachtsmen often changed from inside to outside ballast, and though they thus gained stability and probably speed to windward through the ability to carry more sail, they lost that easy roll that gave pilots a comfortable home afloat.

The normal complement of a skiff was the pilot who owned her and two men. This was the minimum convenient crew for boarding a vessel. The vessel would make a lee. The skiff would sail into it and her punt would be launched from the deck. One of the men would row or scull the pilot over to the vessel in the punt, while the other man handled the skiff, sailing her out from under the vessel's lee so the vessel would not drift down on her. Once the pilot was on board, the skiff would circle back to pick up the punt and then the skiff would be homeward bound, two-handed, to rendezvous with the pilot. If the pilot were taking a vessel out from the home port, the vessel would

often tow the skiff to sea so the skiff would be handy to take off the pilot when he had finished his job.

It was a tough life, taken all in all, but in the early 1900s a hardworking, smart pilot could make $3,250 in a year if he did not have too much bad luck.

In 1908, there were about 100 pilot cutters in the Bristol Channel. Most of the ports were on the north, or Wales, side, the primary ones being Neath, Port Talbot, Barry, Cardiff, and Newport. There was also Swansea, which, for some reason, always had schooner-rigged pilot boats with well-raked masts, short gaffs, and an overlapping foresail, thus showing considerable influence from Holland. At the head of the Channel, there was Gloucester Sharpness, and, on the south side, there was, of course, Bristol itself.

Edgar March quoted one of the pilots, Captain H.S. Watkins, as follows:

"We had all shapes and sizes sailing the Channel by 1912, boats up to 60 ft. long, small flat-sterned boats, boats with sharp raking stems, spoon bows, hollow bows. The *Alpha* of Barry had no forefoot at all, straight stem to the waterline, then a curve

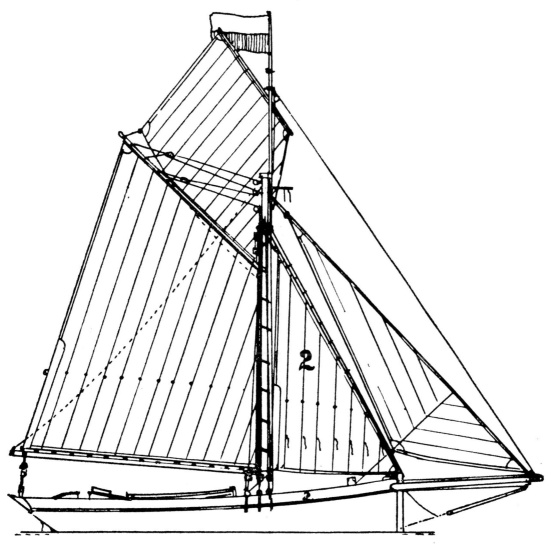

The Hilda, *a typical Bristol Channel pilot cutter at the turn of the century.*

Lines of the Hilda. She was 49 feet long on deck and drew 8 feet of water. (Inshore Craft of Britain in the Days of Sail and Oar *by Edgar J. March)*

Traced from plans lent by Captain H.B Watkins, Pilot, 1966.

Edgar J. March
1966

The Faith *was the first Bristol Channel pilot cutter to be built from plans rather than from a model and the first to have any outside ballast. (The Yachting and Boating Monthly,* 1908)

to the heel; some full-bodied, some had hollow bilges, fitted topmasts, pole masts, steel booms, cross-cut sails, hulls mostly painted black, some near black, one belonging to Barry was blue, the bottoms were treated with anti-fouling black, white, red, green, all the colours of the rainbow. Each expressing the ideas of the owner within the limits of the local bye-laws."

A typical pilot boat of the period was the *Hilda* built by J. Cooper at Pill (on the English side) in 1899. She was 49 feet long on deck, with a waterline length of 43 feet, a beam of 13 feet 5 inches, and a draft of 8 feet. She cost $1,750. She did not have a long life, for on the night of November 4, 1912, she was run down by the tug *Brunel.*

It is interesting to compare the lines of the *Hilda* with those of the French pilot cutter *Jolie Brise,* described in the next chapter. The two pilot boats are quite similar, really, but the French boat is just a bit more graceful and refined.

A skiff would be lofted from a half-model, which would have been much examined and discussed by the owner, the builder, and their friends, and then finally would be approved by the owner. They were heavily built craft. The keel would typically be a single piece of elm some 40 feet long, 18 inches deep, and 6 inches wide. The frames were from 4 inches by 3 inches to 6 inches by 3 inches of sawn oak and were put in doubled from 16 to 18 inches apart. Planking was 2½-inch stuff. The hulls were salted. Decks were of pine, 1¾ inches thick. There were heavy knees throughout, a heavy shelf, and two heavy longitudinal stringers. Ballast was, as said, all inside and usually scrap iron. The pilots had a fetish about keeping weight out of the ends of their boats.

The rig was the usual British cutter with plenty

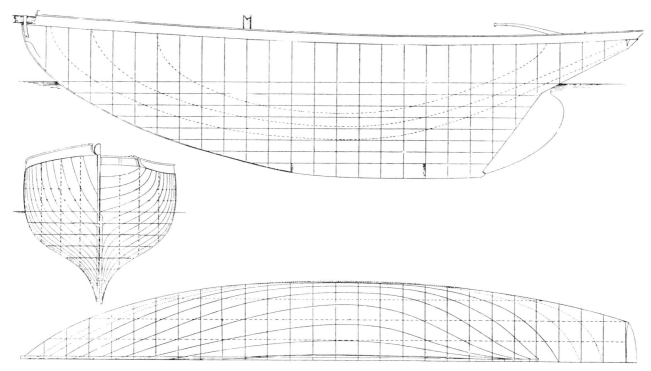

Her lines show a heavy vessel that would hang on well to windward, have a reasonable turn of speed, and perhaps be a bit wet on deck in rough weather. (The Yachting and Boating Monthly, *1908)*

of different-sized sails to suit the conditions. There was generally a small mainsail for use in the winter, and also a storm trysail with a short gaff. The boats normally carried two jibs smaller than the working jib, a tiny spitfire for really heavy weather, and a "slave," so called because it almost always seemed to be set.

A worm roller reefing gear was developed by Williams of Appledore and was adopted by most of the pilot boats soon after the turn of the century. It was often called the Appledore gear.

The roller reefing gear enabled the man on watch to lash the helm and reef the mainsail on most any point of sailing without disturbing his mate below. The gear did have disadvantages, though: when the sail was reefed, its foot couldn't be stretched tight, so the sail became baggy and didn't set as well as did a reefed sail with the clew pennant hauled out hard. Also, the sheet had to be attached at the end of the boom, but as the sail was reefed, the straining leech came inboard on the boom, with the result that a number of booms were broken in heavy weather.

The foresail (or forestaysail as we would call it) usually had two sets of reef points. It was always loose-footed.

Light sails were important, too. Often a big jackyard main topsail of some description would be on board in addition to a working topsail. There was a working jib topsail and also a "spinnaker," or big overlapping jib topsail. In addition, there was a full-cut balloon foresail.

The pilots wanted no standing rigging other than what they deemed absolutely necessary. They had three wire shrouds per side set up with deadeyes and lanyards, and the necessary headstays. There were no running backstays and no bowsprit shrouds. The bobstay was rigged running with a tackle, for the bowsprit was often run inboard in bad weather. There were no topmast backstays. The pilots felt that this kind of rig, which allowed mast and bowsprit plenty of spring and natural play, gave the boats a liveliness that would have been lost with a tightly stayed rig.

All the halyards and sheets led aft to the cockpit where they were belayed to stout samson posts running through the deck outboard of the coaming.

Since the boats were often handled by one man, they were often jibed all standing, and so the main sheet horse was kept quite short and had heavy buffers on either end of it, either of rubber or consisting of coil springs.

The boats were always steered with a tiller from

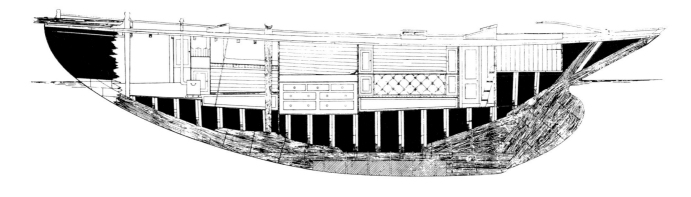

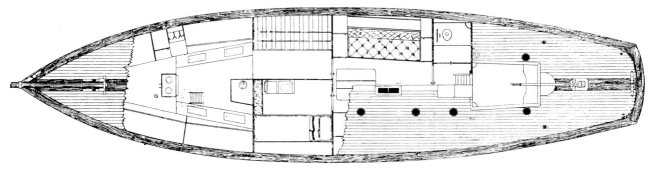

The Faith's *deck and accommodation plans show the standard arrangement for the type except for the little skylight over the saloon and the private stateroom for the pilot. (*The Yachting and Boating Monthly, *1908)*

Who wouldn't trade places with the man on the Faith's *spreader? (*The Yachting and Boating Monthly, *1908)*

a small, self-draining, watertight cockpit whose only seat went across its after end.

Forward, on deck, were huge triple bitts looking outsize for the boats until you remember that they were often towed at some speed by the vessels they were serving. The bowsprit heel was lodged between the center bitt and the starboard one, and the anchor windlass was housed between the center bitt and the port one.

Each pilot skiff carried her own punt, a big, heavy, clinker-built, transom-sterned, round-bottomed dinghy from 10 to 14 feet long. The punts were always carried on deck on the port side. They were launched and recovered usually by simply manhandling them overboard and back on deck, taking as much advantage of the skiff's roll as possible in the process. Sometimes a burton would be rigged to the masthead to take the weight of the punt on a bridle to assist the operation, but most pilots and crews preferred simply to lift her stern up on the bulwarks if they were low, and shove her overboard, or work her stern out through a removable section of the bulwarks if they were high.

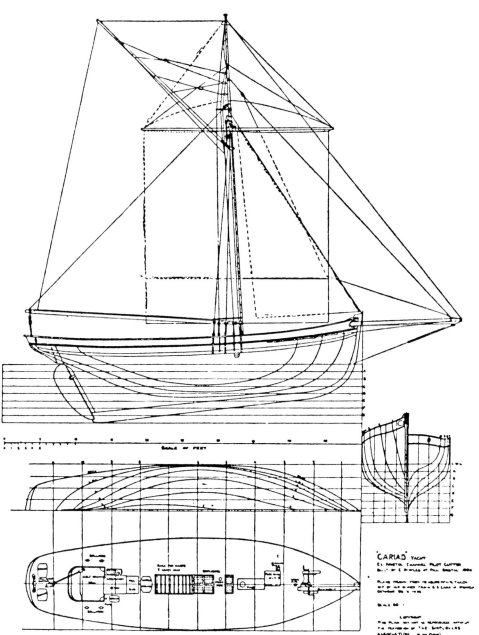

Plans of the Cariad, *a Bristol Channel pilot cutter built by E. Rowles of Pill in 1904 and converted to a yacht in 1926 by Frank G. G. Carr. She is 47 feet 6 inches long on deck, with a waterline length of 41 feet, a beam of 12 feet 9 inches, and a draft of 8 feet. She is preserved at the Exeter Maritime Museum in England.* (A Yachtsman's Log *by Frank G. G. Carr)*

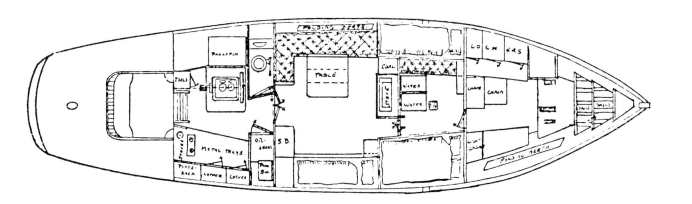

When recovering, the process would be reversed, and the bow would be lifted aboard first as the rail rolled down. The story persists that punts sometimes were made fast to the main boom by their painters and were then jibed aboard!

Manhandling the punt didn't always work smoothly, of course. Peter Stuckey quotes one of the pilots, Captain George Buck, as follows: "Getting the punt back on board, we had lifted her forefoot out of the water when the skiff gave a heavy lurch and my mate slipped on the deck, letting go the painter. I could not hold her and she slipped back into the water, filled and was gone in the darkness." But they found her and picked her up next morning.

To give space for handling the punt, the decks were kept clear of obstructions. The only hatches were the companionway at the forward end of the cockpit and a small hatch forward of the mast leading into the fo'c's'le. There were no skylights, daytime illumination below being through a number of deadlights set flush in the deck. Ventilation below was non-existent. Perhaps it was not wanted by men who spent most of their lives on deck in all seasons.

These were the Bristol Channel pilot cutters as known by Harold Clayton of Penarth, Wales, near Cardiff. He applied his own ideas to the type and drew the plans of the yacht-like *Faith.*

She is 55 feet long on deck, with a waterline length of 43 feet, a beam of 13 feet, and a draft of 8 feet. In her three working sails, she has a sail area of 1,275 square feet, of which 850 square feet is in her mainsail. Her mainmast stands 40 feet high, with the topmast going up another 23 feet. The bowsprit is 14 feet outboard. Her main boom is 35 feet long.

Compared to a typical Bristol Channel pilot cutter, the *Faith* has a spoon bow instead of the plumb stem, a relatively long counter, a cutaway forefoot, less drag to her keel, more hollow garboards, and has her greatest beam farther aft. The *Faith* was the first of the pilot boats to have some outside ballast.

Compared to her ancestors, the *Faith* would be handier in stays, faster, especially to windward, but less steady on the helm. Compared to a boat like the *Hilda,* she would probably have a quicker roll and take more water on deck.

The *Faith*'s sail plan is typical of the type, with the mast set well aft giving a large foresail. The club topsail shown would probably seldom be set except on regatta days.

The interior arrangement of the *Faith* is normal except that her pilot's berth is partitioned off into a separate stateroom, and she appears to lack the usual enclosed berths outboard of the transoms in the main saloon. There is a big storage area in the passageway between the fo'c's'le and saloon and another opposite the W.C. in the steerage aft. Her galley is in the big fo'c's'le.

It is nice to have a big, separate saloon uncluttered by paraphernalia for cooking, navigating, etc. It would seem natural in this boat to move the galley aft out of the fo'c's'le to the storage area on the starboard side abaft the mast.

The era of competitive piloting ended at Barry in 1915, and the *Faith* was sold as a yacht soon thereafter. I don't know what has become of her.

Whether or not the *Faith* is still in existence, a number of the Bristol Channel pilot cutters in England are still around. The *Cariad* is well preserved at the Exeter Marine Museum. This 47½-footer was built at Pill in 1904 by Rowles for Thomas Richards of Cardiff. During part of her career she was sailed as a yacht by Mr. F.G.G. Carr, former director of the National Maritime Museum at Greenwich. The Barry skiff *Kindly Light,* also a yacht during part of her career, is restored at Cardiff.

No longer do the Bristol Channel pilot cutters go "seeking downalong." But the design of these vessels is still highly relevant for ocean cruising, in my opinion, for they did meet their prime objective, that of providing a safe, comfortable craft for people who were at sea in any weather.

7 / The *Jolie Brise*

Length on deck: 56 feet
Length on waterline: 48 feet
Beam: 15 feet 9 inches
Draft: 10 feet 2 inches
Sail area: 2,400 square feet
Displacement: 55 tons
Designer: M. Paumelle

M. Paumelle of Le Havre, France, might not be remembered today, at least in the English-speaking world, were it not for the fact that one of the Le Havre pilot cutters that he modelled and built became a famous English yacht in the Twenties and Thirties.

Even so, in all that has been published on the great *Jolie Brise,* nothing has been written about the man who created her—except that he was simply, M. Paumelle. No one who knew even bothered to indicate whether the M. was his first initial, or whether it stood for Monsieur. I wish I knew more about him and about the other craft he must have designed and built.

We can, at least, be thankful that one of his vessels came to be well known.

The *Jolie Brise* was built in 1913 to serve the Havre pilots, who often took their boats 300 miles to the westward to meet incoming vessels off Land's End. As is well known, the English Channel can be very rough, and what was wanted was a vessel that could keep the sea in most any weather, at the same time providing a comfortable home for her pilots.

There was no need for either large carrying capacity or high speed, though the boats had to be smart under sail and, above all, they had to be weatherly, so they would not be driven off station and perhaps ashore in heavy weather. In other words, the requirements for a pilot boat are remarkably similar to those for an offshore cruising boat.

Lieutenant Commander E. George Martin, Royal Navy, bought the *Jolie Brise* in the mid-1920s for use as a cruising boat. Commander Martin was the founder and first Commodore of the Royal Ocean Racing Club. Then the *Brise* was owned in the late Twenties and Thirties by another well-known English yachtsman, Robert Somerset.

Although the *Jolie Brise* was certainly not built for racing, she gained a great reputation as an ocean racer in the days when ocean racers were not yet designed specifically for that sport and when the races themselves were sailed more in terms of merely making a fast passage rather than in terms of sailing the perfect race.

Commander Martin and his friends came up with the idea of a race down the Channel from Cowes, across a little corner of the Atlantic to the Fastnet Rock off the southern tip of Ireland, and return as far as Plymouth. The distance was 615 miles. It's a tough course, because it involves so much coastal sailing in an area of highly changeable weather and strong tides.

E. G. Martin, who owned the Jolie Brise *in the Twenties, steering his vessel during a crossing of the Atlantic in 1926. The big trysail is set, and her mainsail is covered up, being saved for the Bermuda Race. (*Yachting, *October, 1928)*

The *Jolie Brise* was the boat to beat in the early years of the Fastnet Race. In seven starts, she had three firsts and a second. In the first race she won, the first Fastnet in 1925, Martin beat six other entries in predominantly light going. In 1929, Bobby Somerset brought her home first against nine other competitors in predominantly moderate breezes. In 1930, Somerset did it again against nine competitors in mainly heavy weather.

The *Jolie Brise* also entered two Bermuda Races, which involved four transatlantic passages. In 1926, Martin was fifth in Class A and first in Class C (for "fishermen" types).

In 1932, Bobby Somerset sailed her back to America and set off for Bermuda in the race. Accompanying the racing fleet was the schooner *Adriana*, too big to be officially entered. One night she caught fire, and it was the *Jolie Brise*'s people who saw her distress flare and dropped out of the race to help her. Somerset lay the *Brise* right alongside the *Adriana* and was able to take off all of her crew but her helmsman, Clarence Kozlay, who, by the time he had seen everyone else safely off the *Adriana*, couldn't jump the widening gap between the vessels and fell in and drowned.

The lines of the *Jolie Brise* were taken off the boat by J. Laurent Giles. She is somewhat more delicately modelled than her English counterparts of the same time, the Bristol Channel pilot cutters, although in later years the latter had their forefoots somewhat cut away and were given slight overhangs forward.

The *Jolie Brise* is 56 feet long on deck, with a waterline length of 48 feet, a beam of 15 feet 9 inches, and a draft of 10 feet 2 inches. She displaces 55 tons and has a sail area of 2,400 square feet. As can be seen from her lines and dimensions, she is a very big boat for her waterline length.

Her lines exude sea-keeping ability. There are some beautiful curves in her sections, and her waterlines are slightly hollow at the bow.

Her rig, though generous, is not huge and is very versatile. After the topsails come off in blowing weather, the mainsail is reefed as it continues to breeze on and the headsails are changed to smaller sizes. She would probably have one smaller staysail than the working staysail and at least two smaller jibs than the working jib, including a diminutive spitfire. She often used a trysail, and when George

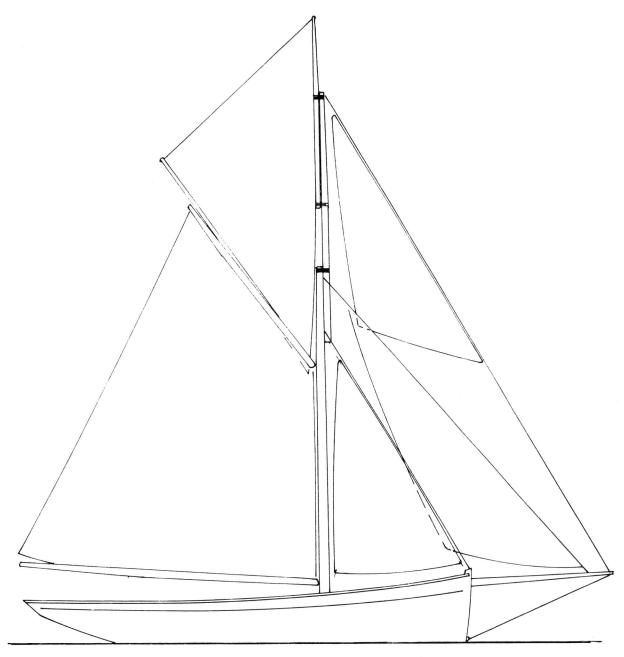

The big pilot cutter carries plenty of sail to drive her heavy hull.

Martin sailed her across the Atlantic to go in the Bermuda Race, he used a gaff trysail with a small topsail set above it and small headsails, so as to save his best sails for the race.

She could also have some bigger jib topsails for light weather and could, of course, sport a huge balloon jib topsail if wanted.

The club main topsail shown was a sail for light weather; she also had a working main topsail without club or yard, reaching just to the topmast head and end of the gaff. Martin had an interesting way of keeping this working topsail to the mast

using running leaders, as shown in his drawing. These allowed the sail to be set or handed from the deck and, because they ran on the mast, let the topsail be set over a reefed mainsail as well as over the full sail.

On his westward crossing of the Atlantic, Martin chose the southern trade-wind route, and for his passage he fitted the *Jolie Brise* with a square rig. The yard consisted of two 14-foot poles fitted rigidly to goosenecks on the mast just below the forestay. As well as spreading a squaresail, these poles were used to spread the foot of a triangular

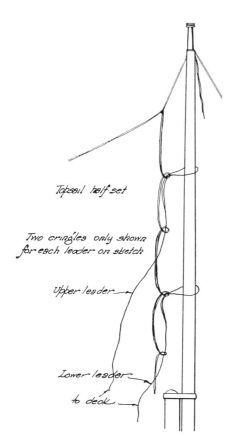

Topsail half set

Two cringles only shown
for each leader on sketch

Upper leader

Lower leader

to deck

The arrangement of the leaders to keep the working main topsail to the mast. (Yachting, April, 1928)

raffee set from the topmasthead. The squaresail and raffee were each made up in two vertical halves laced together up the center. The area of both sails totalled 1,200 square feet.

There was plenty of rolling and plenty of chafe when sailing in the trades under these two sails and Martin learned to use chain in the nips of blocks, just as was done on a big, square-rigged ocean freighter.

Commander Martin never put power in the *Jolie Brise,* at first because he couldn't afford to, and later because he was having too much fun sailing her without an engine. He wrote, "I found such renewed pleasure in handling the ship without it that I lost all desire for a motor and realized that I should be spoiling the ship if I fitted one."

With her wide flush decks and high bulwarks, the cutter provides outstanding working conditions for the people handling her big sails. She steers with a long tiller, the helmsman sitting on a 'thwartships bench that runs right across the vessel.

Below, the *Jolie Brise* is laid out to be a practical sailing vessel. Her saloon is indeed spacious, her

galley is forward where it should be in a boat this size, and her chart table, skipper's berth, and sail stowage are all handy to the after hatch.

It is most interesting to see how experienced sailormen have reacted to this famous French pilot cutter, turned yacht:

John Leather told me that the fishermen of his native East Anglia really respected only two yachts: the *Jolie Brise* and the *Dolly Varden,* Thomas White Ratsey's little thoroughbred cutter.

Henry Scheel, who raced against the *Jolie Brise* in a Fastnet Race in the rakish Marconi sloop *Maitenes II,* told of being wet and uncomfortable beating to windward in a strong breeze and feeling very jealous of the *Brise*'s crew. When the two boats came near each other crossing tacks, all that the exposed *Maitenes* men could see of the *Brise*'s people was the tops of their heads, for they were snugged up under the lee of those nice, high bulwarks along the weather rail.

On the other hand, J. Laurent Giles complained that the *Jolie Brise* was wet and said that you had to go below to get your sea boots in little more than a Force 3 breeze. She is, of course, very heavy and has only moderate freeboard, disguised by her high bulwarks.

These bulwarks, as has been indicated, are an important feature of the vessel. They are 24 inches high. They do give a great sense of security on deck and provide some real protection against falling overboard and against the weather, as those in the *Maitenes* observed. While they keep a lot of spray and slop off the deck, they have to have scuppers, and these have to be of ample size so that should the boat ship a heavy sea, the great weight of water on deck will drain off quickly.

That rarely happened to the *Jolie Brise;* on her first transatlantic crossing, she shipped but one wavetop of any size at all, and that was when Commander Martin admitted he had become a bit careless at the helm after the worst of a gale had passed.

Commander Martin, the man who first decided she would make a good cruising boat, is probably the best qualified commentator on the *Jolie Brise.* He was always very admiring of the steadiness of the *Jolie Brise* when hove to, her only problem when lying to in heavy weather being the common one of putting a heavy strain on her rudder and steering gear.

Martin wrote, "For one who loves ships and

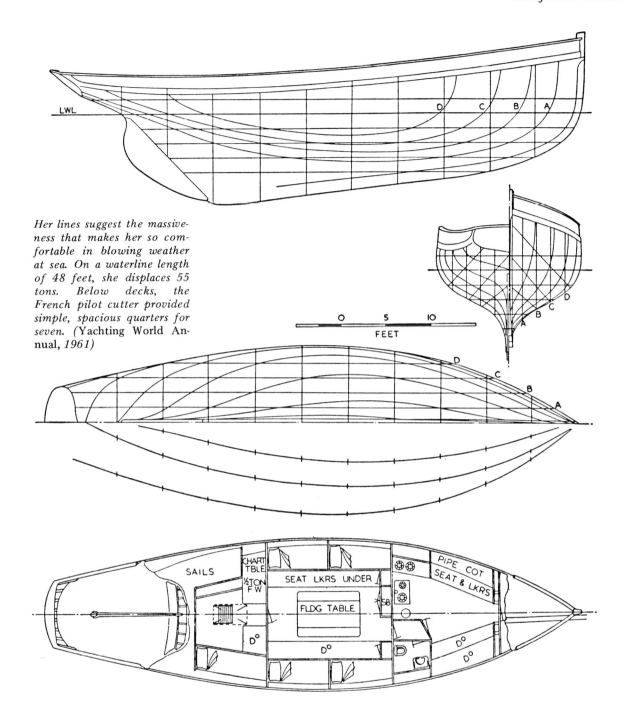

*Her lines suggest the massiveness that makes her so comfortable in blowing weather at sea. On a waterline length of 48 feet, she displaces 55 tons. Below decks, the French pilot cutter provided simple, spacious quarters for seven. (*Yachting World Annual, *1961)*

understands their ways there is no more beautiful sight than the gallant behavior of a fine sea-boat in a gale of wind. It was in this gale that I realized for the first time that the Havre pilots were really speaking the truth when they told me that when hove to in a gale in their boats, they could go below and forget all about it, so easy is the motion and so steadily do they lie."

But much as he admired her, Commander Martin didn't feel that the *Jolie Brise* was his ideal ocean cruising boat. He wrote, "It is, no doubt, this massive compactness which makes her so comfortable in bad weather. I love her for it and do not believe that any other type could equal her in this respect. Nevertheless, I think that a long hull of rather light displacement (he was writing in 1928) and with fine ends, which can be driven with a small sail area, probably makes a ship which is lighter to work."

Martin compared the *Brise* to another cutter he

Left: *This picture of the* Jolie Brise's *businesslike deck has long appealed to me greatly. I'd love to be there.* (Yachting, *November, 1928*). Below: *On the wind in light going, the* Jolie Brise *sports a nice array of overlapping headsails.* (The Oxford Companion to Ships and the Sea, *edited by Peter Kemp, Oxford University Press, 1976*)

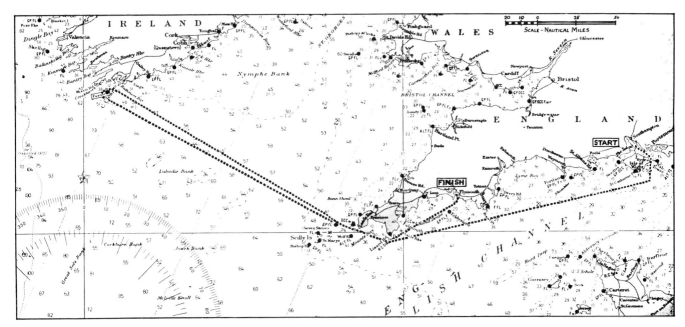

*The course of the Fastnet race, from Southampton Water round Fastnet Rock on the Irish coast and back to Plymouth, a distance of 615 miles. (*The Sportsman, *January, 1937)*

had owned of about the same length: "The square-sterned *Chance* was in every way as reliable a sea-boat as *Jolie Brise* and her dimensions were, length on the waterline 49 feet, beam 13 feet 4 inches, draft 7 feet 5 inches and displacement 35 tons, as compared with *Jolie Brise*'s 48 feet, 15 feet 9 inches, 10 feet 2 inches, and 55 tons.

"The *Chance* was not as comfortable, but was more easily driven and capable of higher all-around speeds in fresh winds. In light winds *Jolie Brise* would have things all her own way unless *Chance* were given a larger sail area than she ever had for cruising."

One might wonder about the rather low stern on the *Jolie Brise*. Martin wrote, "*Jolie Brise* has a counter stern which is beautifully fair although it is quite short, and it never gave us any anxiety though we sometimes ran her before a very heavy sea."

And, in a somewhat similar vein, "*Jolie Brise* has an exceptionally long, fine run, and makes no appreciable wave when running; but nevertheless we found that whenever a following sea began to cause any anxiety we had only to reduce her speed and sailing became easier at once."

Regarding her speed, Martin had this to say: "In *Jolie Brise* it was most obvious that she would make about 6½ knots without the slightest fuss but at 7½ or 8 one knew that she was sailing hard. This

does not quite apply to running dead before the wind, for like most very beamy boats she sailed fastest when she was upright, or nearly so, and we found that when we were running down the trades under the square rig these relative speeds were increased by a knot, or perhaps more. She was capable of higher speeds; the best hour's run we ever made before a strong steady breeze was 10¼ miles, and once when we ran her off before a very heavy squall in the Gulf Stream the log readings gave over 12 for a short time." It seems clear that the *Jolie Brise* was not a boat to be driven and was exceedingly comfortable in rough weather as long as she was not driven. This of course is entirely in keeping with her use as a pilot boat—or as an offshore cruiser.

I had the good luck to see the *Jolie Brise* during the 1950s when the naval vessel in which I was serving called at Lisbon. Even merely tied up in the yacht basin, she had the aura of great sea-keeping ability. Until she was sold in 1977 to the Exeter Maritime Museum in England, she had been owned since World War II by Luis de Guimaraes Lobato, a Portuguese yachtsman who bought her in tough shape and brought her back to excellent condition with the help of former owner Bobby Somerset. All her owners, including now the Exeter Museum, deserve the appreciation of any sailor who admires a handsome and able vessel.

8/ The *Calypso*

Length on deck: 35 feet 9 inches
Length on waterline: 31 feet 3 inches
Beam: 11 feet
Draft: 5 feet 1 inch
Sail area: 827 square feet
Displacement: 10 tons
Designer: Thomas C. Gillmer

Thomas C. Gillmer, a naval architect in Annapolis, Maryland, designs boats under ideal conditions. His house is, appropriately enough, on Shipwright Street, and the balcony of his design office, isolated from the living quarters by a narrow circular staircase, almost overhangs Spa Creek.

Looking at Tom's place from out on the Creek, you'd swear you were in some exotic place like the Italian Riviera. Looking out at the Creek from the balcony just a few steps from Tom's drawing board, you can see hundreds of boats tied up in marinas, on moorings, and passing in review. The inspiration provided by this setting has to be general, however, rather than specific, for there are mighty few boats in sight on Spa Creek nearly as handsome as the ketch *Calypso,* turned out by Professor Gillmer thirty years ago and modified slightly in 1974.

Calypso, as readers of Greek mythology will recall, was the sea nymph who delayed Odysseus on her island for seven years. Her ketch namesake looks fully capable of singing an effective siren song to anyone who would cruise in comfort in an able, good-looking vessel.

Readers familiar with Tom Gillmer's design for the 23-foot yawl *Blue Moon* will recognize marked similarities between the two designs; in any case, the *Blue Moon* is shown in the next chapter.

The *Calypso* is 35 feet 9 inches long on deck, with a waterline length of 31 feet 3 inches, a beam of 11 feet, and a draft of 5 feet 1 inch. Her displacement is about ten tons, and her sail area is 827 square feet.

She has considerable sheer, accentuated at the stern by the high crown of her transom, and this sheerline contributes much to her good looks. Her short ends are businesslike; in redrawing the boat in 1974, Professor Gillmer straightened the stem slightly, but left just enough curve in it to keep it soft.

The *Calypso*'s design is one of moderation. She has moderately hard bilges, moderate deadrise, and moderate draft and depth of forefoot.

She has a hollow entrance, but there is considerable flare above it. This combination makes for a bow that drives into a head sea fairly easily, yet without taking a lot of water on deck.

The ketch has good lateral stability; she should steer well and shouldn't try to round up too much when heeled. The keel has considerable depth below the rabbet line to give an effective lateral plane. Her rather low wetted surface would con-

Tom Gillmer, who designed the Calypso *and her little sister, the* Blue Moon, *in the next chapter.*

tribute to general smartness under sail. All in all, she has a rather easily driven hull, and she should never be cranky.

In the modified design of the *Calypso*, Professor Gillmer has increased her ballast-to-displacement ratio considerably (from about 31 percent to about 43 percent), for 6,250 pounds of iron outside ballast has been replaced by 8,600 pounds of lead.

It is interesting to compare the *Calypso*'s rig of 1945 with the modified rig given her in 1974. With the old rig, the masts were a bit farther forward, and she had a single headsail, a bigger mizzen, and a separate, fidded (offset athwartships, rather than forward) topmast with a bigger topsail. The modification of the rig gave the *Calypso* double headsails and a pole mainmast a little shorter than the older version's lower mast and topmast. In the new rig, the mainsail has 299 square feet; the mizzen, 147; the forestaysail, 121; the jib, 173; and the topsail, 85. All her sails are loose-footed.

The *Calypso*'s new rig is, of course, most versatile. She would balance well under main and staysail, jib and jigger, or staysail and reefed jigger, to name but three combinations.

The roller-furling jib makes great good sense with this rig. It is a most handy sail and can be used reaching or when sailing full-and-by on a passage when weatherliness is not critical. (The problem with roller-furling headsails is you can't set the luff up really hard so the sail loses a lot of its drive when the boat is jammed right up on the wind.) The roller-furling jib could be sent down out of the way when setting jib topsails on this ketch.

She could profit by having perhaps as many as four different headsails to set on the topmast stay. Three of these would be fairly narrow, only overlapping the forestay slightly, and would be designed primarily for windward work. They might have areas respectively of, say, 100 square feet, 175 square feet, and then a really tall one reaching all the way to the masthead with an area perhaps as large as 250 square feet. The fourth sail to set on this stay would be a big ballooner for reaching and running (poled out for the latter) in light going. With all this use of the topmast stay, one might be tempted to return to the staying arrangement of the old rig, with a slightly taller mainmast so that a spring stay could be used between the mastheads in conjunction with upper mizzen shrouds led well aft. One might even find it advantageous to rig running preventer backstays to the mainmast head for use when one of the jib topsails was really pulling.

It would be good if the sail bins also contained both storm and balloon forestaysails. A nice big mizzen staysail is shown, and it would be a rare joy to watch it pull her along if you were ever lucky enough to be on just the right point of sailing to use it.

Would anyone care to play with a club topsail on this boat in light airs? Such a sail might make a fine high note for the *Calypso*'s siren song.

Note the sensibly rigged peak halyards in both sail plans, supporting the gaff throughout its length and, in the case of the new plan, with a long enough bridle so it won't be unduly strained by the pull of its block. For appearance' sake, I find I want to lift the main boom up parallel to the others. Hopefully, readers will already have been mentally trimming the head of that mainsail with a vang led to the mizzen masthead long before I have gotten around to mentioning what a fine rig that makes.

The *Calypso* originally had a Gray 4-40 engine specified, and Professor Gillmer figured it would drive her at a fast 7½ knots.

The new design has a high-crowned flush deck raised to the level of the rail, instead of a trunk cabin. I think that is an improvement, for it makes

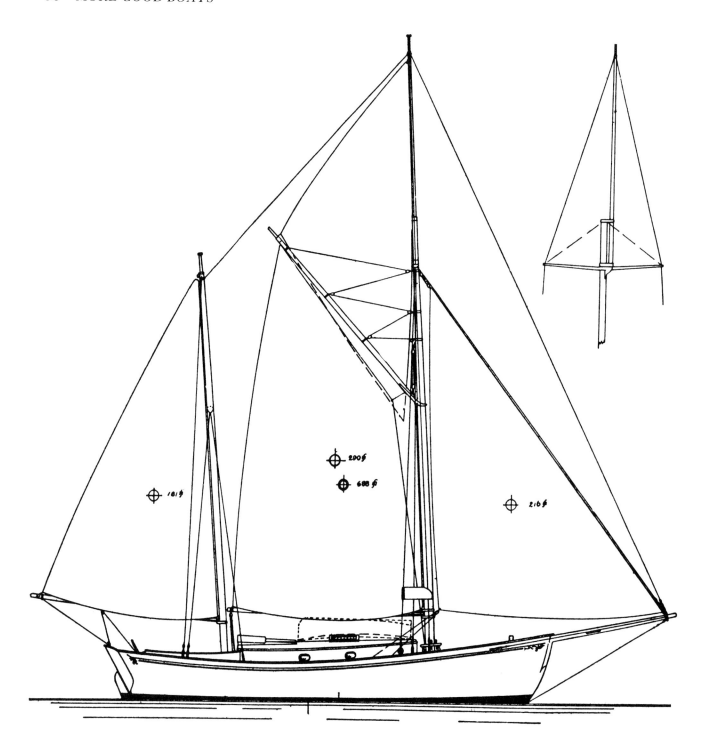

The Calypso *was designed in 1945 and was given a facelift-
ing in 1974. Her original rig had a single headsail, small
mainsail, and big main topsail set on a separate topmast
fidded athwartships.* Calypso's *new rig has a pole mainmast
with a taller mainsail and smaller topsail set above it and a
double head rig.* (Yachting, *September, 1945, and Thomas
C. Gillmer.*)

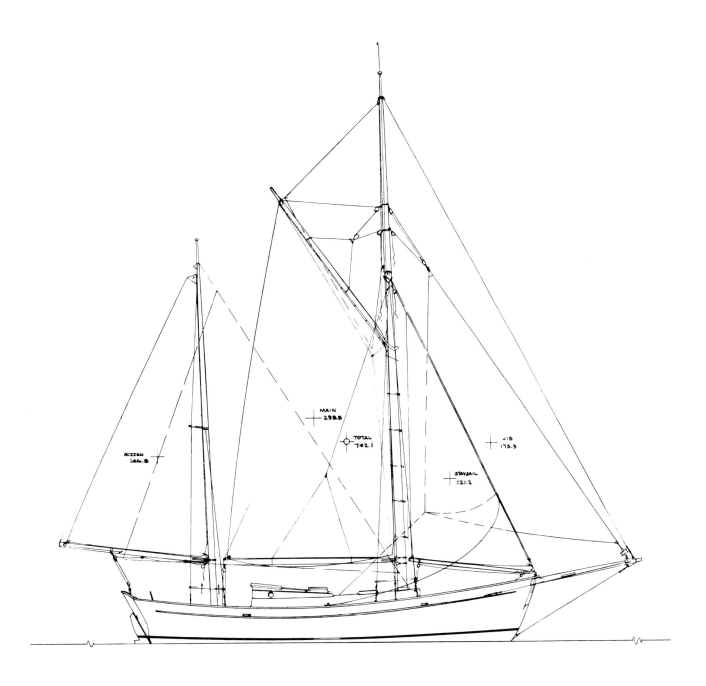

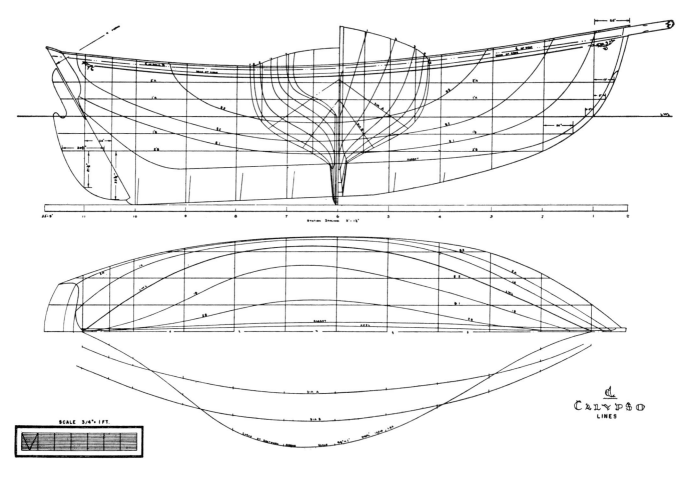

SCALE 3/4" = 1 FT.

CALYPSO
LINES

The only change made in her lines was straightening out the upper part of the stem a bit—I am not sure why. (Yachting, September, 1945, and Thomas C. Gillmer)

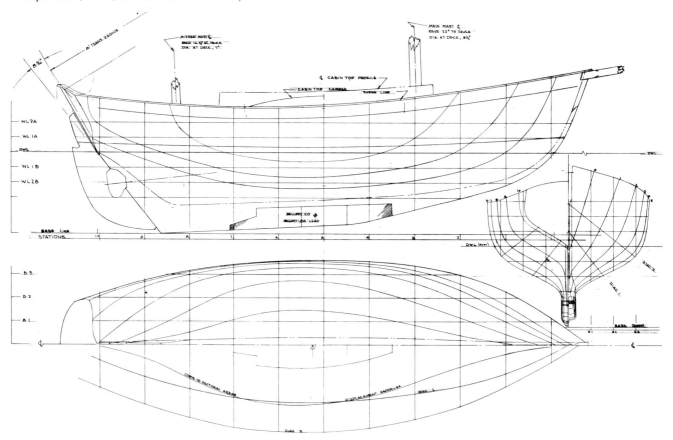

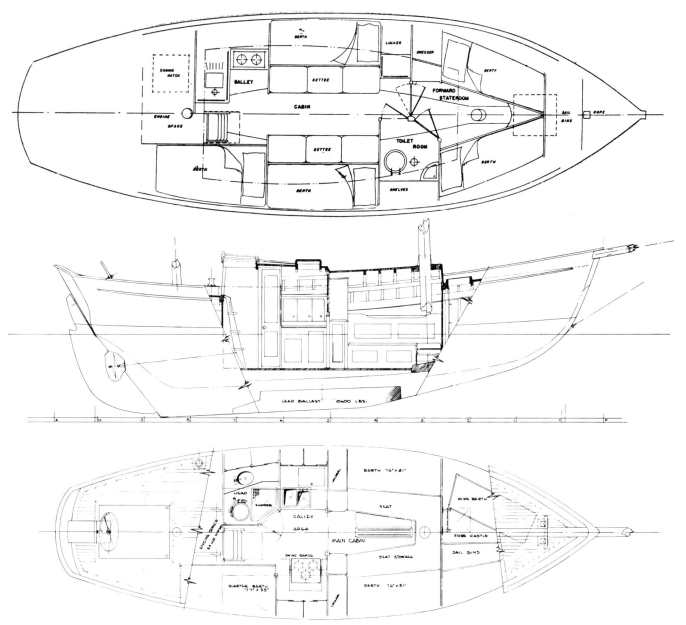

The arrangement plan was changed quite a bit, moving the head aft, the galley and saloon forward some, dead-ending the saloon, and giving her a small fo'c's'le with a single pipe berth instead of a forward stateroom. (Yachting, September, 1945, and Thomas C. Gillmer)

a strong, watertight arrangement and increases the working space on deck. Of course this construction would make it more desirable to have lifelines running between the shrouds.

I would prefer a cockpit coaming on this boat rather than having the cockpit open all the way to the rail. Without a coaming, dollops of water come right into the cockpit when she is being driven a bit, while, with a coaming, the cockpit stays a lot drier.

The original design for the *Calypso* had a standard accommodation plan, with a quarter berth aft to starboard opposite the galley, and a saloon amidships separated from a forward stateroom by a head to starboard and lockers to port. The new accommodation plan shows quite a different arrangement with one less berth but the great advantage of a dead-end saloon. There's nothing like sitting down at the cabin table with the sure knowledge that no one is going to ask you to get right up again so they can "get through." The old arrangement was designed for cruising in the tropics, while the new plan is for cruising in northern waters. In any case, the new layout looks ideal to me for three people for a long cruise. And the separate fo'c's'le makes a simply glorious place for the boatswain to keep his gear and do his work.

A Maine boatbuilder, Roy Blaney of Boothbay Harbor, is building this design for his own use. Now that's really living.

9/ The *Blue Moon*

Length on deck: 22 feet 10 inches
Length on waterline: 19 feet 8 inches
Beam: 8 feet 7 inches
Draft: 4 feet 1 inch
Sail area: 430 square feet
Displacement: 4 tons
Designer: Thomas C. Gillmer

Complete little cruising boats less than 25 feet long seem to have great appeal. There is something exciting about taking a small, well-found vessel offshore. It seems almost like cheating the elements to be able to go out in a little boat and do everything that a big boat can do, though assuredly making fewer knots in the process. You also spend fewer dollars.

Thomas C. Gillmer designed the *Blue Moon* in 1946, the year after he had designed the *Calypso* of the previous chapter. He said the *Blue Moon*'s design was originally inspired by the Falmouth Quay punt (see *Good Boats*, Chapter 23) but the *Blue Moon* has been modified considerably from the true fetch-and-carry boats of Falmouth Harbor and obviously bears considerable family resemblance to her big sister, the *Calypso*.

Professor Gillmer had the *Blue Moon* built for his own use in 1954 by Ivor Bentzen at Arendal, Norway. Two boats were also built to this design by Elmer Collemer at Camden, Maine, one of these being the *Dandy,* owned by Edward B. Stecher.

The *Blue Moon* is 22 feet 10 inches long on deck, with a waterline length of 19 feet 8 inches, a beam of 8 feet 7 inches, and a draft of 4 feet 1 inch. Her sail area is 430 square feet. She displaces

four tons, with outside ballast consisting of 2,300 pounds of iron. The engine specified was a 25 h.p. Universal Atomic 4.

It is interesting to compare the *Blue Moon* with the Stone Horse, a small cruising boat designed by Sam Crocker some ten years before Professor Gillmer designed the *Blue Moon*. The Stone Horse sloop, built in foam-core fiberglass in some numbers by Edey and Duff at Mattapoisett, Massachusetts, is described in Chapter 12. By comparison to the Stone Horse, the *Blue Moon* is beamier, deeper, heavier, and has more sail area. She has more room in her than does the Stone Horse, but is probably not as smart under sail as is the Crocker sloop.

In any event, the *Blue Moon* certainly has a handsome, able look to her and appears to be quite the little ship for so small a vessel. She has bold ends, plenty of sheer, a healthy beam, a nice, hollow entrance, easy sections, and a good run for so small a boat. Her sections show flare forward for dryness and bearing aft for sail-carrying power.

The *Blue Moon* was planked with Oregon pine and fastened with copper rivets. She was given teak decks and trim of mahogany and teak. When Elmer Collemer built the *Dandy* and her sistership, he

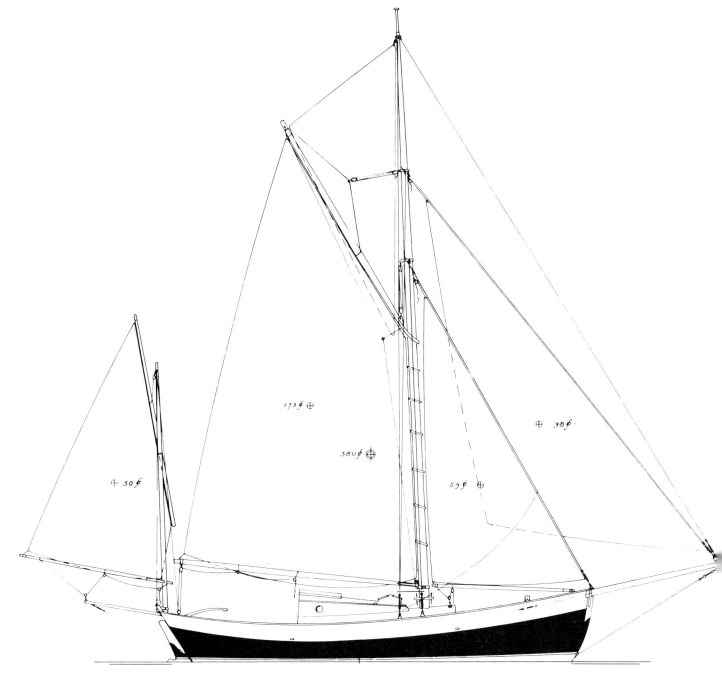

The Blue Moon *is a handsome little vessel. (Thomas C. Gillmer)*

used oak keels and steam-bent oak frames, cedar planking, teak decks, and mahogany trim.

The yawl rig adds considerable versatility to the ways in which the *Blue Moon* can be sailed in a hard breeze. Besides shortening down to mainsail and jib or reefed mainsail and staysail, she can go right down to staysail and mizzen and be well balanced. That makes a good rig for watching to see what develops out of a squall.

All her sails are loose-footed, trading a heavier

strain on the clew for the ability to allow curvature in the foot and vary the draft.

The lug mizzen shown on the sail plan is reminiscent of the sail Joshua Slocum added to the *Spray*'s rig during his cruise around the world, especially since in both cases the mizzen mast is stepped on the transom. In the *Dandy*, the mizzen was gunter rigged. Note that the mizzen boom is cocked up nicely, which looks good and has the practical advantage of keeping it up out of the sea,

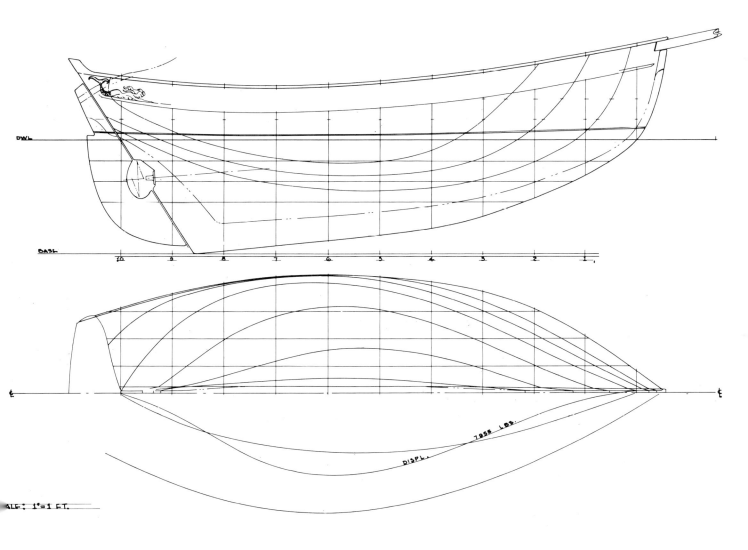

especially important if the boat is sailed under staysail and mizzen in heavy weather.

Mr. Stecher put a roller-furling jib on the *Dandy,* a rig that would certainly make sense, as bowsprits on small boats are likely to be a bit damp if it's rough and you don't have room to run her off to take in the jib. She could have a jib topsail and even a big drifter setting on the topmast stay, but if either sail were carried, you'd want a preventer topmast backstay to keep it all together.

By now I trust you know how to rig a vang on the main gaff of this yawl.

Notice some of the nice details that appear on this sail plan, such as the curved tiller, the shape of the stem, and the gracefully long main truck above the rigging. Another feature of the sail plan that makes the boat look good is having the main gaff set parallel to the forestay.

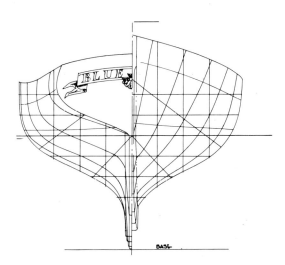

Her lines are unusually easy throughout, especially for such a short, beamy boat. (Thomas C. Gillmer)

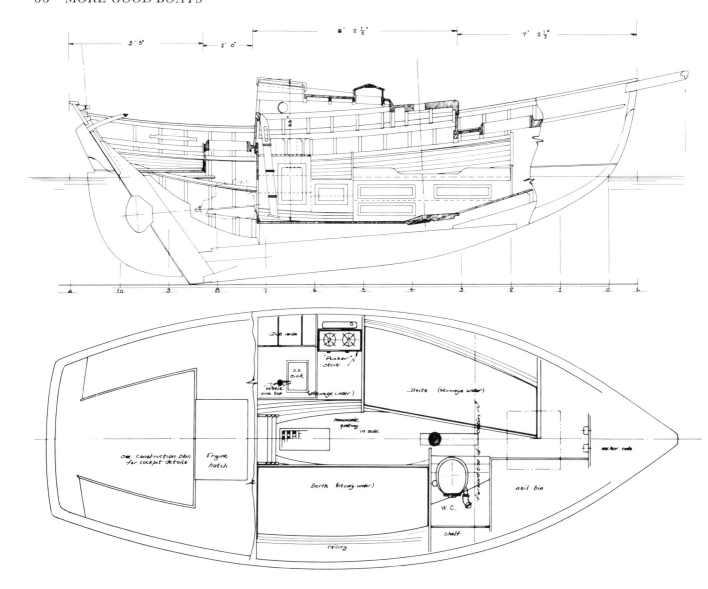

She is laid out for two people. She'd also, of course, make a good singlehander. (Thomas C. Gillmer)

The *Blue Moon* has the well-crowned raised deck that Professor Gillmer gave the *Calypso* when he modified her design. This construction keeps the boat from being cramped either on deck or below.

The little yawl's cockpit was not designed to be self-bailing, but Mr. Stecher had the *Dandy*'s cockpit rebuilt to make it so. The cockpit certainly should be self-bailing in a boat of this type, for she is obviously otherwise well able to handle rough water.

The *Blue Moon* has fine accommodations for two people, including a real galley, so often scrimped in a diminutive cruising boat. Mr. Stecher wrote, "You can see that the galley is large for a boat of this size and my wife has been well satisfied, not being cramped for space, especially as we've spent periods of from sixty to seventy days cruising."

The headroom under the main hatch is 5 feet 4 inches. Her staggered berths give versatile sitting, lounging, and sleeping arrangements. Mr. Stecher rigged a portable table supported by the mast and one leg. He also had an icebox hung from the hatch over the engine, a device arranged by the innovative Ralph Wiley of Oxford, Maryland.

The owners of the *Blue Moon* and *Dandy* were evidently well pleased with the performance of their vessels under sail; the *Blue Moon*'s owner, being also her designer, perhaps isn't her most objective critic, yet there is nothing in Professor

Left: *The* Dandy *and the* Galatea, *both sister ships of the* Blue Moon, *taking shape in the shop of Elmer Collemer at Camden, Maine. (Photo by Frank E. Claes)* Below: *A* Blue Moon *yawl hard at it in San Francisco Bay. (Photo by Diane Beeston)*

Gillmer's praise for his creation that doesn't ring true. He wrote, "I found that I could usually lay the same windward mark as boats of the same size with jib-headed sails, when sailing in company . . . she had a steady, knifing motion that was not easily staggered or thrown off by a little chop. She sailed as honestly as she was built, on a reach or hard on the wind. She ghosted nicely in light weather, but was exceptionally good as a foul weather boat."

Mr. Stecher, the *Dandy*'s owner, wrote: "In light airs, with the topsail set, she does very well and moves along steadily. She will comfortably carry all plain sail up to wind velocities of 25 miles per hour, and taking in the topsail is all that is necessary in anything up to about 35 miles per hour. We have made comfortable passages offshore in *Dandy* while larger powerboats were tossing and making hard weather of it . . . on one occasion I was caught in a blow when winds of 50 miles per hour were reported. We were about ten miles out of York Harbor, Maine, and with mizzen and staysail set, *Dandy* brought us in with no fuss."

All in all, the *Blue Moon* seems to be a great little vessel in which one could see as much of the world as he wished. And, in the bargain, she's just as pretty as a picture.

10/ The *Blue Jacket*

Length on deck: 21 feet 1 inch
Length on waterline: 20 feet 9 inches
Beam: 8 feet 4 inches
Draft: 3 feet 11 inches
Sail area: 417 square feet
Displacement: 3¼ tons
Designer: Arthur Payne

One of the nice things about publishing books is the often rewarding relationships that develop between publishers and authors. This is particularly true in regard to publishing in a specialized subject area, in which case publisher and author usually share a lively interest in the topic of each book produced.

Peter Davies, the English publisher who started the house that still bears his name to publish boating books, and Uffa Fox, the English naval architect and sailor who wrote five great books on yacht design that Davies published, enjoyed such a relationship.

Mr. Davies once spent a Christmas holiday with Uffa Fox. After a long evening of discussing the merits of all the latest developments in yacht design and construction, Mr. Davies decided that he wanted to buy an Itchen Ferry boat, and the older the better. The next day they prowled the boatyards at Cowes, and Mr. Fox found Mr. Davies just the boat he was looking for, a little 21-footer, the *Blue Jacket*. (Fox naturally included the *Blue Jacket* in his next book for Davies, *Thoughts on Yachts and Yachting*, published in 1938.)

The Itchen Ferry boats took their name from their place of origin, a village at the mouth of the River Itchen across from Southampton where the river empties into the head of Southampton Water. The type was a local fishing craft used for trawling for cod, sole, and plaice, and for shrimp and prawns, and, in later years, for oyster dredging in the waters protected by the Isle of Wight. As well as working from the major harbors of the area, these craft worked from small creeks, and, since they were not built to take the ground, their draft was kept moderate. Thus they differ markedly from the deeper, narrower, high-bowed craft developed to fish in the unprotected waters farther westward along the coast.

John Leather, the Lloyd's surveyor and marine historian, has written that in 1872 there were 141 of these little fishing cutters working out of Southampton, 182 from Cowes, and 247 from Portsmouth. He paints a good word-picture of these craft in his book *Gaff Rig*: "Dozens of similar boats were an essential part of Victorian Solent seascapes: fish trawling inside Calshot in a fresh breeze with spitfires a-weather; spray and rain glistening the hulls of the little fleet and soaking the tan canvas as they towed across the ebb, the stovepipe smoke blown to leeward, where a big steamer slid up Southampton Water."

The construction (and many other interesting

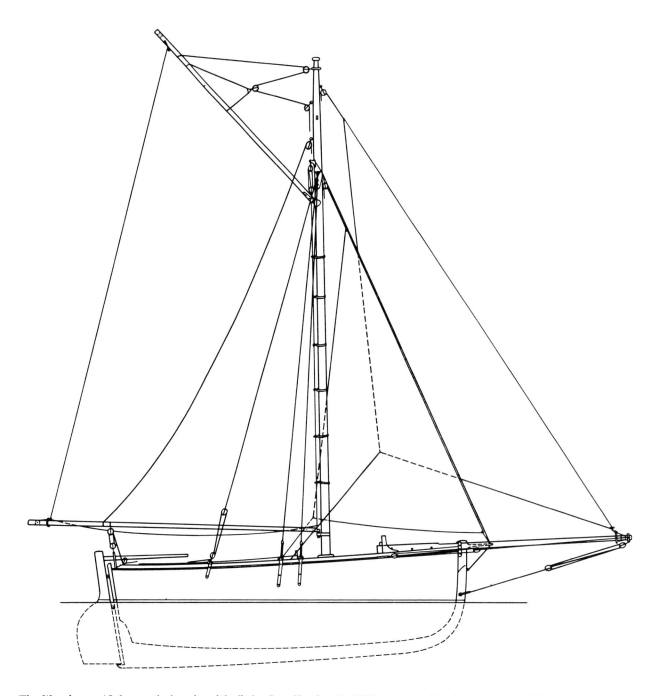

The Wonder, *a 19-footer designed and built by Dan Hatcher in 1860, is the earliest Itchen Ferry fishing boat for which plans exist. The boat herself is still in good condition today. (*Gaff Rig*, by John Leather, International Marine Publishing Co.)*

details) of the Itchen Ferry fishing boats was described by Edgar J. March in his two-volume work, *Inshore Craft of Britain in the Days of Sail and Oar:*

Floors were variously contrived. Sometimes a hogging piece or keelson of wood or iron was worked on top of the keel, its siding being about one-half; this formed a stepping rabbet for the heels of the frames which rested on top of the main keel and were spiked to the hog, the whole being strengthened in some boats by iron floor knees, bolted through frame and plank. Aft, a stepping line to take the heels of the frames was cut in the deadwood; in crack boats the space between plank floor and keelson was filled with cement and boiler punchings, smoothed off level with the top of the keelson.

In the 21-foot class no keelson was worked. A typical boat, *Nellie*, built by Dan Hatcher, was 21

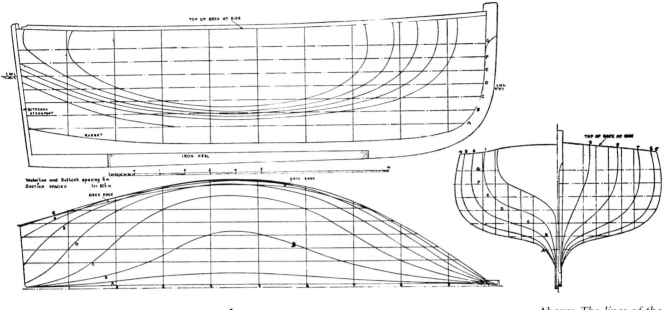

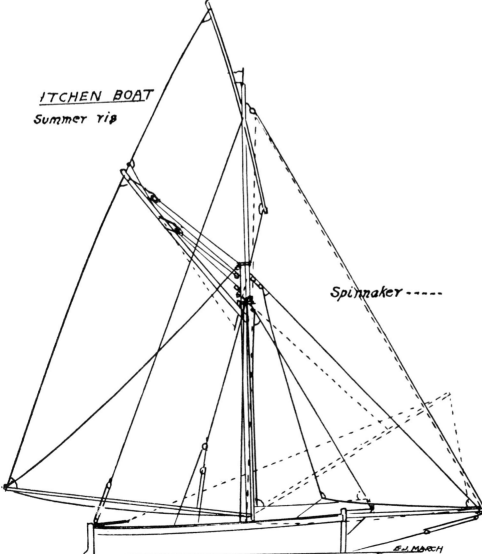

ITCHEN BOAT
Summer rig

Spinnaker -----

NOTE At regattas some skippers-yacht sailing masters-set spinnakers

Above: *The lines of the Wonder as taken off by one of her owners, J. W. Holness. (Edgar J. March)*

Left: *In summer, the rigs of the little fishing cutters were markedly increased for racing. Many of their owners were skippers or crews on the huge racing yachts of the day. (In-shore Craft of Britain in the Days of Sail and Oar by Edgar J. March)*

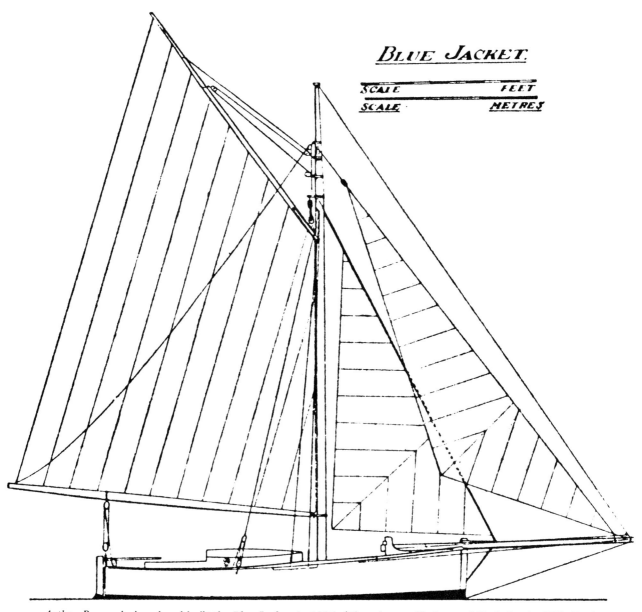

Arthur Payne designed and built the Blue Jacket *in 1894.* (Thoughts on Yachts and Yachting *by Uffa Fox*)

feet 9 inches overall, 7 feet 10 inches in beam, and depth 3 feet 9 inches. The lower waterlines were hollow for'ard, the straight keel was 3-inch sided, 7 inches deep to rabbet; 15 grown oak frames, 3 inches by 2½ inches at heel, 2½ inches molded at heads, were spaced 16 inches center to center; between were steamed frames 1 inch by ¾ inch, beams oak 2½ inches by 2¼ inches, deck planking 6 inches by ¾ inch, side planking 1 inch thick, deadwood knee 4 inches thick, apron 5 inches. . . . the rudder, 2 feet 3 inches wide and 1½ inches thick was fitted with a tiller 5 feet 9 inches overall, socketed into a 5 inch by 4 inch post.

The boats had all inside ballast, in the form of iron pigs. The craft were arranged with a cuddy under the deck forward closed off from the cockpit by a bulkhead. There was no house, and the cuddy had sitting headroom. It contained a couple of berths and a coal stove.

Many boats up to the size of the *Blue Jacket* were fished singlehanded. In the early years they had a boomless mainsail, and John Leather wrote that the boom was added about 1852, the bowsprits being lengthened at the same time. The old boats had a nearly vertical leech to the mainsail, and doubtless the boom took some of the twist out of the sail.

There were typically four rows of reef points in the mainsail and one reef in the staysail. Three jibs

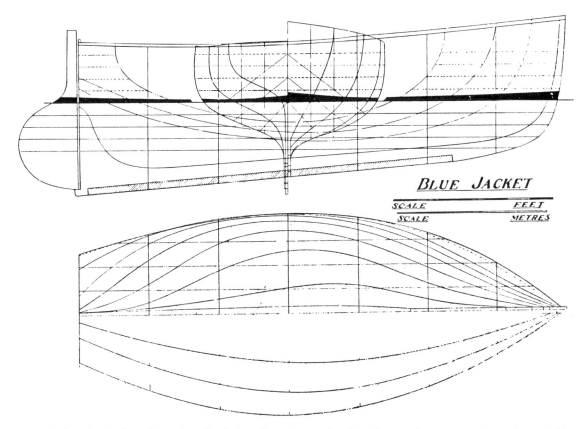

The lines of the Blue Jacket *show that the Itchen Ferry boats developed toward fineness and speed, probably under considerable influence of the racing yachts their skippers and builders knew so well. (*Thoughts on Yachts and Yachting *by Uffa Fox)*

were carried: a working jib, a large, light-weather jib, and a spitfire. The bowsprit could be run in when it was rough.

As a summer rig, the Itchen Ferry boats sported a big, yard topsail and a "spinnaker," a huge balloon jib filling the whole foretriangle.

The owners of the Itchen craft often used them for winter employment only, since in summer they had important jobs as racing skippers and crews in big yachts. These men took their racing seriously, and the influence of the racing yachts was felt in the fishing fleet both in terms of the development of the Itchen Ferry boats and in the practice of holding regattas for them. The fishermen often raced their boats for one of the finest prizes imaginable: a new suit of sails from the great Ratsey loft.

Dan Hatcher, mentioned by Edgar March as the builder of the *Nellie,* had a great reputation as a designer and builder of Itchen Ferry boats. One of his craft, the *Wonder,* built in 1860, still exists in good condition under private ownership, and one of her owners, J. W. Holness, made a complete record of her and drew up her plans. She is 19 feet

long on deck, with a waterline length of 18 feet 9 inches, a beam of 8 feet 3 inches, and a draft of 3 feet 6 inches. Her sail area is 375 square feet.

Among other distinguished Itchen Ferry boat builders were Alfred and Arthur Payne, father and son. Robert Charles Leslie, the marine painter and writer, owned the *Lily,* designed by Alfred Payne, and came to Arthur Payne in later years when he wanted another boat of the same type. Arthur designed him the *Foam II* in 1886, and the craft exceeded both his and Leslie's expectations. Leslie wrote of her as "averaging 7 knots with a fresh beam wind, in sailing from Southampton to Portsmouth and back, about 35 miles, in five hours, the wind being fresh northeast."

Of the type in general, Leslie wrote: "As single-handed boats in tidal waters, the Itchen Ferry shrimpers are not easily surpassed by anything of their size afloat. I have owned one and sailed among them, for more than 20 years, but never knew one to come to grief or leave a widow and orphans as so often happens with other small fishing boats."

Another admirer of the type was the marine

The Blue Jacket *is the very picture of neatness as she waits impatiently to go back overboard. (*Thoughts on Yachts and Yachting *by Uffa Fox)*

artist and boat designer Albert Strange, a few of whose designs are in *Good Boats*. He wrote of the *Foam II:* "Not withstanding the hollow in the waterlines fore and aft and her hollow mid-section, the shape of this boat with her long keel, and her moderate displacement, appeals to me very much as an almost perfect form of a fast, stable, roomy little sea-boat, in which headroom about 4 feet 6 inches could be gotten without an undue amount of cabin top. She would be steadier on her helm than a boat with a shorter and rounder keel outline, and her length would not hinder her from being smart in stays."

Finally, it may be said that the Itchen Ferry boat was probably part of the inspiration for J. Laurent Giles's *Andrillot,* which in turn sired the well-known *Vertue* class sloops (see *Good Boats*, Chapter 25).*

---

*By now, it should be clear to any reader who does not own a copy of *Good Boats* that he ought to.

The Publisher

The *Blue Jacket* was designed by Arthur Payne in 1894 and was built at Summers and Payne at Northam, Southampton. A comparison of her lines with those of the *Wonder* show the development of the type, for the *Blue Jacket* has more deadrise, slacker bilges, less draft forward and more aft. In short, she has a finer and faster hull than does her predecessor.

The *Blue Jacket* is 21 feet 1 inch long on deck, with a waterline length of 20 feet 9 inches, a beam of 8 feet 4 inches, and a draft of 3 feet 11 inches. She displaces 3¼ tons and has a working sail area of 417 square feet.

She has a rather shoal hull and a moderately deep keel. Although the draft has been kept moderate, she has plenty of lateral resistance. At first her waterlines look too curvaceous, but it must be remembered that the buttocks are quite flat, so her hull does not have great resistance. There is just a slight tumblehome to the topsides to keep her from looking boxy.

She has a big rudder, well aft. Like a Cape Cod catboat, she would need it in a strong, quartering breeze. Uffa Fox wrote of her, "Like all Itchen

Ferry boats with their beam and absence of over-hangs, she carries weather helm when pressed."

There is an iron shoe on her keel for protection. When Peter Davies bought her, she was very deep in the water, and, at Uffa Fox's suggestion, a great engine was taken out of her together with consider-able inside ballast. Uffa wrote that they decreased her draft by as much as six inches. They also changed the color of her topsides from white to black, making her look small and neat and setting off well the color of her tan-barked sails.

The *Blue Jacket*'s working sail area of 417 square feet is made up of a mainsail of 270 square feet, a staysail of 72 square feet, and a jib of 75 square feet. The mainsail is loose-footed. This means you can trice up the tack in a twinkling when maneuvering, with the result that the sail area is greatly reduced and the helmsman has a clear view to leeward. If the sail is needed again quickly, the mainsail tack can be dropped and bowsed down even faster than it was triced up.

The bowsprit is off center, and the staysail tacks down to an iron bumpkin supported by a strut to the stem. Mr. Davies and Mr. Fox put a club on the staysail to eliminate the chore of shifting its sheets when tacking. A storm forestaysail and a balloon staysail would be mighty handy cruising sails in this boat. They fitted the jib with Wykeham Martin roller-furling gear, and kept the halyards and the outhaul on the bowsprit rigged so the sail could be taken in as usual if the furling gear gave trouble.

There is room below in this boat for a couple of bunks forward and a couple of seats, some cooking gear, and a cedar bucket aft. Which is everything a pair of people would need to go off for a cruise. Peter Davies cruised in the *Blue Jacket* between the Isle of Wight and Falmouth many times with Uffa Fox on board. And there is no reason why a fine little Itchen Ferry boat shouldn't be cruising today in any of the protected waters of the American coasts.

11/ The Muscongus Bay Sloop

Length on deck: 22 feet 2 inches
Length on waterline: 18 feet 10 inches
Beam: 7 feet 1 inch
Draft: 2 feet 11 inches
Sail area: 340 square feet

Some of the fishermen of Muscongus Bay, on the coast of Maine, used to have a very satisfactory annual schedule. They would build a small sloop over the winter, launch her in the spring, use her for lobstering during the summer, sell her in the fall, and be ready to repeat the cycle. With skill, plenty of hard work, and a little luck, a fellow could keep body and soul together and maybe even put a little money by.

Of course some of the boatmen preferred one side or the other of the cycle, and they became specialists, but since it was easier to build boats in the summer than it was to fish in the winter, there were more boatbuilding specialists than there were fishing specialists.

In any event, Muscongus Bay boatbuilders, both specialists and nonspecialists, were turning out fishing sloops for local use by 1850. By 1870, they had developed a distinctive type of deep-draft centerboarder, and the type has come to be known as the Muscongus Bay sloop. These boats were generally from 16 feet to 26 feet long, though some as large as 35 feet long were built. They were used primarily for lobster fishing, but also for handlining.

The sloops were wholesome and handsome. Their short counter sterns, with well-raked, curved transoms shaped to give tumblehome to the quarters were a good-looking and practical trademark probably adopted from similar sterns on Gloucester sloop boats and Gloucester schooners, with which preeminent vessels Down East fishermen were thoroughly familiar. By the early 1890s, these Muscongus Bay sloops were gradually replaced by generally slightly larger sloops of much greater draft and without centerboards. These later sloops, of course, became known as the famous Friendship sloops, taking their name from one of the principal villages where they were built.

There was nothing fancy about the construction of these local fishing sloops. They were built with whatever materials were immediately at hand, and some shortcuts were taken in their construction. There was no skimping on the scantlings, however, and many of these craft lasted well, through being heavily built and through being well ventilated during their long working lives. The plain and simple construction of these boats was necessary to keep their cost down; still, in 1880, a 22-foot Muscongus Bay sloop would have cost perhaps $600 complete.

Originally, these boats were planked lapstrake, later carvel. Keel and frames were of local red oak. The frames were bent, either being steamed or

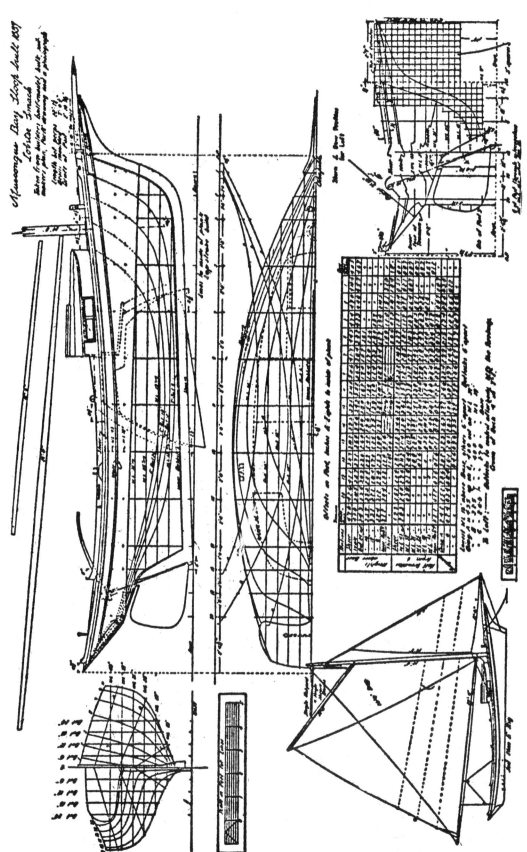

Howard Chapelle's drawings of a Muscongus Bay sloop based on a half model of 1888, the hulk of one of the boats laid up to die ashore, and contemporary reports. (American Small Sailing Craft by Howard I. Chapelle, W. W. Norton and Co.)

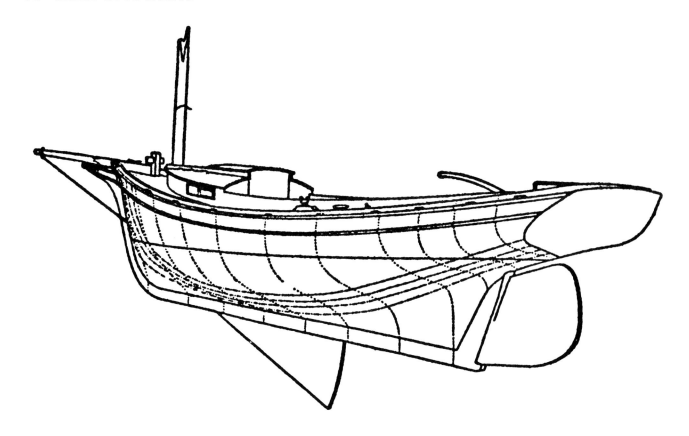

Above: *Mr. Chapelle's perspective lines drawing of the sloop show that she epitomizes the saying, "Moderation in all things."* (American Small Sailing Craft *by Howard I. Chapelle, W. W. Norton and Co.*)

This model of a Muscongus Bay sloop of 1880 is in the National Watercraft Collection at the Smithsonian Institution. (The National Watercraft Collection, *Second Edition, by Howard I. Chapelle, Smithsonian Institution and International Marine Publishing Co.*)

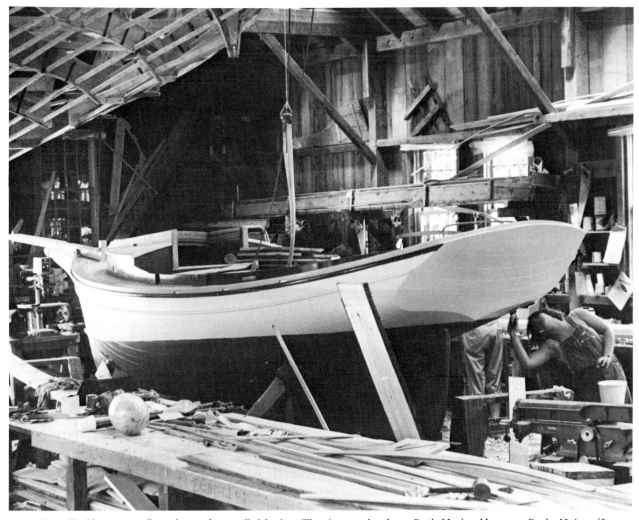

The Chapelle Muscongus Bay sloop almost finished at The Apprenticeshop, Bath Marine Museum, Bath, Maine. (Lance Lee)

softened up a bit in cold water. The boats were planked with oak, yellow pine, white pine, or cedar, and fastened with galvanized iron. All of their ballast was carried inside, at first stone, and later iron. Most of the boats had wet wells built up around the centerboard trunk on both sides.

The lines of the handsome Muscongus Bay sloop shown were taken off a builder's half model by Howard I. Chapelle and were published in 1951 in his book *American Small Sailing Craft.* The boat was built at Bremen, Maine, in 1889. Mr. Chapelle found out details of construction and deck layout from the hulk of a Muscongus Bay sloop that lay dying near Kennebunk, Maine, until 1940. Details of the rig came from contemporary reports of the Fish Commission.

The sloop's length on deck is 22 feet 2 inches;

her length on the waterline is 18 feet 10 inches; she has a beam of 7 feet 1 inch and a draft of 2 feet 11 inches with the board up. She has about 340 square feet of sail, with 280 square feet in the mainsail and 60 square feet in the jib.

This Muscongus Bay sloop would make a fine little daysailer or short-range cruiser. And she is not a boat that would balk at loading aboard stuff like driftwood, a big tent for setting up a base camp on an island, or a crowd of six for an afternoon sail.

She'd have a good turn of speed under a variety of conditions if reefed to meet fresh and strong breezes, but she doesn't have enough sail-carrying power, despite her quite-powerful quarters, to be really driven hard and sailed at high speed when it's blowing hard. Her performance would seldom be disappointing, however.

And under sail . . .

Being a deep centerboarder, she'd have an extremely easy motion in a seaway. I had a somewhat larger deep centerboarder for a decade; her motion was never tiring, though it was undoubtedly somewhat quicker than would be the motion of this Muscongus Bay sloop, for my old boat, the *Aria* (see Chapter 35), was quite lightly built and had outside ballast.

The steepness of the forward buttock lines of this Muscongus Bay sloop is offset by the fineness of her waterlines to give her an entry that would not have great resistance. Her relatively shoal hull gives her a nice, flat run.

Her low freeboard gives her low windage when close-hauled, yet she would not be a wet boat, for she's not going to be driven hard, and when going to windward, most boats, in any event, have a great excess of freeboard amidships on the weather side.

So much of the sloop's rig is in her mainsail that she would be quite handy sailing as a catboat. Of course that wouldn't do when you wanted to get her to windward at her best. But the fishermen, when hauling lobster traps, used to drop the jib down out of the way. That left them with a handy rig indeed.

The rig is a simple one. The mast has no shrouds.

. . . on the Kennebec River.

The mainsail is hoisted by a single halyard led through blocks positioned as they would be for separate throat and peak halyards. The vang shown could be led aft to the weather quarter to take the twist out of the sail on a broad reach or run. There was a wide mainsheet horse to keep the sail from twisting too much when on the wind.

One would be tempted to cut the mainsail with a higher peak, perhaps so that the gaff would be parallel to the forestay. This would give the mainsail a little better shape for windward work, would put the peak of the sail up higher where there is a bit more wind in a light air, but would mean reefing just that much sooner when it breezed up. It would probably be better to add a topsail, set flying on a yard, so as to have something to show off with on holidays and, more practically, to shove her along back to the land in a dying evening breeze. An overlapping jib might be fun for light days and to pole out for running.

One thing that wouldn't do in a boat like this would be to fit her out with a more "efficient" Marconi rig, by which is meant more efficient to windward and less efficient off the wind. This boat just doesn't have the power to stand up to a tall working rig.

These boats were rowed when they had to be in a calm, and could be again, but a less tiring means of manual propulsion would be to scull over the stern with a Chinese yuloh.

She has a big, deep, comfortable cockpit. That's where you would live in a boat this size, and her cockpit would be the envy of people perched on a 60-foot schooner. The cockpit is not self-bailing, so if her crew drive her under, she'll probably get back at them by leaving them to swim for it. That big cockpit, under happier circumstances, can be made a part of the cabin—and the biggest part—by raising the boom until you have full headroom under it, and then putting a tent over it.

In the cuddy there is just room for two narrow berths (each with its clothes hammock of netting), some modest cooking gear, a bucket, and some shelves. There is also just enough depth for sitting headroom.

The Muscongus Bay sloop is indeed a simple boat. She has: four spars (to spread her generous, but low, rig); two working sails (and perhaps two light sails); two pieces of standing rigging; eight pieces of running rigging for the working sails; no machinery; no plumbing; and no electronics "suit." There is, in fact, little about her that could go wrong. Anything that breaks could be repaired relatively quickly by the average handy owner without depending on the availability of parts or materials that might or might not be delivered rapidly from a distance. The result of such simplicity is a highly reliable craft whose owner, if he wanted to, could spend much time sailing compared to the time he had to spend tinkering with complex gear or waiting for people with special skills to make his boat "operable" again. In short, this boat would bring a lot of satisfaction per dollar.

12/ The Stone Horse

> Length on deck: 23 feet 4 inches
> Length on waterline: 18 feet 4 inches
> Beam: 7 feet 1 inch
> Draft: 3 feet 7 inches
> Sail area: 339 square feet
> Displacement: 2¼ tons
> Designer: S.S. Crocker, Jr.

I had a good time at a boat show for used boats in Newport a couple of years ago. There were a handful of old Herreshoffs—a 15, a couple of S boats, and a New York 30 with her original rig. After admiring these beauties for awhile, I went over to where Peter Duff was showing off one of his little Stone Horse sloops. It was Peter who really made the show for me; he made me an offer I couldn't refuse.

Peter said why don't you come down and try out a Stone Horse for a few days and write her up? I couldn't think of any reasons to turn down this offer, so I acccpted it.

Two months later my number-one son and I converged on Aucoot Cove, on the north shore of Buzzards Bay, where the Stone Horses are built by Edey and Duff. We were put aboard the *Pollock Rip,* a good name for a Stone Horse, since the Stone Horse and Pollock Rip shoals lie cheek by jowl in Nantucket Sound.

It wasn't long before we had our gear stowed and were underway, running out of the cove, with mainsail, staysail, and jib set to catch what little remained, by late afternoon, of the northwesterly land breeze. The *Pollock Rip* eased out into Buzzards Bay where she was slowed by a bobble making in from the southwest, hopefully portend-ing the overdue arrival of the breeze from that quarter.

The Stone Horse was S. S. Crocker's design of some 40 years ago for a fine little cruising boat for two people. Nine years ago, Edey and Duff began building her in foam-core fiberglass construction in an attempt to marry a sound design from the past with modern materials now available and to offer the cruising public an alternative to the many racing-cruisers being designed and built to rate well under the IOR first and be cruising boats second. The firm has turned out over 100 Stone Horse sloops to date.

By half-past six in the evening our patience was rewarded by the arrival of the sou'wester. Suddenly instead of running at one knot with the light air being constantly shaken out of our sails by a maddening little head sea, we were boiling along on the starboard tack full and by and just able to lay Woods Hole comfortably. We ran through the Hole with a couple of knots of fair tide, catching a glimpse as we did so of a huge New York Yacht Club fleet barely contained by Hadley's inner and outer harbors. We anchored in Woods Hole harbor at eight o'clock and, after admiring the great ketch *Ticonderoga* moored nearby, went below for supper.

Sam Crocker contemplating the construction of one of the vessels he designed. To be sure, she is a bit bigger than the Stone Horse.(Courtesy S. Sturgis Crocker)

The Stone Horse is 23 feet 4 inches long on deck, with a waterline length of 18 feet 4 inches, a beam of 7 feet 1 inch, and a draft of 3 feet 7 inches. Her sail area is 339 square feet. Her displacement is 4,490 pounds, with 2,000 pounds of outside ballast. Her lines show a stiff boat with hard bilges and quite a flat floor amidships. Yet we found her roll to be slow and easy, rather than quick and tiring. Her buttock lines are easy throughout, for the hull is shoal. She was a bit corky and quick when it came to pitching, which is only to be expected in a seagoing boat of diminutive size.

We found that the *Pollock Rip* got along well under sail in all conditions in which we tried her. Of course she's no real speed demon. The Herreshoff 15, a boat of approximately the same effective sailing waterline length, could sail rings round her, but the Herreshoff was designed as a day racing boat, when that term implied real, rather than relative, speed. It is the Stone Horse's high wetted surface, moderate sail-area-to-displacement ratio, and high freeboard that keep her from sailing really fast, the freeboard affecting only her windward performance, of course.

This is not to imply at all that the Stone Horse is

a dull sailer. She flies along in great style on a broad reach with a 20-knot breeze, and, going to windward, she will stand up to 25 or 30 knots nicely with a double-reefed mainsail and the forestaysail or jib, keeping good headway through the seas if you sail her full. And she does all right in light going without the need to set fancy kites.

We found she was quite steady on the helm; with the tiller lashed she would steer herself for awhile under sail or power in moderate conditions.

Next morning we had a few errands to do ashore in Woods Hole and didn't get back aboard and underway until quarter after ten. We beat out into Vineyard Sound in a light, dry southeaster with a strong east-going tide setting us up to weather nicely. Over near the Vineyard shore, we let her go right across the Middle Ground as there wasn't much of a rip on it and got a minimum sounding of six feet on the depth indicator. (It was one of those that indicated lighted numbers at a rate of about two or three per second, somehow conjuring up the image of a sort of Keystone Kops movie of a leadsman in the chains heaving his lead, hauling it back, and singing out soundings at a terrific rate.) The tide boiled up over the shoal ridge and shoved the boat broadside to windward.

We worked out around West and then East Chop and then beat to Edgartown, staying well ahead of a 35-foot Marconi-rigged (even to the foresail!) schooner, but losing out to a 30-foot IOR sloop with a big Genoa jib set.

The *Pollock Rip* sailed into Edgartown harbor at two o'clock and we worked her through the big fleet of anchored boats and close-reached down into Katama Bay where we found a quiet berth off by ourselves.

There followed considerable swimming and side scrubbing, a bit of ship's work, and then a generally lazy afternoon. The breeze blew fresh out of the east, but as it died down toward evening we rowed the Gloucester Gull dory we were towing over to the beach at the south end of the Bay, went ashore, walked across the wide dunes and watched the breakers for awhile. There were breakers way out on the Wasque Shoal as well as in on the beach. We thought it a lonely and very beautiful place.

In the well-written and thoughtful booklet about the Stone Horse put out by Edey and Duff, five desirable characteristics of a cruising boat are set forth:

1. *She should be easy to handle.* The Stone

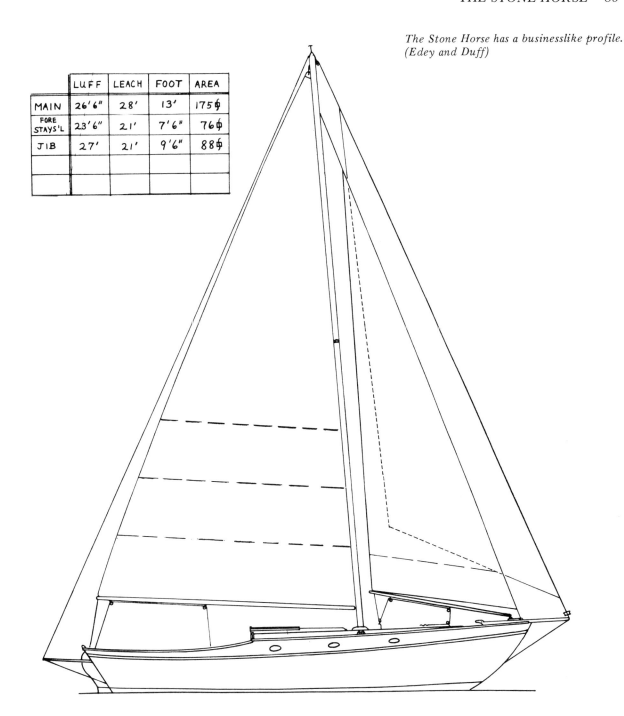

	LUFF	LEACH	FOOT	AREA
MAIN	26'6"	28'	13'	175◻
FORE STAYS'L	23'6"	21'	7'6"	76◻
JIB	27'	21'	9'6"	88◻

Horse certainly is. Her sails are small, her running rigging is ample and is intelligently laid out; her anchor is ready for instant use on the bowsprit; and she does anything that is reasonably expected of her in the way of maneuvering under sail, including beating in through narrow cove entrances in a light and flukey breeze.

2. *She should be comfortable.* Again the Stone Horse rates very high marks; there are many comfortable places to sit, lie, and stand in the boat; after a hard thrash to windward in a strong breeze

and a lump of a sea, not one drop of water finds its way into the cabin from any one of the usual points of entry.

3. *She should be seaworthy.* More high marks for the Stone Horse; her hull, deck, and cockpit are strong and watertight; her hull is able; her rig has a good many combinations to suit the strength of the wind.

4. *She should be fast.* No A+ here, but I would say she is fast for a cruising boat not much over 18 feet long on the waterline.

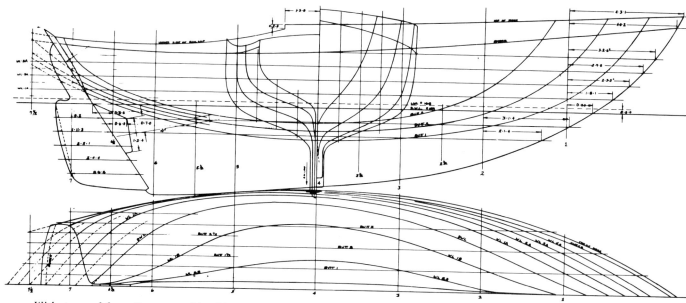

With powerful sections, considerable outside ballast, short overhangs, and great reserve buoyancy, she is a mighty seaworthy 23-footer. (Edey and Duff)

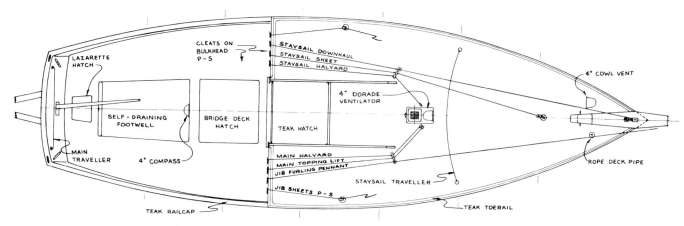

And with her raised deck, she is all deck space. (Edey and Duff)

5. *She should be beautiful.* Now we get into personal taste as well as semantics; I would call the Stone Horse a handsome boat, but not a beautiful boat.

We sailed the *Pollock Rip* out of Edgartown harbor soon after six o'clock in the morning. There was a light, but growing, breeze from the west. We ran to Cape Poge, the northeast point of Martha's Vineyard, and then headed for the Cross Rip buoy in the middle of Nantucket Sound. The breeze backed to southwest and increased to fresh, so we put a double-reef in the mainsail.

On the close reach up to the Tuckernuck Shoal buoy, the breeze increased to strong. We handed the forestaysail. At Tuckernuck, we put her up on the wind and just didn't quite fetch the jetties

leading into Nantucket harbor. Near the end of that leg we reset the forestaysail and rolled up the jib. She had been going well under jib and mainsail, but seemed to do even a bit better under forestaysail and mainsail, or maybe it was that we were getting into smoother water.

We beat up into the harbor and were anchored in the southwest corner by half-past twelve. It blew great guns all the afternoon, but we had no qualms about going ashore to see what progress had wrought in old Nantucket town, for, after all, we had 25 pounds of unpatented anchor on the bottom. She didn't move.

The evening was a most pleasant social one in which we foiled an attempt by the publisher of the *National Fisherman* to escape the office crowd by

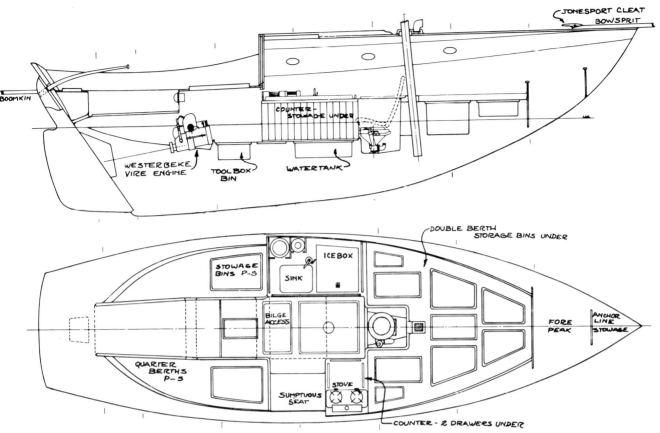

The layout provides comfortable accommodations for two people. All her cruising gear worked beautifully on our cruise south of Cape Cod. (Edey and Duff)

taking his family to Nantucket Island for a couple of days. We met his ferry and he ought to get an Oscar for his "Gee, glad to see you!" act.

The sails on the Stone Horse are small enough to be very easy to set, hand, reef, and stow. The mainsail has an area of 175 square feet, the staysail has 76 square feet, and the jib 88 square feet. The minute you get aboard you can see that the rig was thought out by a sailor. The main topping lift shares a place of equal importance with the main halyard. Tack and clew earings for both reefs in the mainsail are all rove off instead of being thrown in the forepeak. I will say that the reef points for the second reef in the mainsail should be slightly longer. The deeper the reef, the longer the reef point should be. Also, there are times in a gale of wind when the third reef in the mainsail shown in the sail plan would be just the thing.

It's hard to believe how much strain can come on the sheets of even small headsails when it is blowing. The *Pollock Rip*'s jib sheets were single-part; they needed pennants leading to a two-part sheet, so you could really flatten the sail in in a breeze.

The Stone Horse sail plan shows a three-part forestaysail sheet led to a traveller, but the *Pollock Rip* was rigged with a double-part sheet made up so that the sheet itself leads athwartships to form the traveller and make the sail "self-tending." Of course it isn't self-tending; every time after you tack somebody has to go forward to shove the club three or four inches to leeward along its rope traveller. I prefer to put up with the slam-bang of a metal traveller, which will trim the sail just where you want it and really does make it self-tending.

The Stone Horse deck plan shows real cleats for both jib and staysail sheets, but the *Pollock Rip* was rigged with mere jam cleats. Who invented these abortions? Are we supposed to be so lazy we can't take a few turns around a cleat? Where, on a jam cleat, are you supposed to take your turn so you can swig on the sheet to flatten the sail in the last little bit? You can't do it; somebody stream-

It's always the way. You have to beat to windward and along comes somebody in a big schooner running off, just readin' both pages. (Edey and Duff)

lined the cute little thing. Or say there is a heavy strain on the sheet and you want to slack it a bit. Now is when I'd like to call for Mr. Jam Cleat Designer and watch him struggle the sheet out of his contraption and get hauled down the deck before he can jam it back in again. He's now done a bit of dangerous work, but he still hasn't been able to trim the sail where he wants it. I suppose you could say he is in a bit of a jam. Contrast all this foolishness, if you will, with the childishly easy task faced by the proud owner of a real cleat. He takes off all but a couple of turns, eases the sheet out to where he wants it, puts his turns back on.

and goes about his business, never dreaming that there is a fiendish plot to replace his simple, workable cleat with a device that will cause him danger, strain, and frustration. Oh yes, and by the way, the jam cleats on the *Pollock Rip* wouldn't hold the jib sheets in more than a fresh breeze. The sheet just slipped out through them, no doubt causing some damage to the rope. I'd like to pave the bottom of Nantucket Sound with jam cleats. There, now that's out of my system for awhile.

The roller-furling jib worked like a charm. You hear a few horror stories about these sails. A friend of ours was about to anchor in a crowded harbor just as a squall struck. His big overlapping roller jib blew open and filled before you could say, "Let go." The next few minutes weren't much fun. But the *Pollock Rip*'s roller-furling jib worked perfectly and gave no trouble whatsoever. It's an especially handy rig on a little boat where it may be awkward at times to get away out forward to smother a headsail.

The *Pollock Rip*'s sails are brown. It never occurred to me before this trip, but I think brown sails must be a good thing for safety in fog. You know how you can see the shadow of a dark object looming through the mist considerably before a light object will show up.

The little Westerbeke diesel in the *Pollock Rip* was noisy and rough, as are all small diesels. It also ran faultlessly and shoved the boat along at four knots or better for something like seven hours using about two gallons of fuel from its portable three-gallon tank stowed on deck under a cockpit seat. When you need more, you just take the tank ashore under your arm.

Early in the morning it was thick o'fog. But by the time we got underway under power at quarter of seven it had cleaned out a little and you could see across the harbor. We went outside and set all sail to a light west northwest breeze to help the engine shove her along. Then the fog came back in thick and we sent the radar reflector up to the starboard spreader and started thinking about ferry schedules. It turned out to be patchy, though, rather than really thick and by the time we got in to Cross Rip, it suddenly burned right off.

All at once the engine seemed to lose its push. She was turning up the same as ever, but the boat wasn't getting anywhere. We shut down and had a look over the side. Where the propeller used to be, there was a big ball of rockweed. So we rolled up the jib, hauled the staysail to weather, lashed the helm down and held swim call. The *Pollock Rip* was very docile, fore-reaching a little and making a little leeway. The rockweed came right off in our hands and there was the propeller again.

Soon after we got underway again, the breeze dropped entirely, so we furled up the sails and rolled along in true motorboat style. As we approached East Chop on Martha's Vineyard, the head tide got stronger and a look at *Eldridge*'s (in its own neat rack just inside the companionway) showed we still had two more hours of foul tide.

So we went in beside East Chop and anchored in the open and did some more swimming. It was plenty hot on deck, but down in the cabin it was nice and cool.

Four o'clock in the afternoon was slack water so that's when we hove up and got going. As we did so, a moderate sou'wester came in and we had a fine beat over to Woods Hole, taking an extra-long hitch back out into Vineyard Sound just to get a closer look at the big schooner *Bill of Rights* running down the Sound just as pretty as could be. We then went in and beat through Woods Hole with a very strong fair tide. She handled beautifully in the ticklish part where you have to take short hitches across a current that is setting you sideways as fast as you are moving ahead. She also beat up into the cove at Hadley's Harbor against the last of the breeze, made flukey by trees, with neither hesitation nor capriciousness. We anchored at six and rowed the dory out through the northwest gutter to Buzzards Bay before returning to the vessel to admire the sunset. My son knows his birds and was able to identify plenty of species in that lovely haven.

When you first sail a Stone Horse the idea of the cockpit coaming also being the side of the boat seems peculiar, but you get used to it and find it's really kind of nice to be that much closer to the water. That deep bulwark also makes a much better backrest than do most real cockpit coamings.

The tiller might be a foot longer, just so you could reach sheets and halyards more conveniently while steering; we found we would also prefer a bigger-diameter handle on the tiller, because the rather skinny one was a bit tiring to hold after awhile.

The boat has a snug cabin to come down into after a hard sail. There is a lot of wood below; you sense the wood sheathing and all the wood fittings around the cabin far more than you sense the fiberglass overhead.

The two "sumptuous seats" are indeed sumptuous, and they make the cabin one of the most comfortable we have lived in. Well shaped as they are, though, the fiberglass gets a big hard after awhile, and a good cushion might be in order.

The ports in the raised deck are well positioned; from the seats you can look out at what's going on around you, and it's nice to look down below

Of the 36 Stone Horses Lee Ship-building turned out—and sold for $800 apiece—quite a few had trunk cabins instead of a raised deck. The boats set jib topsails rather than jibs on bow-sprits. (Lance Lee)

One of the original wooden Stone Horses built by the Lee Shipbuilding Co. of Harwichport, Massachusetts, in the early Thirties. (Lance Lee)

when she's sailing to windward and spitting seas off to leeward and see the water coming up against the lee side of her hull through these ports from inside. When she's sailing close-hauled on the port tack and heeled well over, a great place to sit is in the starboard seat looking over your right shoulder through the porthole with your eye just at water level. You get a real sense of speed. Under the same conditions, this seat makes a fine place to stand while you lean out the companionway to watch her go.

The galley details in the Stone Horse make great good sense. The sink has no drain and no through-hull fitting. It's portable. When you get through washing dishes, you just lift it out of its nest and dump it over the side from a standing position in the companionway. The icebox has no drain and no through-hull fitting. There is a little pump to pump it out with.

The head has a holding tank, which again means no through-hull fittings.

Throughout the cabin we found nicely made wooden fittings that it would take most of us years of owning the boat to work out the need for and build. These held plates, bowls, tide tables, binoculars, pencils, and a radio. Behind the stove, there is room for a small shelf which would make a nice addition.

The stove was a Swedish-made alcohol wick affair. It was decidedly the very best boat cooking stove with which we had ever been shipmates. She also had a little heating stove which we didn't have the weather to try.

There is no doubt that the Stone Horse's cabin is small. When you first come aboard to stow your gear, it seems cramped. But then, after a bit, you get used to the space there is, and you find that with the smallness is a snugness and a hominess and a downright convenience in reaching for things that you'd be reluctant to give up for mere space. It's the kind of cabin in which you get claustrophobia after five minutes but in which you find real comfort and peace after five days.

On a bright sunny morning in Hadley's Harbor, we found it so necessary to swim and watch the birds and devour a huge breakfast in the cockpit that we didn't break out the anchor until nine o'clock. We ghosted out with a light air from the west, then put her on a nice reach across Buzzards Bay for Aucoot Cove. The breeze increased gradually to gentle and gave us a nice final sail while we took turns packing up our gear and holding field day. The *Pollock Rip* picked up her mooring just at noon. So ends a fine cruise in a fine boat.

13/ The *Tyche*

> Length on deck: 27 feet 1 inch
> Length on waterline: 22 feet 1 inch
> Beam: 9 feet
> Draft: 4 feet 6 inches
> Sail area: 497 square feet
> Designer: John G. Alden

The late Captain Rodman Swift's little Alden schooner is named the *Tyche,* after the Greek goddess of good fortune. She was well named, for she has been a lucky vessel; Captain Swift sailed her many thousands of miles during the half century he had her without serious mishap.

Lucky, yes. But also, of course, she has been handled with great loving care and skill.

I remember a famous athlete being interviewed by the press just after he had led his team to victory in a thrilling demonstration of almost unbelievable physical skill. One of the newsmen even went so far as to suggest that on a few of the plays the athlete might have been a bit lucky. He responded, "Well, I'd rather be lucky than good." To which I would say, "Amen," especially if you're talking about knocking around the coast in a small boat in all weathers. Of course on the water it is often helpful to be both lucky and good. Such was Rodman Swift, and he helped his luck enormously by learning seamanship at an early age, having a seaworthy vessel, and keeping her long enough to get to know her.

His *Tyche* impresses me as a fine little vessel for one or two people. He often used her as a single-hander.

What Captain Swift wanted back in 1922 was a cruising boat for his local waters of Buzzards Bay and Vineyard Sound and also a boat in which he could cruise to Florida and back with his children. For the design he went to the office of John G. Alden.

The *Tyche* is Alden's design No. 172. She is 27 feet 1 inch long on deck, with a waterline length of 22 feet 1 inch, a beam of 9 feet, and a draft of 4 feet 6 inches.

Her lines plan, dated January 9, 1922, was initialed by S.S.C. (Sam Crocker) and J.A.C. (John Alden Crocker, Sam's younger brother). Her sail plan, dated January 24th in the same year, was initialed by J.A.C. only. It shows an area of 497 square feet, made up of a mainsail of 251 square feet; foresail, 143 square feet; and jib, 103 square feet. Then there is a dotted line drawn in that cuts about a foot off the leech of the mainsail from boom to gaff, diminishing the area of that sail to 230 square feet and her total area to 476 square feet. She was evidently built with the reduced sail plan, and undoubtedly steers a bit easier for it.

The little schooner was built in 1922 at Baker's Yacht Basin, Quincy, Massachusetts.

A sister hull was built in 1929 by G.L. Chaisson at Swampscott, Massachusetts, and was rigged as a Marconi yawl. This boat was built for W. Candler

John G. Alden (Chester M. Sawtelle)

Bowditch of Boston and was later owned for a few years by an uncle of mine, Frederick C. Buffum, who named her the *Wah Wee*. I was too small to know the *Wah Wee* when my uncle had her, but I remember seeing pictures of her.

The *Tyche* is the smallest of the hundreds of cruising schooners turned out by John G. Alden. In fact it is said that Captain Swift had to exercise a bit of persuasion to get Alden to put a schooner rig in such a small boat. The year before, Alden had designed a schooner with a waterline length of 24 feet 6 inches, but he must have thought making the *Tyche* a schooner was going just a bit too far. Nonetheless the boat has certainly proved successful for the uses to which Captain Swift put her.

One of Rodman Swift's growing-up pals around New Bedford was Llewellyn Howland, the man who later developed the Concordia yawl (described in Chapter 2). Skipper Howland wrote an article about Captain Swift and his *Tyche* published in the May, 1954, issue of *Yachting*. He told how he and Swift contracted an "irresistible contagion," an "enduring love of seafaring." In Swift's case, the symptoms were much harbor work in a heavy punt

all of five feet long; extensive coastal cruising in a 16-foot, two-masted, sprit-rigged open boat during which spartan voyages Swift became a "hard case"; and a year-long voyage in the full-rigged ship *Astral*, carrying case-oil to the Far East. Then he got the *Tyche*, and it was clear that the disease was incurable. You might say he lived of it.

When we look at the *Tyche*'s plans, we see at once that Captain Swift did not go afloat in order to get from one place to the next as fast as he could. Rather he was clearly interested in being able to enjoy the performance of a seakindly craft in any reasonable weather. Captain Swift loved being in his easy-going *Tyche* and paced his life on board her to her own steady, comfortable reactions to wind and sea.

The *Tyche* was never laid up ashore while Captain Swift had her. For 50 years, he had that good feeling of a sailor that he could always go on board his vessel.

The *Tyche*'s hull is husky rather than graceful, but she is well proportioned and well balanced. Her short ends, curved stem, springy sheerline, buttock lines, and waterlines are all well formed. She has plenty of freeboard for dryness in rough water and, with her powerful sections, is certainly a stiff boat. She has 4,440 pounds of lead on her keel. John Alden wrote, "On a boat of this size, I like all the ballast outside as the chief weights are relatively far higher than on a larger boat and, therefore, it is necessary, in order to obtain satisfactory performance to windward, to have the center of gravity of the ballast correspondingly lower."

The schooner was built with a white oak backbone and ribs and was planked with cypress. She was given copper sheathing at the waterline for ice protection.

Captain Swift gave his *Tyche* a long life by taking good care of her in the traditional manner. Her masts in way of the hoops were carefully slushed down. Her wire rigging was kept rust-free with generous applications of linseed oil. Her ironwork was carefully red-leaded and kept painted. Nor was the linseed spared on her pine deck.

Her schooner rig is snug indeed, even as originally designed with the larger mainsail. Were she mine, I'd be sorely tempted to give her topmasts and much paraphernalia for summer, but that would do away with her simplicity. Rodman Swift was far too wise to succumb to any such shenanigans.

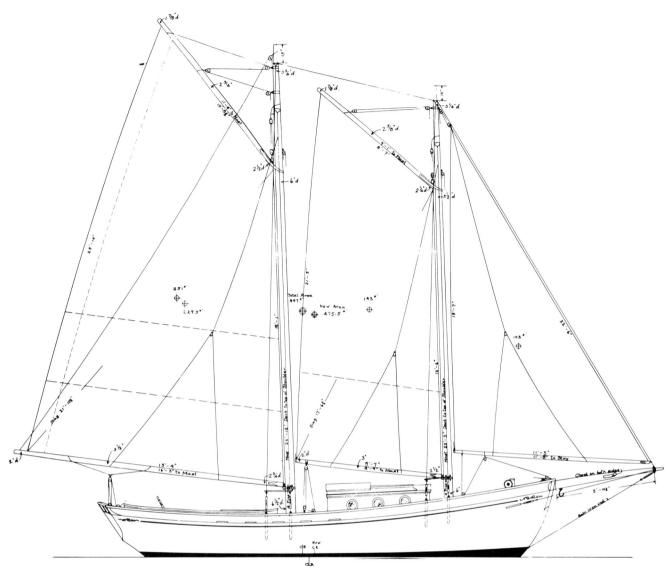

The Tyche, *designed and built for Captain Rodman Swift, is the smallest-ever schooner designed by John Alden.*

The single headsail makes sense in so small a schooner. Her bowsprit, flat on top, extends six feet outboard.

There ought, of course, to be a vang on her narrow, rather square foresail.

Though she would not need to be reefed often, she has reefs that are deep enough to be worthwhile when you put them in. You'd want to keep both clew earings rove off on the mainsail. Note the lazy jacks all round, a big help to a single-hander.

She would balance with reefed main, foresail, and jib; or with jib and reefed mainsail without the foresail; or she could heave to, run, or reach under foresail alone.

She would have a good enough turn of speed under most conditions, but she wouldn't do well to windward in a seaway, and she'd be sluggish in a light air without topsails and a balloon jib. When things weren't going her way, she would need her engine, a 10-h.p. Frisbie, or, preferably, a master with Captain Swift's patience and oneness with the water.

When sailing the *Tyche* singlehanded, Swift rigged lifelines from stem to stern tied off to the shrouds. He also used to tow a line from each quarter just in case the lifelines failed at their appointed task. (When sailing my old Herreshoff sloop alone, I used to tow a line astern with a small, balsa, white-painted buoy on the end of it. I

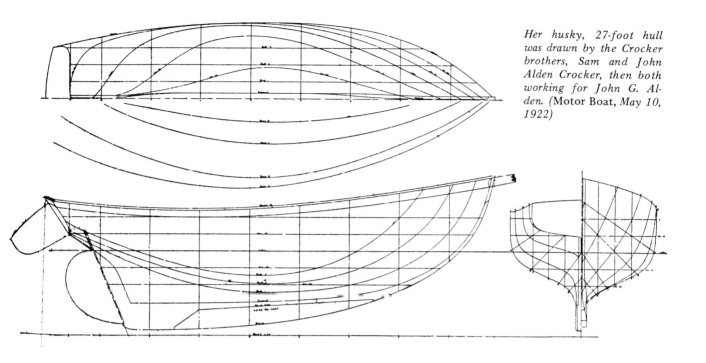

Her husky, 27-foot hull was drawn by the Crocker brothers, Sam and John Alden Crocker, then both working for John G. Alden. (Motor Boat, May 10, 1922)

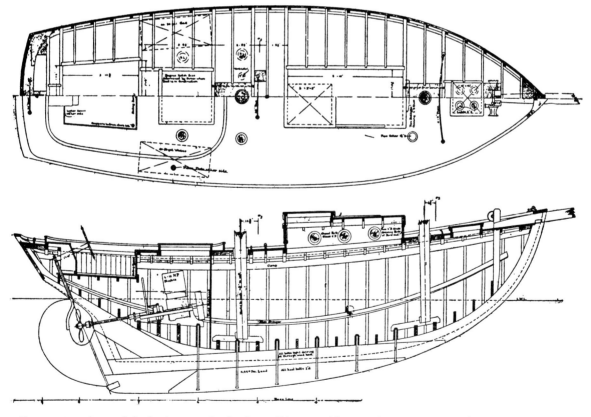

Her construction and deck plans emphasize her solidness and her spaciousness topside. (Motor Boat, May 10, 1922)

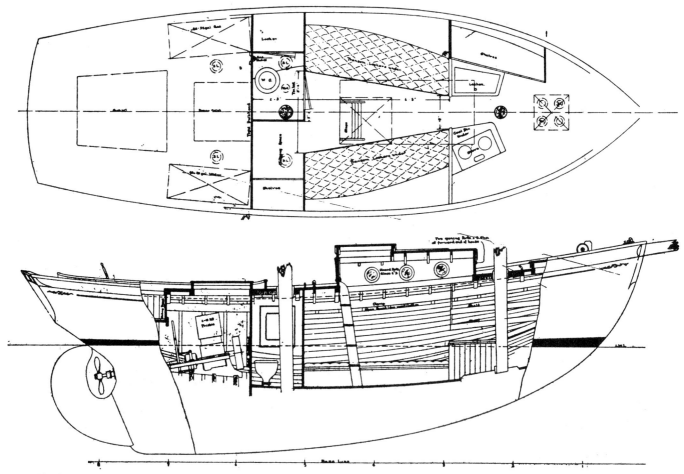

She has a snug cabin for two with an enclosed head and a completely separate engine room. (Motor Boat, May 10, 1922)

never had to use it, but it made me feel as if I was acting like a responsible citizen.) The *Tyche* has an added sense of security on deck in that she has seven-inch bulwarks.

The *Tyche* carries a pair of old-fashioned iron anchors, and with them she and Captain Swift rode out the 1938 hurricane in Padanaram, Massachusetts, no mean feat, and one not duplicated by many craft, even on "permanent" moorings.

The schooner's very small cabin house makes great good sense in a boat of this type. It gives her nearly six feet of headroom under its carlins, and the space on deck is far more useful than would be a larger area of headroom below. For one thing, she can carry her dinghy on deck on the port side of the house, a very valuable ability for a cruising boat that wants to be at home in rough water. Her tender was a 9-foot 9-inch dory, said to be tippy enough to discourage borrowing.

Down below she has a snug, warm little cabin. The head is well located back under the deck in way of the mainmast. Opposite is a big hanging locker, which I'd be tempted to turn into a desk. There are good-sized deadlights abreast the mainmast. Her galley is at the forward end of the little house with just room to stand up to the stove with various degrees of slouching depending on your height. There is considerable stowage space in the forepeak, which has a hatch to the deck.

The schooner's engine has its own room with plenty of space around it and a pair of deadlights in the deck for when the big hatch is shut. As may be seen in the photo, the engine room hatch was built up considerably higher than shown in the plans. The engine room is separated from the cabin by a full-width watertight bulkhead. Alongside the engine are a 50-gallon gas tank to port and a 50-gallon water tank to starboard.

The Tyche *lying on her mooring behind the breakwater at Padanaram, Massachusetts. (Photo by Doug Cabral)*

So the *Tyche* is a fine little coastwise or offshore cruising boat for a small crew. She conjures up all sorts of seagoing images, one of which was nicely expressed by Skipper Howland:

I keep in mind the picture of *Tyche* hove-to under her reefed, tan foresail, well offshore on a day of early spring, in the Gulf of Maine where a strong, cold nor'easter has piled up a heavy, white-capped sea—formidable conditions for so small a vessel bound east under sail—and catch a glimpse of the captain's uncovered, gray head as he pokes it out for a "squint" between the lower fashion-board and the closed slide of the companionway of that glorified booby hatch—the trunk of his little cabin abaft the foremast—while *Tyche*, appearing and disappearing, breasts the seas, steady as the ticking of a clock, and except for an occasional burst of spray at her weather fore rigging, as dry and unconcerned as a great black-backed gull. And as she slowly drifts to leeward, I can almost catch a whiff of that wood smoke from her stovepipe mingled with that of her captain's stub-stemmed briar—sure signs of warmth and comfort and—yes—serenity of mind down below.

14/ A Knockabout Schooner

Length on deck: 30 feet
Length on waterline: 23 feet 3 inches
Beam: 7 feet
Draft: 4 feet
Sail area: 374 square feet
Designer: Philip C. Bolger

As an antidote to extreme and freakish racing craft, a type of small, keel sloop that could be sailed comfortably in rough weather was developed in the 1890s by some New England yachtsmen. These craft had outside ballast and either a very short bowsprit or no bowsprit at all. They were such handy little vessels that they earned the nickname "knockabouts."

Thomas F. McManus of Boston, trying to design safer Grand Banks fishing schooners at about this time, came to realize that the bowsprit was responsible for considerable loss of life in these vessels. It was not just that the bowsprits of the big schooners were inherently dangerous places to work in heavy weather, but also that most of the fishermen had neither time nor inclination to keep footropes and sail stops in good order so that this gear carried away all too often, many times with fatal result.

McManus struck on the idea of solving this safety problem by adapting the concept of the knockabout to fishing schooner design. He designed a schooner with the bow drawn out and raised to take the jib stay and fore topmast stay. The resulting lines showed a vessel nearly half again as long on deck as she was on the waterline. The new design measured 65 feet on the waterline and had a

molded length on deck of 105 feet 6 inches. Her molded beam was 20 feet 6 inches, and her draft was 12 feet. Her sail area was 5,200 square feet.

Tom McManus designed this first knockabout fishing schooner in 1900, but it was a year before he could interest anybody in building his innovation. Captain William Thomas of Portland, Maine, and Cassius Hunt decided to build a schooner to the new design and had her put up by Oxner and Story at Essex, Massachusetts. The schooner was launched in the spring of 1902 and was named the *Helen B. Thomas.*

All of this knockabout fishing schooner development was reported for us by Howard I. Chapelle and appears in his last book, *The American Fishing Schooners: 1825-1935.* Chapelle wrote of the *Thomas,* "This vessel was a fast sailer and very handy. She was exceptionally quick in stays and was well balanced. She tacked in 20 to 25 seconds in smooth water."

The drawback to the knockabout fishing schooners was that they were relatively small carriers for their length, and thus, to a certain extent, for their cost. But they are an interesting type of schooner, especially the early ones with their very long, high bows and strong sheerlines. Later knockabout fishing schooners, such as Jim Sharp's

Phil Bolger (Paul Kenyon)

Adventure, still sailing out of Camden, Maine, were given conventional Gloucester schooner bows, and their rigs were adjusted as to balance and sail area by shortening the main boom and increasing the height of the lower masts.

Charles G. Davis' drawing of the sail plan of the *Helen B. Thomas* in his excellent book, *Ships of the Past,* published by the Marine Research Society at Salem, Massachusetts, in 1929, had great fascination for me as a youngster. The long-ended, springy hull of the big schooner and her huge, well-proportioned sail plan stirred in the imagination a vision of the vessel strapped down and going to windward with everything set in a strong breeze, her great bow spitting off sea after sea to leeward. As part of my study and enjoyment of this sail plan, I found it necessary to measure up her sails and pencil in their areas.

This same knockabout fishing schooner disease thoroughly infected two young admirers of the type, Philip C. Bolger of Gloucester and Albert M. Barnes of Falmouth, Massachusetts. The former is a naval architect still working in Gloucester, and the latter is on the staff of the Mariners Museum at Newport News, Virginia, and is a well-respected authority on Gloucester fishing schooners. Three decades ago Barnes gave Bolger his requirements for a little knockabout fishing schooner, and Bolger turned out for him the accompanying design. She is, to my eye, a very pretty boat.

While she has an obvious Gloucester heritage, she is, of course, a very fine-lined boat compared to a working fisherman; there is more emphasis on speed and less on carrying capacity.

The little schooner would make an admirable daysailer and short-range cruiser for two. She'd be a bit sensitive to weight and so shouldn't be loaded down with gear and people. Putting ashore permanently the large piece of machinery outlined amidships in her construction plan would make an admirable first step for her loading plan. Then the drag-creating propeller could be dispensed with and its aperture closed up. One can almost feel the gratitude of her rudder for these kind deeds.

This knockabout schooner is 30 feet long on deck, with a waterline length of 23 feet 3 inches, a beam of 7 feet, and a draft of 4 feet. Her least freeboard is 18 inches. Her outside ballast is 1,395 pounds of iron. Her mainsail has an area of 209 square feet, the foresail 118, and the jib 47, for a total of 374 square feet.

Her diagonals may be seen to be very fair indeed; it would be good to see one more diagonal drawn in above the load waterline.

Her forefoot is well cut away and her hull is quite shoal, giving very easy buttock lines. She is really almost a fin-keeler and should sail fast. She has a fine entry and is a narrow boat. The flare to her sections just above the load waterline should contribute considerably to her stiffness.

The shape of the schooner's stem and the crown of her transom are good-looking details. Her construction plan shows that her scantlings have been kept moderate; she has no need to be nearly as heavily built as were her ancestors.

The rig has been kept simple, with single shrouds leading to deadeyes and lanyards, and she has no extraneous gear. Yet it is interesting to note that even this simple schooner rig with a single headsail has no fewer than a dozen pieces of running rigging, six pieces of standing rigging, and seven spars. And I would propose replacing the engine with a main topmast so that a main topsail and a fisherman staysail could be carried in light weather; this

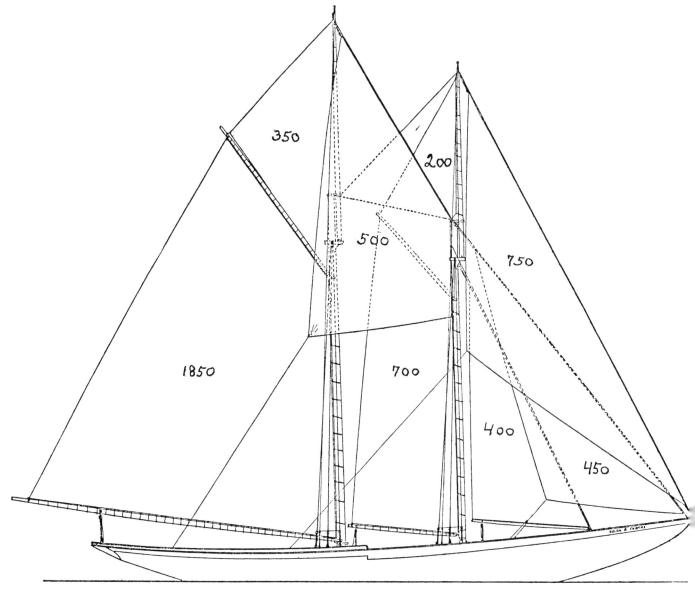

Charles G. Davis' sail plan of the knockabout fishing schooner Helen B. Thomas *is enough to conjure up a full-color, three dimensional image, complete with sound effects, of the big schooner thrashing to windward, smashing up and over one head sea after another. (I'm afraid it was I who wrote in those numbers for the areas of the sails on Mr. Davis' nice drawing.) (*Ships of the Past *by Charles G. Davis)*

would add seven more pieces of running rigging, three more pieces of standing rigging, and one more spar. It is all this sailorizing kind of gear that makes a little schooner the greatest of fun to some but the greatest of frustrations to others.

The center of effort of the sail plan is just at the luff of the mainsail, farther aft than on many schooners. She would still balance all right, however, under the foresail alone. You would shorten sail initially by reefing the mainsail. A third reef in that sail and a couple of reefs in the foresail would

not go amiss in such a small schooner. There would, of course, be a vang from the fore gaff to the mainmast and down to the deck.

As long as we are thinking of giving her a main topmast, we might as well go whole hog and send out a running bowsprit so that a big balloon jib could be carried with a light, leading breeze.

One of the things that makes this schooner pretty to look at is the way her booms cock up nicely.

It is good to steer a little schooner like this with

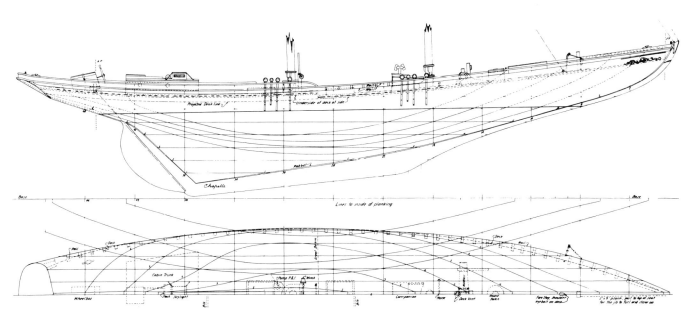

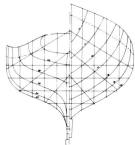

Howard I. Chapelle's lines drawings of the Thomas *give a good idea of her long-ended beauty. The bow profile in this drawing is undoubtedly more accurate than that shown in the Davis sail plan. (The American Fishing Schooners by Howard I. Chapelle, W. W. Norton & Co.)*

a tiller. Some folks feel that every schooner must have a wheel to be right, but the decision really ought to be based more on the size and weight of the vessel than on her rig.

This boat has a big cockpit; its seats are eight feet long, and there is another three feet of flush deck inside the coaming between the seats and the house. The cockpit is apparently not self-draining; I think it would be worth making it a little shallower so that it could be. What is needed when the cockpit floor is only an inch or two above the waterline is a wooden plug for each drain made big enough and shaped so that you can get a good grip on it with one hand. These plugs are kept in the drains when sailing so to keep water from coming into the cockpit when she heels, but may be removed quickly if a sea should come aboard.*

---

*Since this was written, I have learned that all you need do is criss-cross the drain lines and forget about the plugs. Oh to be clever enough to think up stuff like that.

She has enough room around her masts to make working her halyards a pleasure. It would be particularly pleasant to work at the foot of her mainmast which is on deck and inside the coaming instead of on top of a house, as is often the case in a small schooner.

A good tender for the little schooner might be a 15-foot canoe either towed or stowed on deck on the port side with one end tucked inside the fore shroud and the other stopping just short of the end of the tiller so the steersman could still choose his side.

Her cabin house is nicely shaped indeed, and the low taffrail looks good. You'd want a tarp to go over the main gaff for a rainy day.

Below, her headroom is four feet at the after end of the house, just enough to sit up in. You could have two transoms in the after part of the cabin extending under the midships flush deck to form bunks. The galley could be nicely located at the forward end of the house with a stool for the cook. An important item to have on board would be a cedar bucket. The schooner has plenty of stowage space in the bow and along the sides of the cockpit.

I suggested to Phil Bolger that he might want to include this little vessel in a book of his designs, *The Folding Schooner* (which, obviously, took its title from a different Bolger schooner than this one). He declined on grounds that the design might

W. B. Jackson's photograph of the Thomas *shows her close-hauled and footing fast. (*Ships of the Past *by Charles G. Davis)*

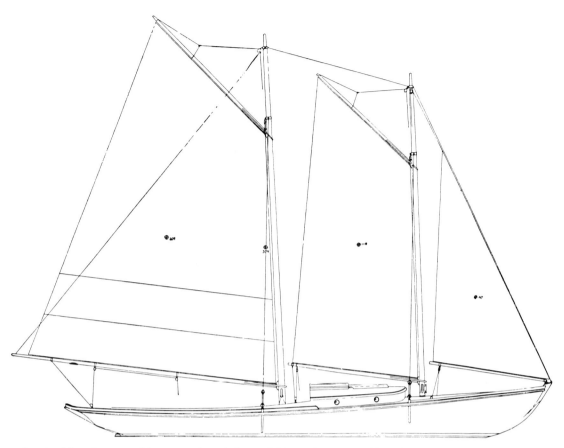

Above: *Inspired by the great Gloucester knockabout fishing schooners, Phil Bolger turned out this little beauty of the same type for his friend Albert M. Barnes. (Rudder, August, 1950)*

Below: *The lines of the 30-foot knockabout schooner show her to be light, narrow, fair, and slippery-looking. (Rudder, August, 1950)*

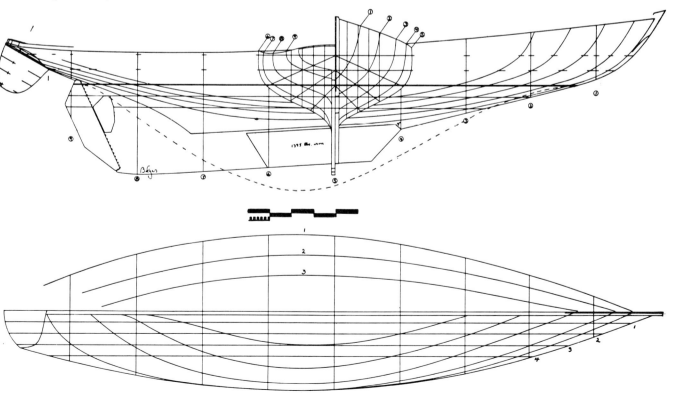

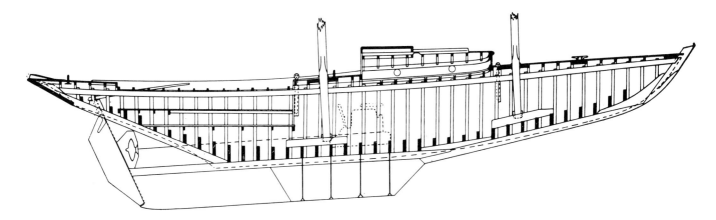

It is just as well to show machinery in dotted lines in a boat of this type, for the presence of such foreign matter in such a smart, handy boat may well be ephemeral. (Rudder, *August, 1950*)

better be an example of a designer's immature thinking, since he was so young when he created her. Not that he still didn't like the little schooner. He wrote, "Once one gets by the crudity of the drawing, it's a surprisingly good design, I must say. If she'd been built by somebody who knew enough to fix up the detailing decently, I think she'd have been a very good sailer on most points. In fact, she wasn't built, or even seriously meant to be built; she was one of those exercises a young designer does to specifications furnished by a friend for practice."

All this is undoubtedly true, but if a young designer's work is immature, it is also, perhaps, somewhat idealistic and romantic. I catch a sense in this design of the power, majesty, and speed of the great *Helen B. Thomas*. Would that more designers, as they mature, could keep a firm hold on the idealism and romanticism of their youth as they turn out craft ever more nearly able to meet all the needs of their owners. Anyone familiar with Phil Bolger's work over the years would have to agree he has stayed young at heart.

15/ The *Rain Bird*

> Length on deck: 40 feet
> Length on waterline: 27 feet 7 inches
> Beam: 10 feet
> Draft: 6 feet 6 inches
> Sail area: 751 square feet
> Designer: William Garden

It is always interesting to study a vessel drawn up by a designer who knows that he himself is going to be the one to sail and maintain her. The schooner *Rain Bird* was designed by William Garden for his own use. And in this case, as with a number of Bill Garden's designs, he did a good bit of building of the boat.

Mr. Garden commented on this business of a designer designing for himself with regard to the *Rain Bird* in 1951:

I'm sorry that I can't divulge any startling reasons for building *Rain Bird* other than that I enjoy looking at her. Much the way we select our wives and sweethearts—not because this one can cook or that one has an income, both excellent practical reasons—but because we like to look at one in particular. If the boat will also sail well enough to be a constant source of enjoyment, the reason is doubly sufficient.

The principal complication for the designer is caused by the stream of boats that go sailing across his board each year, providing an enthusiasm during the work and the recurring thought that this would be a dandy little ship to have. Probably much the way it would be if you knew intimately about 500 chorus girls of, say, 20 basic models, and had to decide which one to run away with.

Originally I worked out a canoe-sterned yawl, more of a motor sailer, intended as an ideal boat for my purposes of a month's cruising in the summer and weekending the year around. She looked to be ideal and most practical, but then I made a little sketch of a schooner one day and she looked to be so much fun to build that I rolled up the motor sailer and started on the schooner.

The schooner Mr. Garden "started on" has a length on deck of 40 feet, a waterline length of 27 feet 7 inches, a beam of 10 feet, and a draft of 6 feet 6 inches.

She has the relatively long, high bow of the knockabout schooner, the kind of structure that the British marine historian Edgar J. March might call a "sea-fendy bow." (Marvelous expression!) To balance her wonderful bow, the *Rain Bird* has a fairly high, well-shaped stern with a nicely curved wineglass transom.

Her ends are connected by a lively sheerline, and note the lovely curve of this sheerline in the plan view as well as in the profile. This is a hull that maintains its beauty when viewed from any angle.

She has quite hard bilges and a rather deep draft with her outside ballast hung low. With these features and her long run, she should be stiff, fast, and weatherly. Her hull is powerful enough to carry well her rather tall and generous rig.

It is interesting to compare the design of the *Rain Bird* to that of the 30-foot knockabout

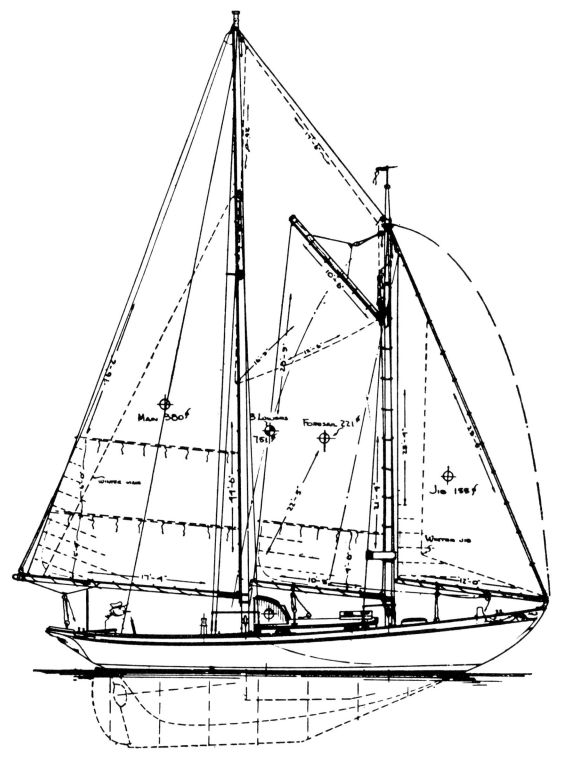

Bill Garden designed the Rain Bird *30 years ago for his own use. (*Yachting, *November, 1951)*

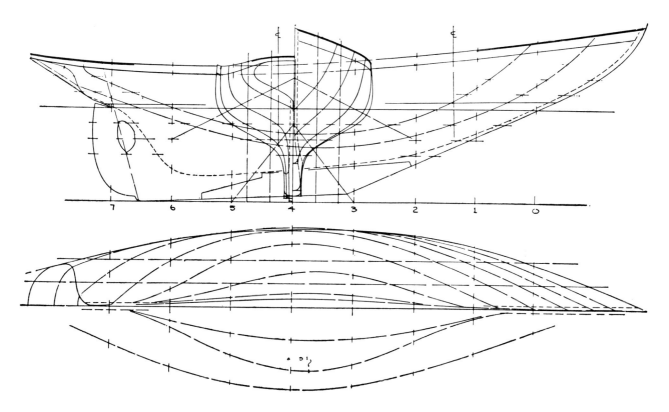

Above: *Her lines show a shapely hull with high ends and a lively sheer, a long run, and considerable power to carry sail.* (Yachting, *November, 1951*)

Below: *The schooner's cockpit is big, well-laid-out, and eminently livable.* (Yachting, *November, 1951*)

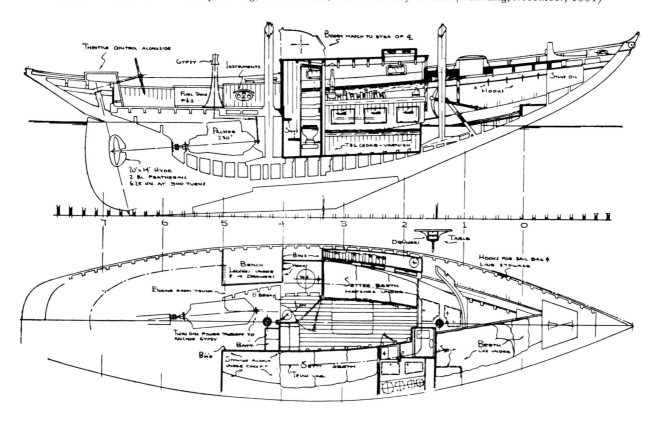

The Rain Bird *a
decked out in he
finest, even to
stylish deck
sweeper. (Phot
by Roy Mon*
gomery, courtes
of Sailing)

schooner designed by Phil Bolger that was described in the previous chapter. The Garden design, besides being a bigger boat, is proportionally heavier, deeper, and more powerful than Bolger's knockabout schooner. The Bolger schooner would be quicker on her feet.

Bill Garden reported that the *Rain Bird* was well balanced whether sailing upright or rail down. Her mainsail has an area of 380 square feet, the foresail 221 square feet, and the jib 150 square feet, for a total working sail area of 751 square feet. The fisherman staysail adds 208 square feet for a full-sail area of 959 square feet. Rather deep reefs are shown in the mainsail and foresail, and a small jib is dotted in on the sail plan. She has enough sail area to be a good performer in light weather, yet can be readily shortened down to do every bit as well in a breeze.

To make best use of the foresail when running before it, you'd want to rig preventers on both fore and main booms, coasting schooner style, so you could run her off wing-and-wing without fear of jibing. This is nice work if you can get it, sitting at the wheel of a little schooner like the *Rain Bird* running off with the sails wung out; the oldtimers called it "readin' both pages." You might even want to go whole hog and have a balloon jib that could be poled out opposite the foresail.

Note that the schooner has no spring stay, so you don't have to lower the fisherman staysail and reset it when tacking. The sail works like any double-sheeted headsail, so that all you have to do when tacking is let go one sheet and take in the other. The sail sets inside the fore gaff on one tack and outside it on the opposite tack. The single-part sheets lead to the quarters, and the sail has enough area so that it would be something of a chore to flatten it in in a breeze. Of course it is little trouble to give a cruising vessel a luff to make such a job easy. This sail should be cut quite flat for windward work.

The *Rain Bird* could carry a ten-foot dinghy on her port side, with one gunwale up on top of the house and the other down on deck. Such a boat could be hoisted out quite readily with a pair of Spanish burtons, one rigged on each mast. This ability to stow a dinghy on deck is an important one for a cruising boat. It's all right to tow a dinghy sometimes, but you certainly want the choice of being able to bring her on board. The

The Rain Bird *full-and-by under working sail.* (Yachting, *November, 1951*)

unwanted feeling of towing a dinghy along behind has perhaps never been expressed better than by Sarah Orne Jewett in her book about the Maine coast, *The Country of the Pointed Firs.* Captain Bowden takes Sarah sailing. She wants to land on a certain island where a hermitess once lived. She writes, quoting Captain Bowden, " 'I don't know as we can make an easy landin' for ye,' he remarked doubtfully. 'May get your feet wet; bad place to land. Trouble is I ought to have brought a tagboat; but they clutch onto the water so, an' I do love to sail free.' "

The *Rain Bird*'s engine is a Palmer 230. It swings a 20-inch by 14-inch Hyde two-bladed feathering wheel, which drives the boat at 6¼ knots at 900 r.p.m. The engine is placed slightly off center and at an angle to the centerline, but with the wheel on center. The turning moment to the right caused by the angle of the shaft would be counteracted by the turning moment to the left generated by the right-hand rotation of the wheel.

The engine drives a gypsy head mounted upright in the cockpit. This is primarily to handle the anchor line but also could be used to make a neat project out of hoisting the mainsail, getting the dinghy on board, or even sheeting flat the fisherman staysail.

Her fuel tanks are under the cockpit seats on both sides. These seats run only half the length of the cockpit, leaving plenty of room around the good-sized steering wheel.

Instead of a full-width bridge deck, she has a half-width bridge deck on the port side, forming an engine room trunk and leaving a clear passage at the level of the cockpit deck to the booby hatch over the companionway just to starboard of the centerline. You can enter the engine room either through the hatch at the top of the trunk or through the head compartment below. With the head open into the engine room, neither compartment would seem like a closet. There is a workbench to port in the engine room.

She has a single berth in the fo'c's'le and two transom berths in the main cabin. Aft of the starboard transom is a big storage area under the cockpit deck.

Her galley range is oil-fired for heat as well as for cooking. The tank for the stove oil is away up in the eyes of her. The skylight at the forward end of the house would be a good vent for the galley.

A small schooner like the *Rain Bird* makes an admirable cruising vessel. Particularly practical is her basic arrangement with the cabin house stopping short of the mainmast, leaving a big, useful cockpit—in this case a dozen feet long—needed by the crew to work the vessel and enjoy her ability to sail well. The *Rain Bird*'s cockpit, with features seldom achieved in far larger vessels, might not be fully appreciated on a short visit, but it would be a great place to live.

In 1968, the *Rain Bird* was entered in a race from Victoria, British Columbia, to Lahaina, Maui, Hawaii, by her then-owner, William B. Johnson. Leonard Wibberly, skipper of a modern racing sloop sailing in the race, wrote in his book, *Hound of the Sea: The Story of a Racing Yacht,* "We beat *Rain Bird* by two hours *on corrected time* although *boat for boat* she finished some hours ahead of us. [Emphasis supplied.] This is worth noting because *Rain Bird* is a schooner, modeled after a Gloucester fisherman, and schooners are not supposed to be able to compete with modern racing sloops."

16/ Two Schooners

Grey Gull II	Williams Schooner
Length on deck: 36 feet 2 inches	Length on deck: 36 feet
Length on waterline: 32 feet 2 inches	Length on waterline: 30 feet 10 inches
Beam: 11 feet 1 inch	Beam: 11 feet
Draft: 4 feet 6 inches	Draft: 5 feet 10 inches
Sail area: 847 square feet	Sail area: 730 square feet
Designer: S.S. Crocker, Jr.	Designer: Fenwick C. Williams

If you asked the Old Timer, "What's the best school of naval architecture around?" he'd likely reply, "Well I don't know about nowadays, but in my time it was down at 131 State Street in Boston, the office of John G. Alden." The design firm wasn't actually a school, of course, but the place did turn out, in addition to the plans of many a fine vessel, a steady stream of designers made competent by translating John Alden's ideas for good boats into detailed plans and specifications under his inspecting gaze.

An amazingly large percentage of the best designers drawing boats in the 15 years before World War II had served their apprenticeship under Alden. Each had his own distinctive style, of course, yet in the boats turned out by all of them you see characteristics here and there that were Alden's hallmarks.

Two designers who graduated summa cum laude from the Alden shop were S. S. Crocker, Jr., and Fenwick C. Williams. Each went off on his own to design cruising boats; for a time, Fenwick Williams paired up with Murray G. Peterson, another Alden alumnus. Crocker and Williams each had his own style in boat design, but, on one occasion at least, both happened to design quite similar small cruising schooners. It is interesting and fun to compare the two designs side by side.

The Crocker schooner is the *Grey Gull II* built by H.H. Ellsworth of Cohasset, Massachusetts, some half a century ago, for Luther W. Turner (who next owned the *Amos Judd*, described in Chapter 28). She is 36 feet 2 inches long on deck, with a waterline length of 32 feet 2 inches, a beam of 11 feet 1 inch, and a draft of 4 feet 6 inches. Her sail area is 847 square feet.

She is a stiff little vessel with her generous beam. She has quite a bit of flare up in the bow to help keep her deck dry. Her entrance is fine and hollow for such a beamy boat. Her transom is quite broad; she picks up considerable bearing aft as she heels. Her buttocks are long and easy, her draft moderate, her forefoot well cut away, and her sheerline springy. The diagonals are very fair. She has a comfortable motion combined with a fair turn of speed.

The schooner has a generous rig. The mainsail has 407 square feet, the foresail 262, and the jib 178. Her reefs are deep enough so that when they are tied in she is snugged down to a very modest sail plan.

The Marconi mainsail makes good sense in a

small schooner. With this rig you don't have to bother with a topsail, which couldn't be much more than an oversized handkerchief in any case. (Of course some of us do like to fool with such objects.)

Her tall, narrow foresail would twist rather badly unless, of course, one were to vang it aft to the mainmast.

The *Grey Gull*'s single headsail on a club with lazy jacks is a very easy sail to handle indeed. Pete Culler said this size of schooner is too small for a double head rig, and I agree with him.

Note that the running backstay on the mainmast has two parts, one pulling opposite the main "topmast" stay and the other opposite the spring stay.

The schooner has a Gray 4-30 engine specified. It takes up most of the after cabin, which is labeled, "Engine Room." Let's yank that engine out and sell it. Now, instead of an engine room with two bunks in it, we have a fine, big cabin handy to the cockpit. Doze in it at night while your watchmate steers, or use it to get in out of the cold and wet on a rough-and-tumble run. Turn it into a big chart room when cruising or the ship's office when living on board. If you must have an engine, put the thing up alongside the mainmast to port with the shaft canted in to the centerline and relegate the head to the bow.

Another idea would be to give her an Uffa Fox *Wishbone*-type deckhouse. For the big ketch *Wishbone*, Mr. Fox designed, just forward of the cockpit, a deckhouse the after half of whose roof could slide forward over the forward half, like a huge hatch. The deckhouse was like any other in rough or rainy weather, but in fine weather could be opened up to become a deep, protected part of the cockpit. (If such a device were built into one of today's stock "cruising" boats, I suppose her advertising copywriter would call it a "sun roof.")

For all her steady comfortableness, the *Grey Gull* was fast enough to win races on Long Island Sound in her early years. She also won praise from George A. Bleyle of St. Augustine Shores, Florida, who wrote me as follows:

> I was the first paid-hand on the schooner *Grey Gull II*, when she sailed from Cohasset Harbor (Massachusetts) on her maiden voyage, Luther W. Turner, owner/skipper, commanding.

Fenwick C. Williams.

If my memory serves me right, she was originally powered with a four-cylinder Kermath 20 h.p. engine turning a two-bladed, self-feathering propeller, which greatly reduced prop-drag when under sail alone.

Yes, the engine sat uncovered in the middle of the aft-cabin floor, which served not only as an engine room but also for sleeping quarters for "Uncle Luther" and me. Obviously, this was a most unusual feature, but it had many desirable properties. First and foremost, the engine, from all sides, was accessible. It was kept wiped down and spotlessly clean. One did not have to hang by his ankles or be a contortionist to check the oil level in the crankcase, or any other simple task. Furthermore, the engine room was very well ventilated, a most desirable feature in preventing explosions, and there was an air-tight-water-tight full width thwartship bulkhead at the forward end of the cabin which prevented any fumes or water from entering the bilge of the main cabin where the passengers "lived" when below.

Grey Gull II was an excellent sailer. She could carry sail and move with the best of them. I vividly remember coming around Race Point, Provincetown in a real breeze and with the tide at odds. We were carrying full sail. The lee scuppers were not quite awash, but not a drop of water came on board. In my opinion, she was *great*.

Turning now to the Fenwick Williams schooner, we find she is 36 feet long on deck, with a waterline length of 30 feet 10 inches, a beam of 11

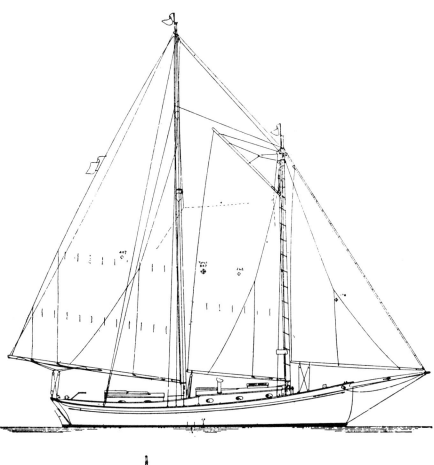

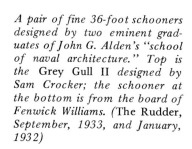

A pair of fine 36-foot schooners designed by two eminent graduates of John G. Alden's "school of naval architecture." Top is the Grey Gull II *designed by Sam Crocker; the schooner at the bottom is from the board of Fenwick Williams. (*The Rudder, *September, 1933, and January, 1932)*

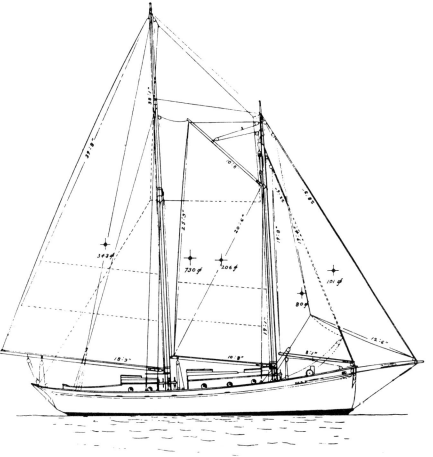

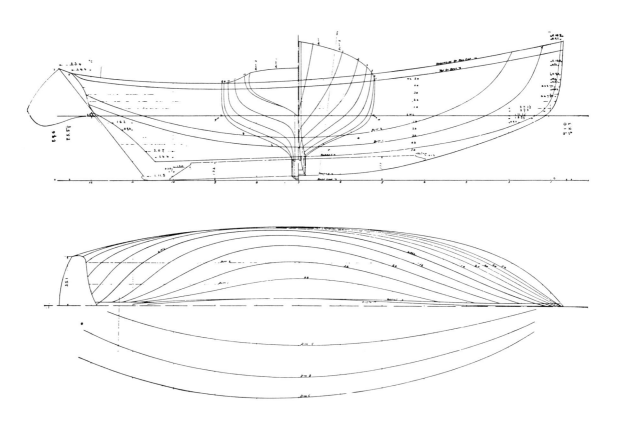

*A comparison of the lines of the two schooners shows many similarities, but the Crocker schooner has a shoaler keel, a finer entrance, and a broader transom. (*The Rudder, *September, 1933, and January, 1932)*

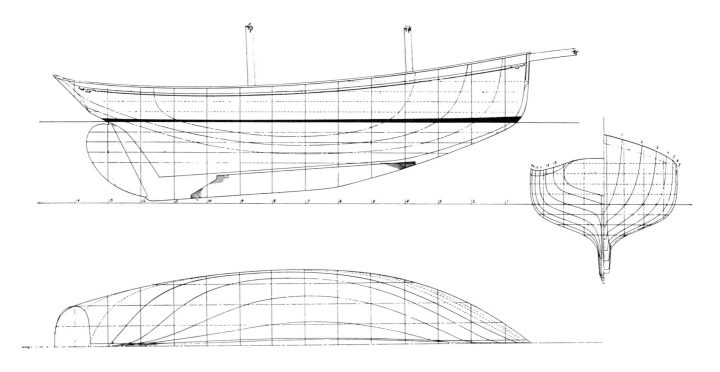

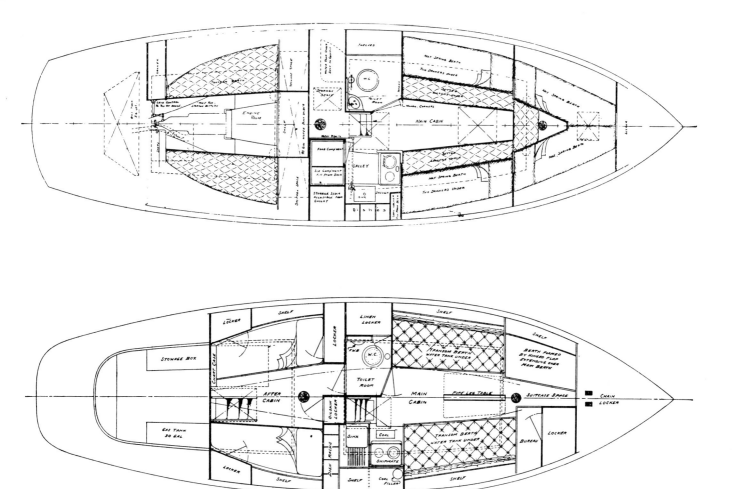

The arrangement plans are quite similar except that in the Grey Gull, *the after cabin has been turned over to—of all things—the engine. (*The Rudder, *September, 1933, and January, 1932)*

feet, and a draft of 5 feet 10 inches. Her sail area is 730 square feet. Her ballast consists of five tons, three tons on the keel and two tons inside.

Although the Williams schooner is deeper than the *Grey Gull,* most of that extra depth is in her keel; the deadrise in both schooners is about the same. The Williams schooner shares a hollow entrance with the Crocker craft, though the former is not as fine forward as is the latter.

Compared to the *Grey Gull,* the Williams schooner is a bit under-rigged. Fenwick Williams' central purpose in this design was to produce a vessel that would stand up to her sail in a fresh breeze without reefing. Her mainsail has 343 square feet, the foresail 206, the fore staysail 80, and the jib 101. Note that the combined area of her jib and staysail is only three square feet more than that of the *Grey Gull*'s jib.

Mr. Williams has drawn in a vang for the fore gaff—for which I thank him from the bottom of my heart. Note that the backstay arrangement is the same as that used on the *Grey Gull.*

The Williams schooner has a sensible arrangement for her after cabin. The engine is beneath the companionway ladder. You can go forward into the main saloon through the head.

The **Grey Gull II** *looking a bit "pitchy" as she works to windward under a rather bizarre combination of sails. (Morris Rosenfeld and Sons)*

Away forward on the port side is a high berth "formed by hinged flap extending over main berth," to quote from the accommodation plan.

This schooner's headroom is 5 feet 10 inches in the after cabin and 6 feet 2 inches under the forward house.

Here are two fine little schooners from the boards of two of the most distinguished graduates of John G. Alden's school of naval architecture. Which one do you pick?

17/ The *Gloucesterman*

Length on deck: 51 feet 6 inches
Length on waterline: 42 feet 6 inches
Beam: 14 feet
Draft: 8 feet
Sail area: 1,718 square feet
Displacement: 30½ tons
Designer: Fenwick C. Williams

One of the most noteworthy of American vessels in terms of her influence on later designs was the fishing schooner *Fredonia*. She was fast and able, and her general type was copied widely; she spawned a general class of Gloucester fishing schooners that became known as *"Fredonia* models."* Her influence can also be seen distinctly on other smaller craft, such as the Friendship sloop.

Actually, naming this class of schooner after the *Fredonia* is a bit like naming the New World America instead of Columbia. The *Fredonia* was a near sistership to another schooner built from the same design, and the other vessel was built before the *Fredonia*. It's something of a mystery why the class of vessels started by this design didn't become known as *Nellie Dixon* models. Perhaps it was because the *Fredonia*, when first launched, was used as a yacht for a short time by J. Malcolm Forbes, and thus gained a wider reputation than her slightly older sister.

The man who created this important design was the great yacht designer Edward Burgess.

The *Fredonia* was launched in 1889 at Essex, Massachusetts, from the yard of Moses Adams. She had a relatively short life, for she foundered in a gale on the Grand Banks on December 18, 1896.

The chief difference between the *Fredonia* and the *Nellie Dixon* is that the *Fredonia* was shortened on deck by some 2 feet 6 inches from the original design. The *Fredonia's* dimensions were: length on deck 112 feet 5 inches; length on the waterline 98 feet; beam 23 feet 5 inches; and draft 14 feet 5 inches.

The *Fredonia* inspired not only fine fishing schooners, but also fine yachts. One of the best is the schooner *Gloucesterman*, designed some half a century ago by Fenwick C. Williams of Marblehead, Massachusetts. Howard I. Chapelle's description of the *Fredonia*, given in his book *The American Fishing Schooners: 1825-1935*, fits the *Gloucesterman* quite well.

The design for these two schooners [the *Fredonia* and the *Nellie Dixon*] showed a moderate, graceful sheer; a slightly rockered keel . . . the forefoot had much rounding. . . .

The sternpost had much rake, above which was a short counter and a rather small, heart-shaped transom. The run was long and somewhat convex without straight buttocks, but with very little rounding. The entrance was long and very sharp with a slight hollow in the forefoot. The midsection was formed with a much hollowed garboard, a sharp rise of floor carried straight well outboard, a high and rather hard turn of the bilge, and strong tumblehome

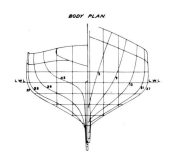

BODY PLAN

The lines of the Nellie Dixon *and the* Fredonia *from a copy probably made from the plan drawn by Edward Burgess, the designer of these important fishing schooners. (The National Watercraft Collection, Second Edition, by Howard I. Chapelle, The Smithsonian Institution and International Marine Publishing Co.)*

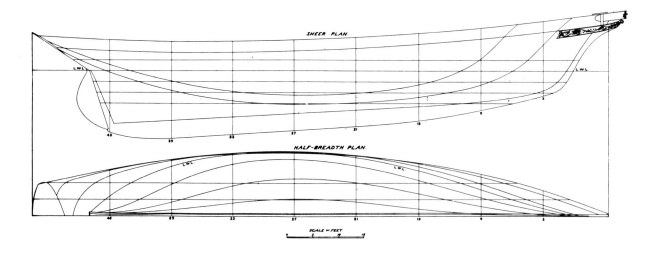

SHEER PLAN.

HALF-BREADTH PLAN.

SCALE IN FEET

in the topside. In these vessels Burgess seems to have been somewhat influenced by the then scientific "wave-line theory," insofar as the entrance was designed very sharp and long, with the run a bit full and short.

The *Gloucesterman*'s entrance is not nearly as long and fine as that of the *Fredonia*, of course, for the *Gloucesterman* is a much smaller vessel. Her maximum fullness is also farther forward than that of the *Fredonia*. And her transom is oval, rather than heart-shaped.

The *Gloucesterman* is 51 feet 6 inches long on deck, with a waterline length of 42 feet 6 inches, a beam of 14 feet, and a draft of 8 feet. She displaces 30½ tons, with 7½ tons of outside ballast in an iron keel.

The schooner's sail plan is simply a big triangle filled in with six sails. The shape of the triangle, with its rather low-lying leading edge, would be more efficient off the wind than on, which, of course, makes good sense in a cruising vessel that

doesn't particularly care that it takes her 20 minutes instead of 15 to beat a mile dead to windward but wants to be sure of being able to sail at hull speed with ease and safety once the wind frees.

But who can long look at a gaff-rigged schooner sporting a main topmast as a geometrical figure or an aerodynamic exercise? She's a true, living vessel with elegance and huge potential for romance.

Fenwick Williams has made the most of the possibilities. Everything about the hull and rig of the *Gloucesterman* is proportioned just right. Look at the relationship between the profile of her stem, her sheerline forward carried out by the well-steeved bowsprit, and the angle of the foot of her jib. This all looks exactly right, and it looks right because it works well in a head sea. The tack of her jib is 8 feet 3 inches above the water, precisely the same height as the clew of her mainsail.

The schooner's sail area is 1,718 square feet, made up of a mainsail of 598 square feet; foresail,

The drydock manifests the size and beauty of the great Fredonia. *(The Smithsonian Institution)*

359 square feet; staysail, 171 square feet; jib, 189 square feet; main topsail, 155 square feet; and fisherman, 246 square feet.

She has deep reefs in both mainsail and foresail. With the first reef tied into the mainsail, that sail is reduced to 450 square feet, an area that can normally be handled by one person. Her reefed foresail is a snug 250 square feet.

Her main gaff would not sag off unduly, for it is peaked up reasonably high and the long foot of the mainsail would help keep the twist out of the sail. The foresail, being tall and narrow with a low-peaked gaff naturally has a vang with which to control the shape of the sail.

The *Gloucesterman*'s engine is right in the middle of her galley, an arrangement with both advantages and disadvantages.

The good news is that there is plenty of room to work around the machine, and you can hardly forget to keep it clean. Hers would not be a neglected power plant. Also, the engine box would serve as an admirable galley table.

The bad news is that clean and polish though you might, the bread might always taste just a tiny bit of diesel oil. Also, if you were making a passage under power in a prolonged calm, you'd probably have to shut her down during meal preparation or the cook would mutiny. Maybe that item should come under the heading of good news also (not the mutiny of the cook, but the occasional, forced shutting down of the engine).

There is a 100-gallon fuel tank in the galley (is this wise?) and a 150-gallon fuel tank back aft in the lazarette. The lazarette also contains a 150-gallon water tank and racks for six 5-gallon water carboys, so you have something substantial to take ashore and hold under that lovely waterfall.

The after companion ladder can be removed to get to the door of the lazarette. A good arrangement here might be to replace that ladder with two vertical ladders, one on either side of the companionway, with the rungs oriented fore and aft. With the boat upright, you can use either ladder or, better yet, use alternate rungs of both ladders.

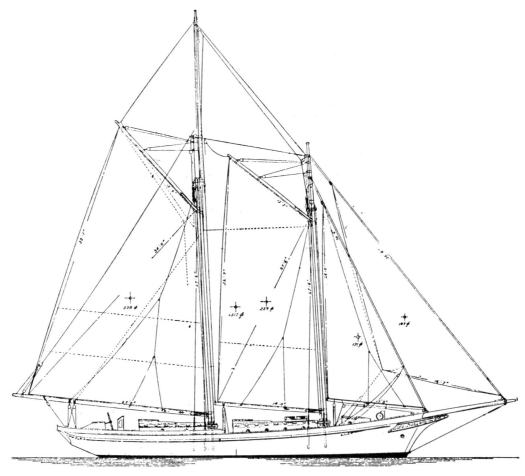

Above: *The* Gloucesterman *is a beautifully proportioned schooner of the* Fredonia *model. (*Yachting, *August, 1932)*

Below: *Though she is less than half the length of the* Fredonia, *the* Gloucesterman *shows unmistakable characteristics inherited from the big fisherman. (*Yachting, *August, 1932)*

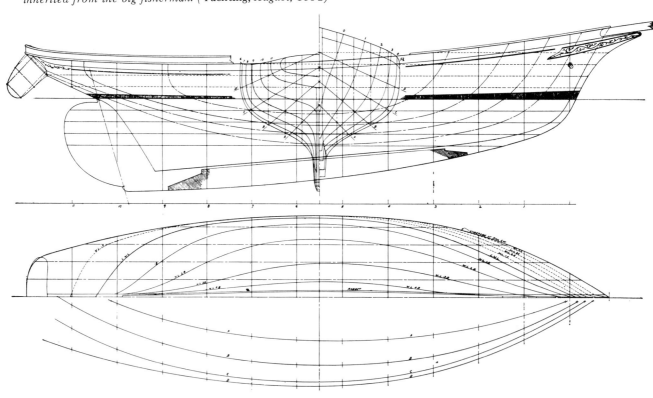

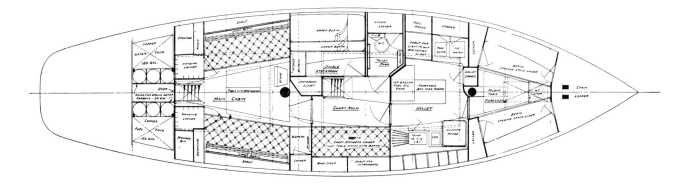

The schooner's layout is versatile; two people could live in her in luxury, nine could squeeze in, and five would find her ideal for cruising. (Yachting, August, 1932)

When she's heeled over, these ladders come into their own, for the ship's crew appreciates the nicely slanted leeward ladder, while the ship's monkey gets ecstatic about the overhanging windward one. The first designer to use this double ladder idea, as far as I know, was Ralph Wiley.

The schooner's saloon is a most comfortable place, with its heating stove alongside the mast and its two big hanging lockers on either side of the companionway.

The forward companionway comes down into a chart room, which has a high bunk with chart drawers underneath. The chart table drops down onto this berth.

A pleasing feature of the fo'c's'le is its folding table, extending out from the foremast.

The *Gloucesterman* has nine bunks, but she would be far more comfortable with five people on board for a cruise of any length. You could have four watch-standers and a navigator-cook. In easy weather, the watch-standers could stand one in four, with the oncoming watch being on call during the preceding watch to take in and reset the fisherman when tacking, or whatever. In hard weather, you'd probably want to double up with two on deck all the time, standing watch and watch.

But I am getting ahead of myself. I guess we'd better lay the keel before we plan the watches.

18/ The *Blackfish*

```
Length on deck: 51 feet 7 inches
Length on waterline: 41 feet 10 inches
Beam: 13 feet 8 inches
Draft: 7 feet 6 inches
Sail area: 1,400 square feet
Displacement: 27 tons
Designer: Henry A. Scheel
```

Every small-boat sailor has felt that twinge of envy, I suppose, when his little craft is being buffeted by rough seas and there are in sight people on board a more powerful vessel having a relatively easy time of it.

I experienced an extreme case of such feeling one time when Pop and I were in the 32-foot yawl *Brownie* and didn't quite make it to Cuttyhunk before a northeast gale sprang up. We were struggling along into a quickly rising sea under forestaysail and mizzen with the engine ticking over to help her along, but going up and down a lot more than ahead.

A "big" tanker (she must have been all of 350 feet long) came by heading up into Buzzards Bay for the Cape Cod Canal. The seas that were making us hang onto our teeth crashed harmlessly off her bow and her people looked over at us from a platform that had no perceptible motion other than rapid progress in the desired direction. It was almost enough to make a young fella want to chuck sail and go into steam.

Another occasion on which this sort of thing happened was one time when we were coming out of Newport bound to the westward in the little yawl. It breezed on quite hard from the sou'west, and by the time we got to Point Judith we had had

enough and ducked in to anchor behind the long breakwater at the Harbor of Refuge.

The schooner *Blackfish*, a vessel I had admired many times in various harbors, left Newport after we did, headed in the same direction. The hard breeze was just what her people wanted, and after we had anchored and wiped some of the salt out of our eyes we saw her go by. I climbed up on top of the main gaff so I could get a good view of her over the breakwater.

She had taken a hitch offshore and had now tacked again and it looked as though she was just about fetching up the beach to Watch Hill Point. She was about rail down under her four lowers and was going like a train of cars. I didn't dare tell Pop that I wished I were out there on board her, but that's sure how I felt.

The *Blackfish* was designed some 40 years ago by Henry Scheel, then of Provincetown, Massachusetts, and now of Rockport, Maine. She was built by Jacob Story, obviously no stranger to the construction of this sort of vessel, at Essex, Massachusetts, and was owned throughout her 26 appointed years of life by Mendum B. Littlefield of Mamaroneck and later Larchmont, New York.

Henry Scheel is a delightful gentleman of considerable charm and amazing wit. He is an ex-

Henry Scheel.

perienced seaman and has a rare ability to command with an authority that is not to be denied yet that cannot stifle his impish sense of humor.

I don't know how old Henry is. It doesn't matter. He's right up to date. A recent tour of his office produced no evidence of the *Blackfish* or anything like her (her plans had to be dredged from the files of the Mystic Seaport), but there was lots of evidence of his current design work consisting of very modern sloops and cutters that are very good looking (I can't quite bring myself to say handsome) and that have what is rapidly becoming known as the "Scheel keel."

As its name suggests, the Scheel keel is an innovation of Scheel's. One time Henry was watching that curlicue of cavitation that you sometimes see trailing off the heel of a boat's keel, and, unlike all the rest of us, he decided to do something about it. He reasoned that if you could stop that from happening there would be a benefit in terms of reduced leeway. Hence the Scheel keel, which has a flared-out section that traps most of the water on the lee side of the keel and doesn't let it cross under to the weather side. No curlicue. It seems to work.*

Getting back to the subject at hand, in *Blackfish* Henry Scheel designed a great cruising schooner. He stayed pretty much with the fisherman type; the design of the *Blackfish* is a lot closer to that of a working fisherman than, for example, is your typical John Alden schooner. She is, of course, a very able boat and would carry a big load easily for long-range cruising without hurting her sailing qualities.

The Blackfish is 51 feet 7 inches long on deck, with a waterline of length of 41 feet 10 inches, a beam of 13 feet 8 inches, and a draft of 7 feet 6 inches. She displaces 27 tons and has an iron keel of 10½ tons.

Her profile shows a fairly deep forefoot and a rather long run. She has deep, powerful sections with easy bilges and no hollow to the garboard until you get aft of amidships. Her quarters avoid heaviness; she would not gripe when heeled. She has the handsome elliptical stern of the true Gloucesterman.

The construction of the *Blackfish,* as expected, is quite heavy. Incidentally, on her construction plan Mr. Scheel noted for the builder with respect to her keel and keelson, "Keep scarphs away from mast steps!!" [double emphasis his], probably advice that turned out to be superfluous at the Story yard.

She has double-sawn oak frames 3 inches by 2½ inches at the heads spaced on 15-inch centers. The planking is 1¾-inch hard pine; the ceiling, 1½-inch fir. Her clamp is 3 inches by 6¾ inches, with an under clamp of 2¼ inches by 5¾ inches. Deck beams are 2¾ inches by 3¾ inches, doubled in way of the masts. The deck is 1¾ inches thick. She has plenty of big knees in her, her hanging knees being of wrought iron and her flat knees of 2¾-inch oak. The sides of her small house are 2 inches thick.

*I'd really like to know who designed the 25-cent toy boat models we used to have as children. They had shoal, flat hulls, and a free-standing spade rudder, a skinny, high-aspect-ratio keel with the Scheel flare so they would stand upright on a table. Whoever dreamed up those little boats was either a bit ahead of his time, or emulating the Star boat designed in 1911 by William Gardner.

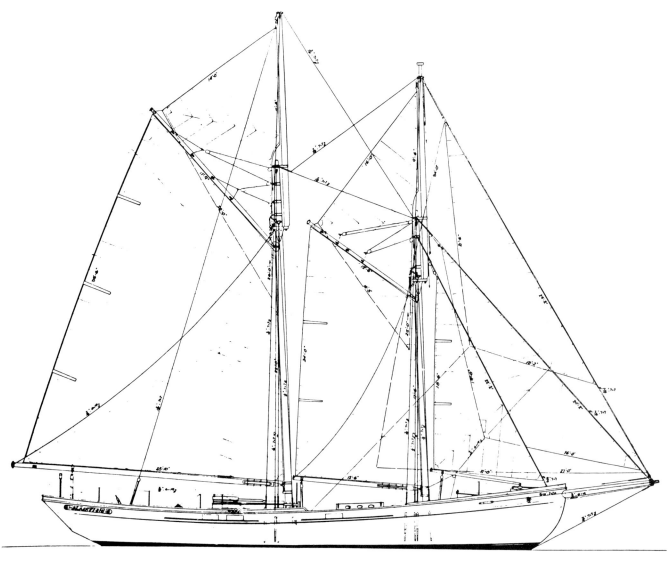

The Blackfish *was designed forty years ago for Mendum B. Littlefield. (Courtesy Mystic Seaport Museum)*

The sail plan of the *Blackfish* shows a typical full-rigged gaff schooner with both fore and main topmasts. She has a handsome rig (you have to get into clipper ships before you find anything prettier than a two-topmast gaff schooner) in which the proportions are those of the working fisherman, with rather generous topsails to keep the lower sails relatively small and easy to handle.

Her jumbo is loose-footed with its club mounted back from the forestay. Note the big ballooner shown.

No fisherman staysail is drawn in, though you'd have to have one on this boat. There is a preventer backstay on the main topmast.

Of course this rig has lots of spars, sails, and rigging to it. It all makes great good sense if you have the time and inclination to take care of it. This is a vessel for living aboard and for sailing a lot of miles. She ain't no daysailer.

The deck structures on the *Blackfish* have been kept small with the result that there is plenty of space to work the rig. Her T-shaped cockpit well makes sense, for it gives you plenty of useful room around the wheel.

She has permanent lifelines fore and aft but not between the fore and main rigging where they could easily be set up temporarily if needed. This gives you a clear space between the masts for

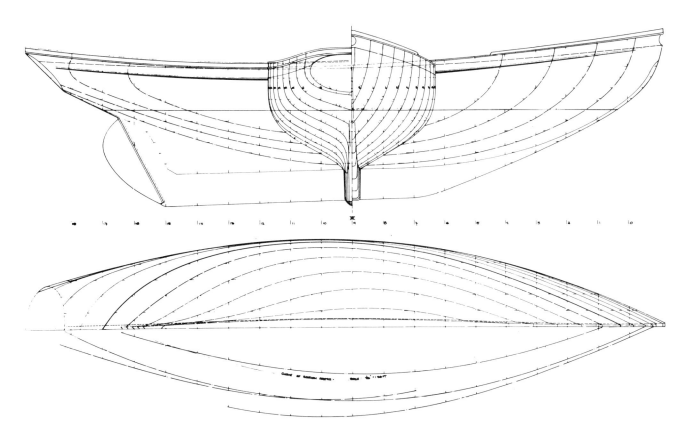

Above: *Her lines show little departure from the true fishing schooner type, and she is a handsome, able vessel.* (Courtesy Mystic Seaport Museum)

Below: *Mr. Scheel drew up quite complete construction plans for her. (Courtesy Mystic Seaport Museum)*

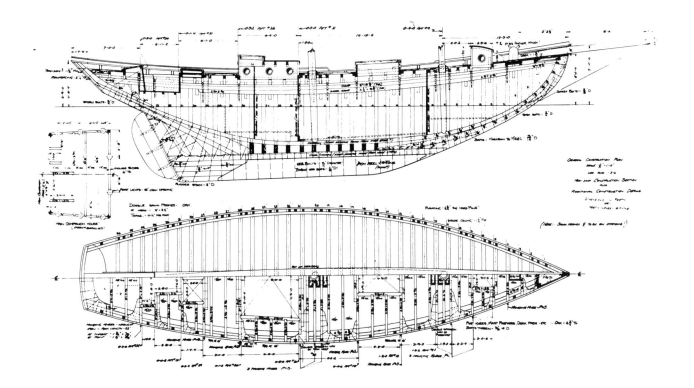

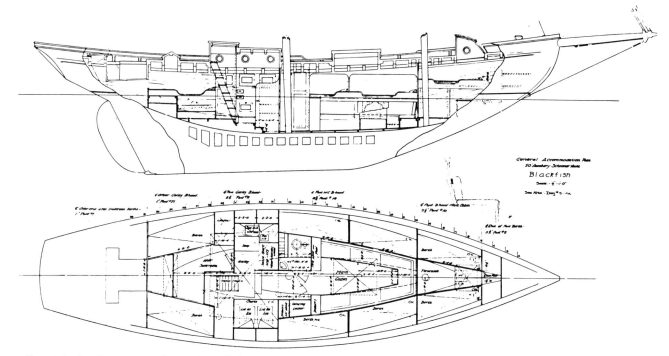

Her eight bunks are spread out through her length, each tucked away for a reasonable amount of privacy for off-watch sleeping. (Courtesy Mystic Seaport Museum)

swinging a boat in and out. Mr. Littlefield always carried a 13-foot Swampscott dory on board.

Below, her layout is straightforward and practical. I particularly like the berths tucked in behind the transoms in the saloon. And the forward end of the saloon is a cozy place, for, sensibly, there is no passage through into the fo'c's'le.

Back by the companionway, the icebox on the starboard side doubles as a chart table. The galley range sets athwartships to port and is near the centerline.

On September 28, 1963, the *Blackfish* got underway from her home mooring at Larchmont bound for winter lay-up at Greenport, Long Island. Mr. Littlefield kindly sent me an article from the *Riverside Yacht Club Burgee* about that trip, and it is worth quoting here:

When *Blackfish* left Larchmont that Saturday morning, it was a beautiful day. She had five in crew: owner/skipper Mendy Littlefield, his son Jack, Charles Geoffroy of Portland, Oregon, Chuck Standard of Riverside and Bob Bennett of Greenwich. Jack and Geoff formed one watch; Chuck and Bob the other.

All through Saturday they had a fine and lovely sail under a fresh northwester, the sort that makes you think you may be laying up too early. During the night the weather began to break down, wind changing to a heavy southeaster and raising a short, steep and lumpy sea. Where other yachts might find this punishing, *Blackfish* found it to her liking. She just shouldered her way east down the Sound.

At about 5 a.m. Sunday morning, Chuck and Bob relieved Jack and Geoff. As Jack turned the helm over to Chuck he told him to tack when Horton Pt. Light east of Mattituck came abeam. Then he and Geoff went below. Jack crawled into a starboard bunk knowing it would soon be the leeward one. Geoff was in the head and about to turn in. At about 5:15 Horton Light came abeam and Chuck headed into the wind to bring *Blackfish* from starboard to port tack. She never filled away on her new tack. As she started about, Mendy and Bob heard a 'thunk' and went on deck immediately. Jack heard something he'd never heard before on *Blackfish*—coal sliding across the cabin sole, then dishes. Then water started pouring in. When the wind had hit the sails on the port side while *Blackfish* was tacking she didn't just heel—she rolled until she lay on her beam ends on her starboard side. The rush of water flushed Geoff right out of the head but the two-position door was half under water and blocked him. Somehow, with Jack's help, he got clear and they 'swam' out through the hatch. All this within 60 seconds of coming about.

Blackfish had lost her keel! But of this her crew had no certain knowledge since she lay on her side almost awash with only two feet of freeboard.

Blackfish always carried a 13-foot Swampscott dory on deck, happily portside, and fortunately it

The Blackfish *reaching along under full sail on a bright day in 1963. (Photo by Peter Barlow)*

was not tied down and came loose. Unfortunately, the crew couldn't find the dory's wooden plug. So Mendy, then Chuck got in the dory to bail, aware how desperately they might need it should *Blackfish* founder. They bailed with Bob Bennett's boots. The other three sat on the topsides and lashed themselves to the stays. Except for Chuck and Bob, the others were in the sack, or getting ready for it, and neither then nor at any time were they able to get their foul weather gear, boots or more warm clothing.

The wind was southeast in the range of 25-30 knots and *Blackfish* had been running under shortened sail. Her masts had gone in the water pointing northwest. Acting as a drag they worked her around so they headed southeast. And the seas wrenched up by the strong wind and incoming tide frequently passed over the schooner—and the crew. The wind

was picking up; it was raining. They were soaked and getting very cold.

By 8:45, after three and a half hours in this predicament, they had drifted to about six miles north of the fuel oil unloading station east of Mattituck. They concluded there would be no traffic in the area because of the conditions and the southeast squalls would only increase in intensity. And they were not far enough out for shipping to spot them. The likelihood of rescue was remote. Further, they didn't know exactly what had happened or how long *Blackfish* would float. She was beginning to break up.

The decision was made to abandon ship and all five climbed into the dory which could be rowed with two pairs of oars, which, unlike the plug, were in place. For two and a half hours they rowed four to five miles in those big waves, the wind, the rain, and

Who wouldn't want to take a trick at her wheel? (The Rudder, *March, 1944*)

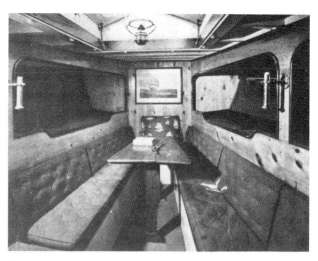

The forward end of her saloon is a cozy place. (The Rudder, *March, 1944*)

the cold, bailing with Bob's cut-down boots all the while. They seldom saw land, but kept wind and waves on the port bow. Finally, as they neared the gas buoy west of Mattituck, they were spotted by two fishermen in an outboard and taken in tow to Naughley's Dock on Mattituck Inlet. It was about noon when they came ashore.

Meantime, Gay Littlefield, Mendum's wife, had driven over to Greenport to bring them back to Larchmont. She had arrived about eleven and was concerned because *Blackfish* was not in sight. She decided to have lunch and left word at Brigham's boatyard where she could be reached.

And meantime, scarcely able to walk they were so cold, Chuck, the only one even warm enough to dial a phone, called the yard and was given Gay's number. He reached her and told her only that they were in

Mattituck. She drove the 10 to 12 miles over there and seeing neither them nor *Blackfish* asked the two fishermen if they'd seen the schooner. "Oh yes, she sank." And so did Gay's heart. But quickly she spied her crew and felt better. She took them back to Larchmont arriving about 4 p.m.

Within 24 hours, *Blackfish* came ashore on rocks at Sound Beach, Long Island (north shore). Her keel bolts were still in place. But not her keel. She was declared a total loss and sold for $25 to a skindiver for what he could salvage. She eventually broke up completely. Her two masts still stand as flagpoles on Long Island.

In his report to the Coast Guard and the insurance company the day after *Blackfish* capsized and had to be abandoned, Mendum Littlefield had concluded laconically, "No lives were lost." True.

19/ A Chapelle Schooner

> Length on deck: 64 feet
> Length on waterline: 56 feet
> Beam: 17 feet 8 inches
> Draft: 9 feet
> Sail area: 3,500 square feet
> Designer: Howard I. Chapelle

Sometimes when we seem to be getting more buried than usual in office paper, *National Fisherman* Editor Dave Getchell and I stand looking out the window at Penobscot Bay and ask each other, "What are we doing in here when we could be out on that Bay, running a schooner-load of cordwood up to Boston?" Here's a candidate for that kind of job, a burdensome, medium-sized, versatile auxiliary schooner designed by Howard I. Chapelle more than 30 years ago.

Mr. Chapelle modelled this vessel after the earliest of the deep-draft Gloucester fishing schooners of the 1880s and 1890s, rather than after the more yacht-like schooners developed after the turn of the century that John G. Alden emulated in many of his schooner-yacht designs. The kind of Gloucesterman that Mr. Chapelle had in mind when he created this design was a vessel like the *Arthur D. Story.*

The *Story* was modelled in 1885 by Dennison J. Lawlor, a well-known designer of the time, and was built by the man she was named after at Essex, Massachusetts. She was one of the deep, "improved" fishing schooners that Captain Joseph W. Collins of the U. S. Fish Commission was advocating as being safer than the "clipper" schooners. The *A. D. Story* was 93 feet 6 inches long on deck,

with a beam of 23 feet, and a draft of 11 feet 4 inches ready for sea.

Of course Chapelle's schooner is a couple of "sizes" smaller. She is 64 feet long on deck, with a waterline length of 56 feet, a beam of 17 feet 8 inches, and a draft of 9 feet. Her sail area is 3,500 square feet.

The schooner has a heavy, able hull, and she needs her big rig. It is a shapely hull, though, with plenty of tumblehome worked into the topsides aft, a slight hollow to the garboards, a well-raked transom, a hollow entrance, fine, high shoulders, and a sweeping sheer. Her diagonals are extremely fair.

All the schooner's ballast is inside; she'd have a very easy motion in a rough sea. She also should be easy on her helm and with her somewhat cutaway forefoot, she wouldn't gripe when running off in a big quartering sea, and she wouldn't take all day to go about.

This is a vessel that would have to be driven some to make fast passages. She was designed to operate well under power as well as under sail, and should be reasonably dry under power when driven into a head sea, certainly drier than the schooners modelled after her later ancestors with their fairly long spoon bows. This quality would be most appreciated in winter icing conditions.

Howard I. Chapelle. (Zayma Chapelle)

It would take some crew to handle a schooner like this. Of course plenty of people were always available in the fishermen—except when the dories were all out, when the vessel would have to be handled under easy sail by the skipper and the cook. That's the great versatility of the schooner rig: with a big, willing crew, there is plenty of working sail and upper kites to set to drive her as hard as you please; yet, she can also be shortened down to a very easy working rig, especially when the big mainsail is replaced by a trysail.

(I still remember the thrill—don't you?—in *Captains Courageous* when Disko Troop, after filling the *We're Here* with fish, hauled out the big mainsail. It was the signal that all the salt was wetted, that the vessel had all the catch she could stow, and that the riding sail could come down. Now they could put the big mainsail on her and roll and go for home!)

The Chapelle schooner's mainsail has 1,050 square feet. Setting, reefing, trimming, and handing it would take some manpower, and the sail would have to be reefed often to keep the vessel going at her best. This would be especially true in fall, winter, and spring, for the cold, heavy air always makes you need one more reef all around than you need for the same breeze in summer. She has a footrope on the outer end of the main boom to enable a man to climb out to haul out the clew

earing when reefing and to tie off the outboard reef points. Which would be a good reason to rig double lifts on the boom, inspect them often, and renew them at the slightest provocation.

The schooner's topmasts are not overly long; she carries no fore topsail, but has a big fisherman staysail and a big jib topsail, both with lots of overlap. She would need these sails, together with her generous main topsail, in even a fresh breeze to sail fast. If sail were crowded to her, she'd go all right even in light weather, and well shortened down, she'd be a most able performer in a big breeze and heavy sea. Under a triple-reefed foresail alone, she'd be as snug and comfortable in a strong gale at sea as a vessel can expect to be.

Howard Chapelle wrote me about this design: "This was a heavy displacement vessel well suited to heavy weather areas. If I were designing for such conditions I would use this design as a point of departure. This boat could go around the Horn with a reasonable chance of making it."

The schooner has the standard fisherman arrangement, with the cabin aft with four bunks; a small hold abaft the mainmast, given over to the engine room; a big hold from the mainmast forward; and right forward a big fo'c's'le with the galley in its after end. It's that big midships hold that makes this schooner such a versatile vessel. It could be used for fish, cargo, be fitted with bunks

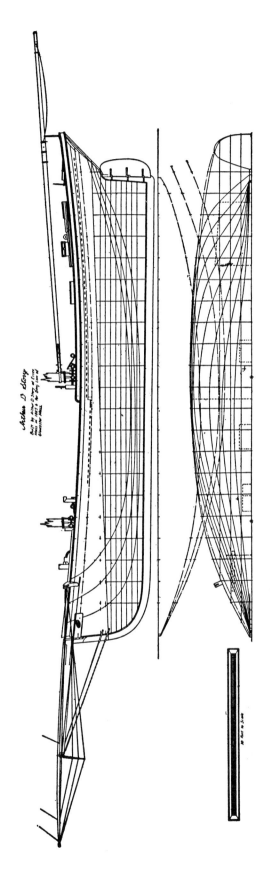

Arthur D. Story

Built by Arthur D. Story at Essex
Model by Tho' Irving Lawlor
Gloucester Mass

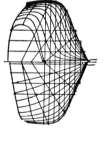

The Arthur D. Story, a Gloucester fishing schooner of 1885, is the type Mr. Chapelle was emulating with his 64-footer. The Story was designed by Dennison J. Lawlor. (Lines by Howard I. Chapelle from his American Sailing Craft)

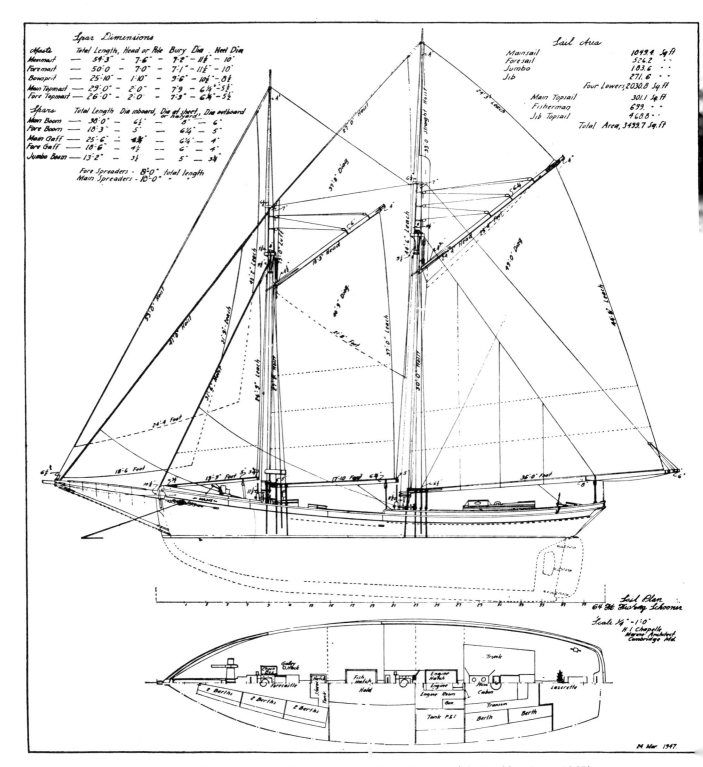

The Chapelle schooner has plenty of spars, sails, and bunks. (The Rudder, *June, 1947*)

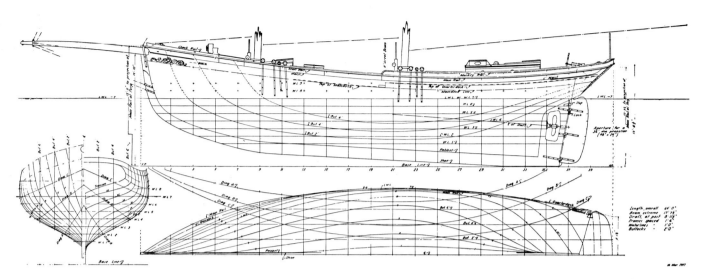

Her lines show a heavy, able hull with some beautiful, subtle curves. She's the kind of rugged lady that would need—and want—a bit of driving now and then. (The Rudder, *June, 1947*)

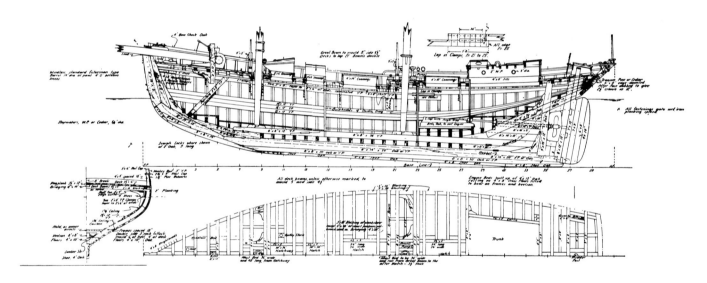

The schooner's construction plan shows heavy scantlings, such as a stout backbone made up of an 8" x 8" keelson, 8" x 14" keel, and 8" x 4" shoe; double 6" x 3" frames making up to 6" x 6", spaced 18" apart; 2" planking and 1¾" ceiling. (The Rudder, *June, 1947*)

for paying passengers, be made into a school room, a huge saloon, a laboratory, or be used to house salvage gear and the products thereof.

On deck, she has a slightly raised quarterdeck, with the break coming just forward of the main-mast. She cries out for a nest of at least two or three dories on deck between the masts, with tackles rigged on the fore and main masts to whisk the boats overboard.

In short, Howard Chapelle has produced here what to my mind is every inch a real schooner, with her double topmasts, big gaff mainsail, well steeved bowsprit, and long, outboard chain plates. I can just see her driving off down the Bay on the wings of a winter northwester, an enthusiastic crew having given her all plain sail even to the full mainsail as long as they are up under the weather shore.

You could move a lot of cordwood to Boston in her. Maybe we should just get an idea what she'd cost to build.

20/ The *Swift*

> Length on deck: 70 feet 5 inches
> Length on waterline: 59 feet 4 inches
> Beam: 18 feet 3 inches
> Draft: 9 feet
> Sail area: 5,166 square feet
> Designer: Howard I. Chapelle

The Deptford Dock, London, must have been an exciting place to work in, say, the year 1783. Deptford was one of the docks into which the Admiralty would bring, for scrutiny and measurement, worthy, foreign-built vessels that had fallen into its hands. So the men who worked there had paraded before their very eyes some of the finest examples of naval architecture the world could produce.

It is thanks to this British practice of measuring foreign vessels whenever the opportunity presented itself that the plans of many notable craft, including many American-built vessels, have survived.

Into the Deptford Dock in the year mentioned came a fine, little, American-built brig to be examined and have her lines taken off. She was a Baltimore Clipper type that was manned by a crew of 40 and carried ten three-pounder carriage guns. Her original name is unknown, but the Admiralty renamed her the *Swift*.

Howard I. Chapelle described her as follows in his book *The Search for Speed Under Sail:*

The *Swift* was originally designed for a fast sailing vessel, as is obvious in her plans. She had fine ends, much drag to the keel, a very raking curved-stem rabbet, raking post, square-tuck transom stern, and moderate sheer. Her midsection was formed by sharp-ly rising, straight floor, and a high and easy bilge carried up to the sheer to form some tumblehome. Her quarterback buttock became straight as it approached its intersection with the after load line, then slightly reversed as it approached the transom. The load line, just abaft the stem rabbet, showed a slight hollow, when projected in the half-breadth plan.

This vessel was very well built and finished. On her stern she had a carved panel showing three fleur-de-lis and two partial wreaths. Her quarter badges had false windows and formal carvings.

Mr. Chapelle implied that the *Swift* was probably no great sail carrier when he commented on her probable performance: "She should have been a fast sailer, at least in light and moderate weather when she could carry sail." The Admiralty evidently felt the same way about her, for when they fitted her out for service, they decreased her sail area and increased her ballast. The sail plan shows her as rigged when she came into the dock, presumably as the Americans had rigged her when she was built in 1778. She would perhaps be more properly termed a brigantine than a brig, for she set no main course, but she was generally referred to as a brig.

This fine, little brig vanished long ago, of course, but she was recreated as a topsail schooner by

Mr. and Mrs. William Albert Robinson and Howard Chapelle at the christening of the Swift. *(William A. Robinson)*

William Albert Robinson in 1938. Robinson had considerable seagoing experience under his belt. He had sailed around the world in the 32-foot Alden ketch *Svaap,* and later had sailed her from New York out to the Galápagos Islands. He had also sailed his own big brigantine, the *Florence C. Robinson.*

Mr. Robinson put together a building yard at Ipswich, Massachusetts, in August, 1937, to build ocean cruising vessels based on traditional craft, not out of sentiment, but because he believed they would make the best vessels for the purpose. He obtained the services of Howard Chapelle to make his research on traditional craft available and to design the cruising vessels to be built and help supervise their construction.

The first vessel turned out by the new yard was the topsail schooner *Swift,* a somewhat smaller and simpler version of the brig *Swift.*

In creating the new *Swift,* Mr. Chapelle changed the basic lines of the original vessel but little. While the brig *Swift* had some hollow to her sections forward, the schooner *Swift* has none; all her hollow is aft. The schooner has moderate lines throughout; she is without extremes, though by modern standards she does have a deep forefoot and a long, straight keel. Her tumblehome and wineglass sections aft are particularly handsome.

The brig *Swift* measured 85 feet 9 inches long on deck, with a waterline length of 74 feet 4 inches, a beam of 20 feet 10 inches, and a draft of 9 feet 6 inches. The schooner has comparable dimensions of 70 feet 5 inches, 59 feet 4 inches, 18 feet 3 inches, and 9 feet.

At Mr. Robinson's yard, the *Swift* was built by Essex County shipwrights, men who had worked on such famous vessels as the great Gloucester racing fisherman *Gertrude L. Thebaud.* It took a year to build the *Swift.* All of her fittings and ironwork were made at the yard of Norway iron, and Mr. Robinson still has half a hundred detailed pencil drawings of all this nice work.

The brig *Swift* spread 5,320 square feet of sail, not counting the square spritsail set under the bowsprit. The sail area of the schooner *Swift* is 5,166 square feet, of which 3,488 square feet is in her fore-and-aft sails, with the remaining 1,678 square feet in her fore course and fore topsail. Her

(continued on page 143)

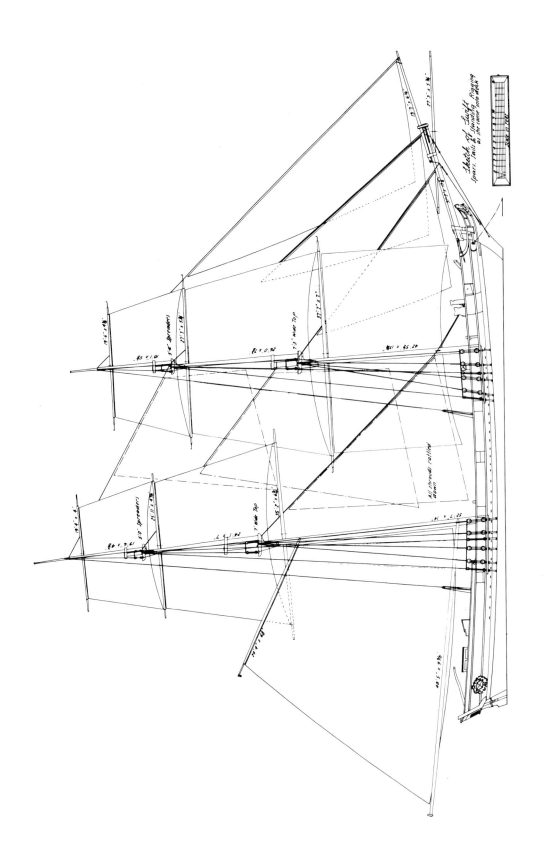

The sail plan of the American brig Swift, as originally rigged in 1778, drawn from an Admiralty plan by Howard Chapelle. (The Search for Speed Under Sail by Howard I. Chapelle)

The lines of the brig Swift, as taken off at the Deptford Dock and drawn by Howard Chapelle. (The Search for Speed Under Sail by Howard I. Chapelle)

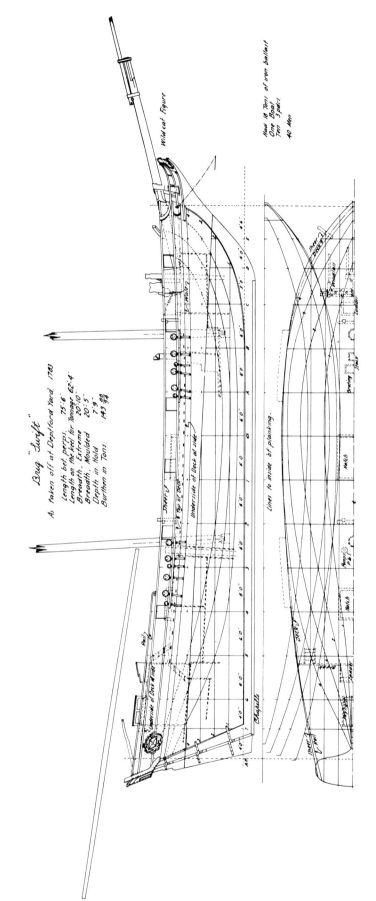

Brig "Swift"

As taken off at Deptford Yard 1783

Length bet. perps.   75'-6"
Length on the keel for Tonnage 62'-4"
Breadth, Extreme   20'-10"
Breadth, Moulded   20'-5"
Depth in Hold   7'-9"
Burthen in Tons   143 88/94

Wild cat Figure

Had 18 Tons of iron ballast
One Boat
Tent 3 pairs

40 Men

Three fleur-de-Lys in wreath

Scale of Feet

Underside of Deck at side

Lines to inside of planking.

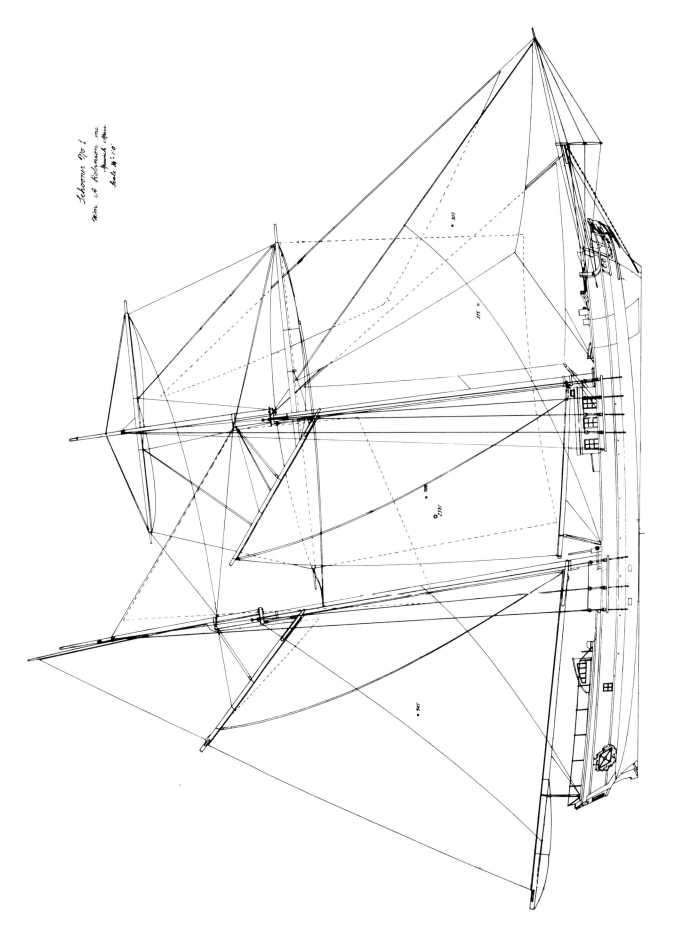

Mr. Chapelle's design for the smaller topsail schooner Swift for William A. Robinson was based on the plans for the brig. (William A. Robinson)

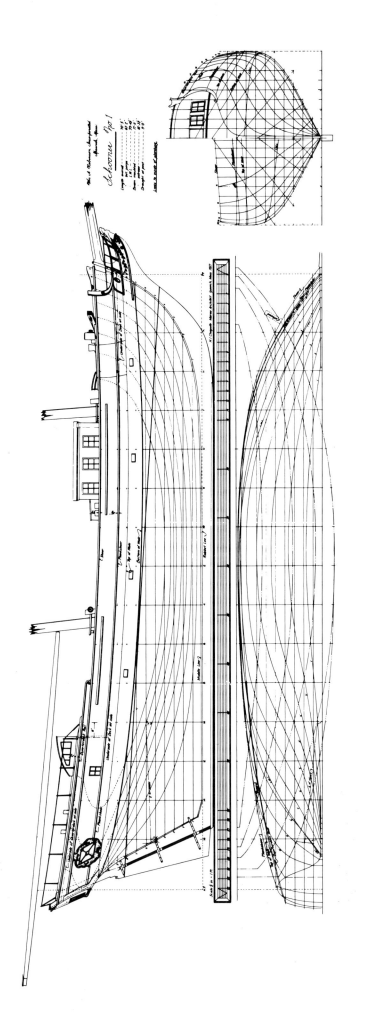

The lines of the schooner Swift show her to be very closely modeled on the brig, perhaps the most notable difference being the lack of hollow in her forward sections. (William A. Robinson)

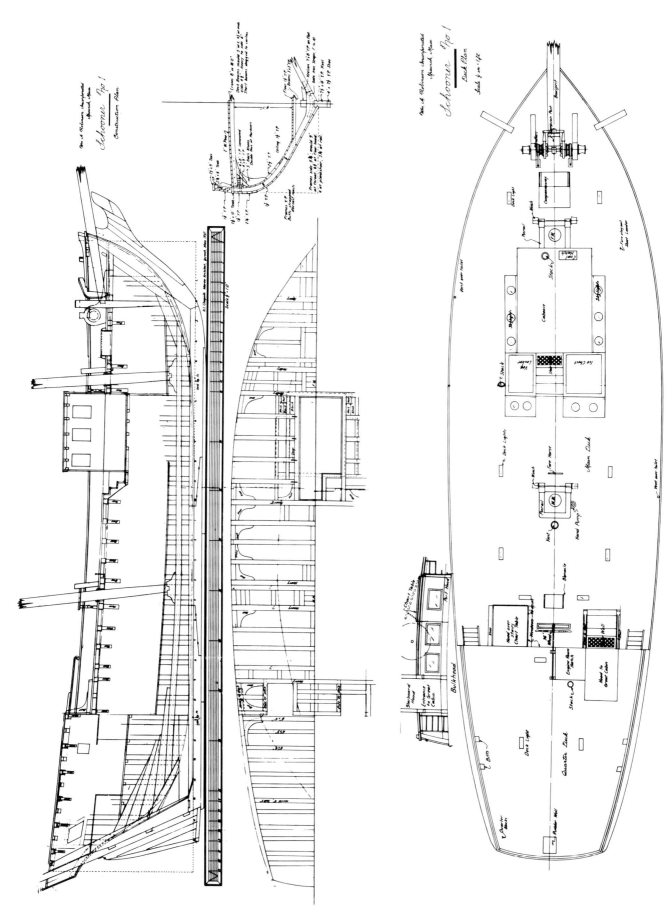

Her construction plan shows some interesting details. Note the massiveness of her stem. Her deck plan is worthy of study. In addition to four hatchways leading below, there are four small skylights, and eleven decklights, small rectangular prisms let into the deck. (William A. Robinson)

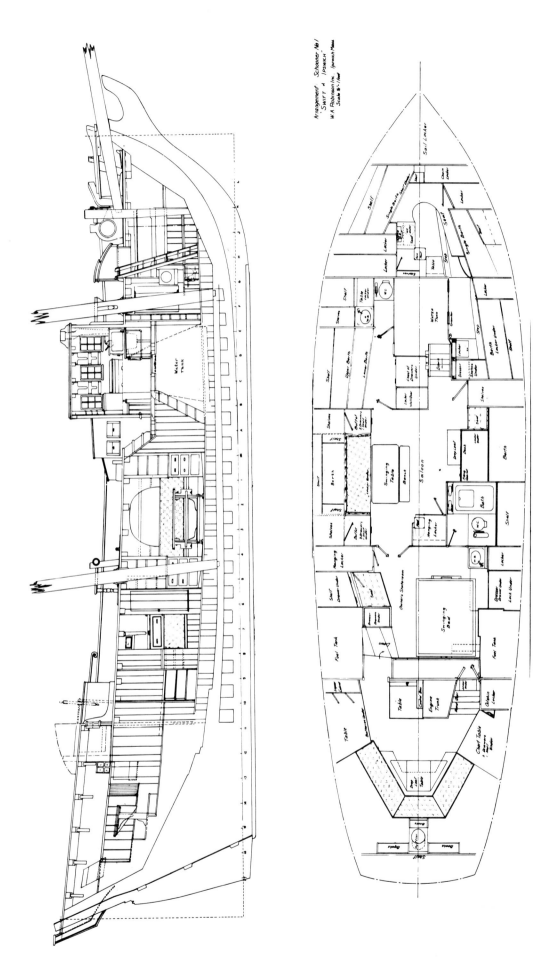

The Swift's arrangement plan shows the sumptuous quarters possible in a 70-foot hull in which the accommodations stretch from stem to stern. (William A. Robinson)

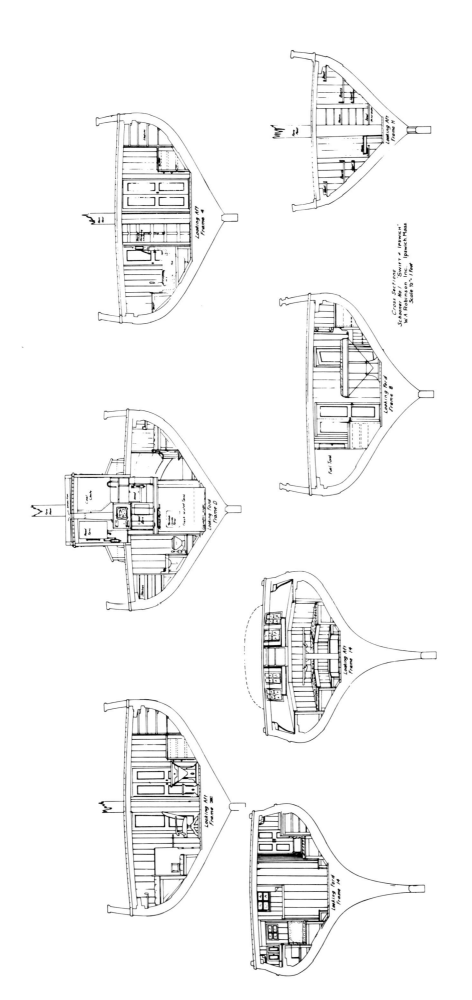

The sectional views of her interior arrangement clarify some of the complexities of her cabins. (William A. Robinson)

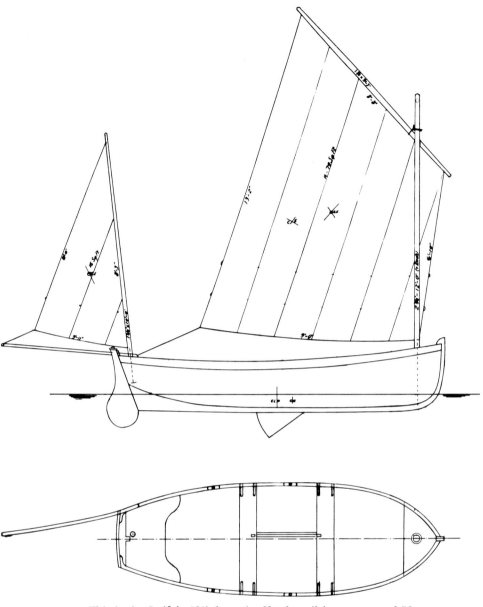

This is the Swift's *13½-foot gig. Her lugsail has an area of 79 square feet; there is but 15 square feet in the mizzen. (William A. Robinson)*

fore course and gaff foresail would probably not generally be set at the same time. In her four lower fore-and-aft sails, the schooner sets an area of 2,331 square feet. The fore course is the biggest sail in the ship at 1,100 square feet; her mainsail has 945 square feet.

Although the *Swift*'s topsail schooner rig is far simpler than the brig rig of her ancestor, she still looks grandiose today. She has plenty of sail area, to be sure, but a relatively low center of effort by today's standards, especially when shortened down to her lower sails. This is a vital feature in a vessel whose hull does not emphasize sail-carrying power.

In any event, the topsail schooner rig is certainly handsome and has much versatility. She could jog in heavy weather under foresail and forestaysail, or foresail alone, but to work to windward in a hard chance she would go best with forestaysail, foresail, and mainsail, all reefed. Her long foreyards give her a generous spread of squaresails for chasing away before the wind.

Note that the leeches of her mainsail and main topsail make a straight line. The main topsail sets on a yard and thus would be handled from the deck, but the vessel's shrouds are still rattled down fore and aft. Her big main topmast staysail (610

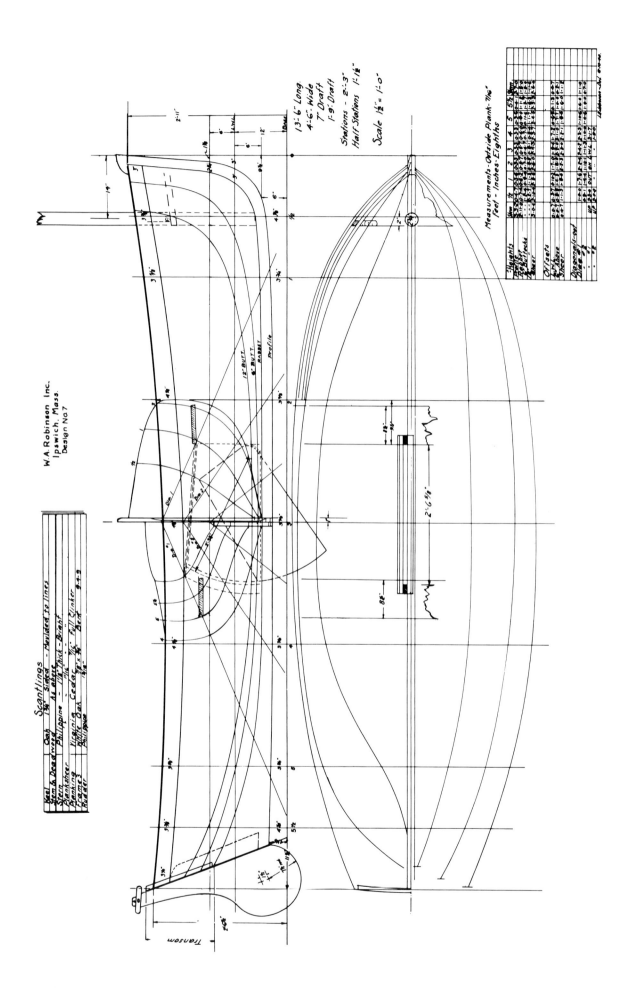

The gig has a beam of 4 feet 6 inches. She is clinker built and planked with 7/16-inch Virginia cedar. The frames are bent, of white oak, 7/8'' x 3/4''. (William A. Robinson)

15 Foot Ships Boat

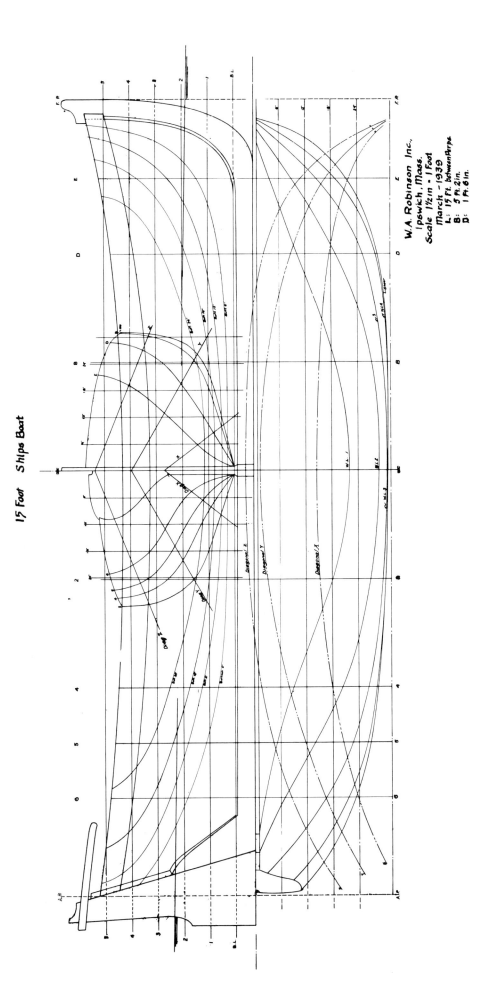

W.A. Robinson Inc.,
Ipswich, Mass.
Scale 1½in - 1 Foot
March - 1939
L: 15 Ft. between Perps.
B: 5 Ft. 2 in.
D: 1 Ft. 6 in.

Here are the lines of her 15-foot shallop, a heavy rowing craft with a beam of 5 feet 2 inches and a narrow, heart-shaped transom. (William A. Robinson)

The Swift *about ready to launch at Ipswich. (Photo by E. Morgan Savage, courtesy William A. Robinson)*

square feet) would be a great sail on a reach. Note the footropes on the main boom to facilitate getting at the reefing gear outboard.

She has nine sails, set on 14 spars, steadied by 29 pieces of standing rigging, and controlled by 50 pieces of running rigging, not counting outhauls, reef earings, lazy jacks, and various and sundry Spanish burtons, handy billies, and come-alongs.

On deck, the *Swift* has deep bulwarks. There is a high break from the main deck to the quarterdeck in which there are windows opening into the great cabin. Her wheel is at the break of the quarterdeck and just forward of it is a stout and decorative binnacle built up of wood to house the steering compass and to stand and lean against. On the port side of the helm, the quarterdeck is extended forward in a rectangular hood that gives headroom

over a stairway below; the flat top of this hood is used for an on-deck chart table.

She has plenty of open space on deck, particularly around the foot of the mainmast and on the quarterdeck, though some of this would undoubtedly be taken up by her small boats.

Four skylights flank the forward deckhouse, and there are 11 deck lights scattered around the main and quarter decks.

There are wells in the deck leading down to the entrance in the after side of the forward deckhouse and to the entrance to the great cabin at the break of the quarterdeck on the starboard side. In the deckhouse well, big boxes flank the entryway, that to starboard being an ice chest, and that to port a vegetable locker.

Up forward, there is a big anchor windlass at the

The Swift *under sail with everything set but the main topsail and main topmast staysail.* (William A. Robinson)

bowsprit heel. She has winch heads mounted on the pin rails at the foot of both masts.

Two small boats were specially designed and built for the *Swift,* a 15-foot shallop and a 13½-foot gig. The latter was rigged with a standing lugsail up in the eyes of her and a little leg-o'-mutton mizzen set on a mast stepped just inboard of the transom and sheeted to a long pole boomkin. These are real ship's boats entirely in keeping with the vessel.

The accommodations possible in a 70-foot hull with a great cabin in the stern seem nearly limitless. The *Swift* has her galley in the sunken deckhouse forward, a big fo'c's'le for three people, a double stateroom forward, a big saloon with two berths tucked away outboard, and a sumptuous stateroom aft with a huge bed in gimbals and its own bathroom, these last reminiscent of the master's quarters in the whaling bark *Charles W. Morgan,* but even more spacious and convenient. Then there is the great cabin in the stern.

She has a notable amount of desk and table space throughout, many big lockers and, in fact, plenty of room for up to nine people for a lengthy voyage.

The engine is under the great cabin sole, with a trunk from the engine room to the deck entered by a hatch at the break of the quarterdeck. She has a three-bladed, solid wheel, off center to port. The fuel tanks are outboard in way of the after stateroom. There is a huge water tank beneath the galley.

William A. Robinson was well satisfied with the vessel he, Howard Chapelle, and his Essex shipwrights had created. He wrote of her performance:

The *Swift* proved under sail to be all that her famous predecessors were—fast, able, comfortable and, above all, safe. She requires almost no steering, none at all on the wind. She has a very easy motion and is sure in stays. She takes a comfortable angle of heel and holds it steadily, slipping through the water without fuss. She sails as close to the wind as can be expected of any cruising schooner, and with her large squaresails she should make great passages in the trades. Under average conditions at sea she will hold her own with the abler of modern schooners, and when it blows she will be sailing comfortably long after most of them are hove to.

These words were written, to be sure, after some stability problems with the vessel had been solved. Trials showed her to be much more tender than

Here she is lying to a mooring. Her starboard bower hangs from its cathead; fender boards and boarding ladder are at the ready; quite a large crowd is working on deck amidships; and there's a man aloft on the foremast. (Edwin Levick Collection, Mariner's Museum, Newport News, Virginia)

anticipated, and the weight of her upper spars and fittings was reduced considerably.

Regarding the *Swift*'s later career, Robbie wrote me from his home in Tahiti:

I sold her to the Cagney brothers, William and James, and she was in numerous Hollywood films. She was later un-rigged, masts lifted out, and was taken through a highway bridge in California to a lagoon where she was re-rigged and put on display as the last privateer, or some such nonsense. Later she reversed the process and spent years as a charter boat in California. I had frequent communications from the new owners. Recently someone sent me newspaper clips indicating that the *Swift* is now engaged in some research project. She is apparently still sound, the salting process we used a success. Also involved in her longevity is the fact that she was completely "trunnel" fastened (locust tree-nails) so there were no fastenings to corrode or plugs to leak and start soft places.

The *Swift* is a fascinating vessel with many features that mark her as a true ship: her complicated bow, with figurehead, head rails, hawse holes, trailboards, broad, built-up headpiece outside the stem, catheads, bowsprit, jib boom, and martingale, with their stays and guys; her galley deckhouse with its rectangular windows; her carved badges on her quarter windows and her square windows in the broad transom; her well-raked masts crossing a couple of yards; her deadeyes and lanyards, set up to outboard channels for the shrouds; and her salmon-colored topsides with their broad, black wales.

Her figurehead is a likeness of the owner's wife. (William A. Robinson)

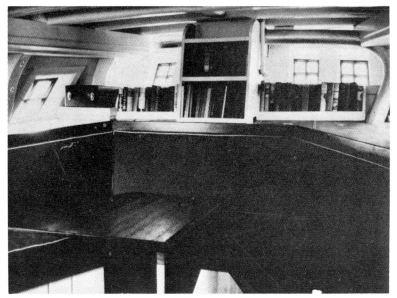

It's hard to beat the look of her traditional, functional stern, either from inside or outside. (Photos by Richard H. Anthony, Yachting, July, 1939)

Her deck structures give her the feeling of a much bigger vessel. (Photo by Richard H. Anthony, Yachting, *July, 1939)*

It was interesting to note that when William A. Robinson perfected his ultimate ocean cruising vessel after World War II, he stuck to square rig but went to a somewhat less romantic but probably somewhat more utilitarian vessel, at least in terms of the size of crew required, in the 70-foot brigan-tine *Varua,* whose plans were drawn for him by two of the greatest designers of the recent past, W. Starling Burgess and L. Francis Herreshoff. The *Varua* has proven to be a highly successful cruising vessel, and she is still going strong. But the *Varua* is another story, one reserved for the next chapter.

21/ The *Varua*

> Length on deck: 70 feet
> Length on waterline: 60 feet
> Beam: 16 feet 3 inches
> Draft: 7½ feet
> Sail area: 2,700 square feet
> Displacement: 15 tons
> Designer: W. Starling Burgess

William A. Robinson, like many another young sea dreamer, used to go down to the docks during his lunch hour to watch ships arrive from and depart for exotic-sounding ports of call. He was an engineering graduate working in a textile mill in Brooklyn. The year was 1926.

Unlike others lounging on the pier heads, Mr. Robinson made his dreams of sailing to far-off places come true. He bought the *Svaap,* a 32-foot Alden ketch, for $1,000, and sailed her around the world from June of 1928 to the fall of 1931. And this voyage, beyond the wildest dreams of most dockside "supervisors," was only the beginning. He had called at Tahiti, that alluring goal of many an ocean voyager. Some who get there are disillusioned. Most find about what they expect, move on, and cherish the memory. Mr. Robinson is one of the few for whom sailing to Tahiti had an overriding impact on the rest of his life.

After his circumnavigation, Mr. Robinson again set out for the South Seas in the *Svaap,* but had to be taken off the boat in the Galápagos Islands with a ruptured appendix. His life was saved, but the *Svaap* was confiscated and wrecked by Ecuadorians.

He went on to Tahiti by steamer and established a home on the island in 1934. Three years later, he

came back to the States to establish a shipyard at Ipswich, Massachusetts, for the purpose of building traditional sailing yachts. The first vessel built was the *Swift,* described in the last chapter.

Because a number of the vessels he contemplated building would have square rig, Mr. Robinson wanted practical experience in handling and rigging a square-rigged vessel. He went out to Colombo, Ceylon, in 1938, bought a handsome, 90-foot, teakwood brigantine named the *Annapooranymal,* renamed her the *Florence C. Robinson,* and sailed her to Gloucester. The dreams were being carried out almost as soon as they were being dreamed. (The *Florence C. Robinson* went out to Tahiti before World War II and was used as an inter-island trading vessel. She was lost on the barrier reef of Papeete harbor in 1957.)

World War II interrupted many a sailor's dreams and their realization. As the nation went to war, Mr. Robinson's little yard was expanded to a work force of 600 that built mine sweepers, submarine chasers, and landing craft. But whenever men could be spared from building boats and vessels for the Navy, they were put to work finishing off a dream ship Mr. Robinson was building for himself. This craft was launched on March 19, 1942. She was christened the *Varua,* Tahitian for spirit or soul.

W. Starling Burgess on board his raised-deck sloop, the **Pomelion.** *(Muriel Vaughn)*

As the war wound down in 1945, Mr. Robinson liquidated the shipyard and put to sea from Gloucester in the *Varua.* He sailed his dream ship to his dream house in Tahiti.

Mr. Robinson took up a purposeful, rather than an indolent, life in the South Seas. He spearheaded and for many years stayed involved with a successful medical research campaign against filariasis and elephantiasis. He bought a low coral atoll, Taiaro, three miles in diameter, and used it for the production of copra and for the study of the ecology of the region.

He also made significant ocean voyages in the *Varua.* On the last day of 1951, he sailed from Papeete harbor on an 11-month, 15,000-mile cruise that took him to Patagonia, up the west coast of South America to Panama, and back to Tahiti. In 1956, he embarked on a 15-month-long voyage from Tahiti to Bangkok and back in connection with his medical research program and to study the early movements and possible origins of migrating Polynesians. He also made a number of what he calls "milk runs" in the *Varua* from Tahiti to Honolulu and back.

Mr. Robinson sold the *Varua* a few years ago. She is now a research vessel operating out of Tahiti to the Western Pacific and owned by Marine Environmental Research, Incorporated. She was completely rebuilt at Samoa during 1977 by Paul Rollins.

Now in his mid-70s, Mr. Robinson lives in Tahiti with his four daughters, a lifetime of dreams come true to look back on, and, still, dreams for the future.

William A. Robinson has recounted his voyages in four books: *10,000 Leagues Over the Sea* told the story of the *Svaap*'s circumnavigation and was published in 1932; *Voyage to Galápagos* told of the *Svaap*'s second cruise and came out in 1936; *To the Great Southern Sea* recorded the *Varua*'s cruise to South America and was published in 1957; and *Return to the Sea,* published in 1972, told of the *Varua*'s passage from Gloucester to Tahiti, of her cruise to Bangkok, and of Mr. Robinson's life and work in the South Sea islands.

I find William A. Robinson's dream ship, the *Varua,* a fascinating vessel. She was designed to make long ocean passages, to be home, workshop, and laboratory for Robinson and his family, and to be comfortably handled, if necessary, with a crew of three.

Her design was the culmination of Mr. Robinson's thinking after his considerable experience with the *Svaap* and with building traditional sailing yachts of some size at Ipswich. In 1940, he took his ideas and drawings for the design of his dream ship to W. Starling Burgess, an outstanding yacht designer and the son of one of the greatest of designers, Edward Burgess. Starling Burgess was to work out the final design of the dream ship according to Mr. Robinson's ideas and was also to collaborate on construction details.

When given the design requirements, Mr. Burgess said, "She must be able to run before it with safety in any weather." He paid particular attention to the vessel's stern. Her model was tank-tested at the Stephens Institute with simulated following seas. The stern was altered until she could run at various speeds without disturbing them. The result was the interesting shape seen in the lines drawing, which Messrs. Burgess and Robinson dubbed her "double chin" stern.

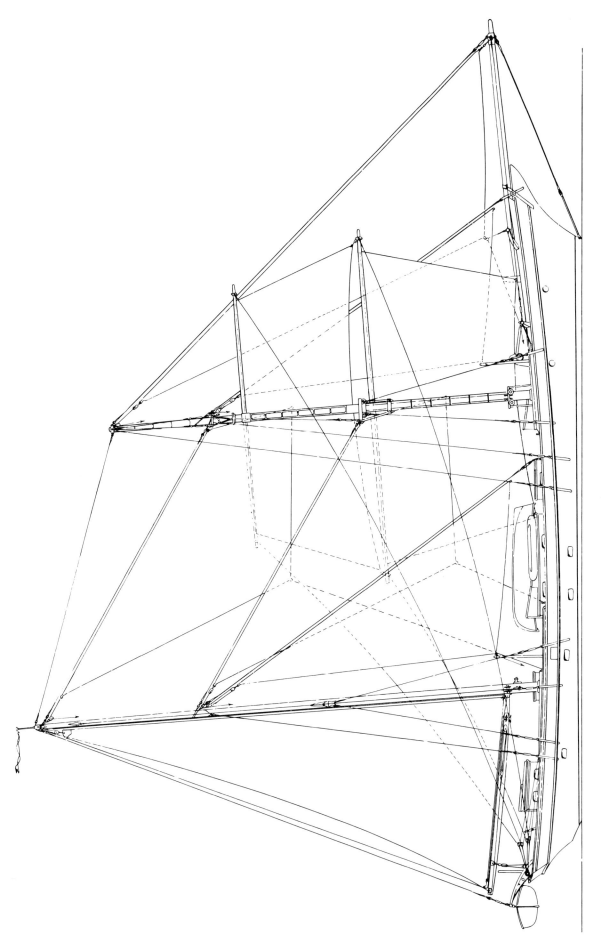

The 70-foot brigantine, Varua, built in 1942 at the yard of William A. Robinson at Ipswich, Massachusetts, was and is Mr. Robinson's idea of a world cruiser and home afloat. The concept for the design was worked out by Mr. Robinson; final hull lines were drawn by W. Starling Burgess; the final rig was designed by L. Francis Herreshoff. (Muriel Vaughn)

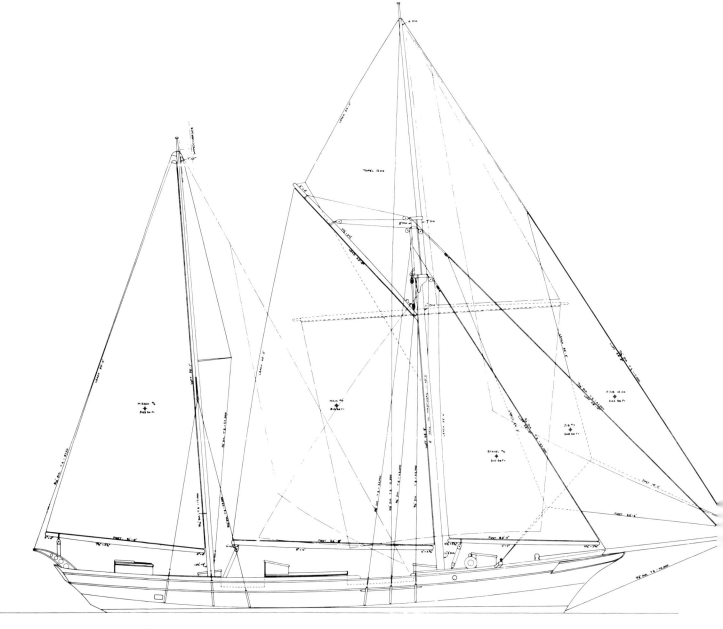

The Varua's *original ketch rig as drawn up by Starling Burgess. The area of the four lowers is just over 2,000 square feet, with 813 square feet in the mainsail. (William A. Robinson)*

The vessel was built of composite construction with all of the cross members of the skeleton being of steel and the planking, deck, and deck structures being of wood.

She was originally designed as a gaff-headed ketch with a Marconi mizzen, because it was contemplated that she would be used on the East Coast for a few years and even possibly enter the Bermuda Race. Then, when she could go out to the South Seas, she was to be re-rigged as a brigantine, according to Mr. Robinson's well-considered concept. The masts would be in the same position for both rigs. When, during the War, Mr. Robinson wanted to finish up the design for the brigantine rig, Mr. Burgess was swamped with work, so Mr. Robinson turned to L. Francis Herreshoff. It was Mr. Herreshoff who designed the brigantine rig shown in the sail plan following Mr. Robinson's concept. (Francis Herreshoff also designed a most interesting 49-foot ketch for ocean cruising for Mr. Robinson in 1942 and 1943, but she was never built. Her design appears in Mr. Herreshoff's book *Sensible Cruising Designs.*)

When Robinson left Gloucester in the *Varua* in

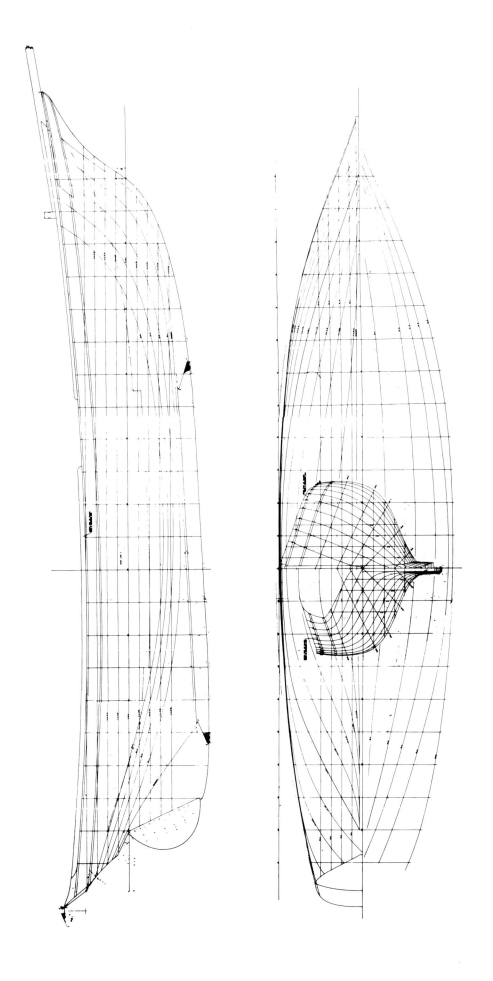

She is a fine-lined vessel, long, narrow, and of very moderate draft. (William A. Robinson)

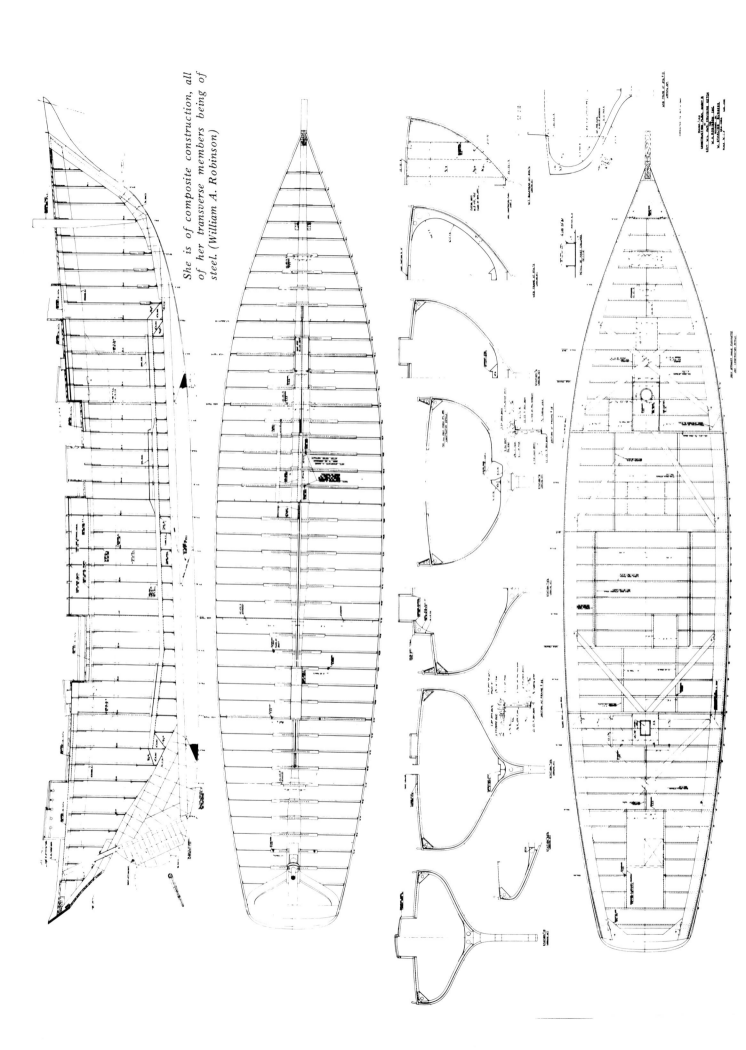

She is of composite construction, all of her transverse members being of steel. (William A. Robinson)

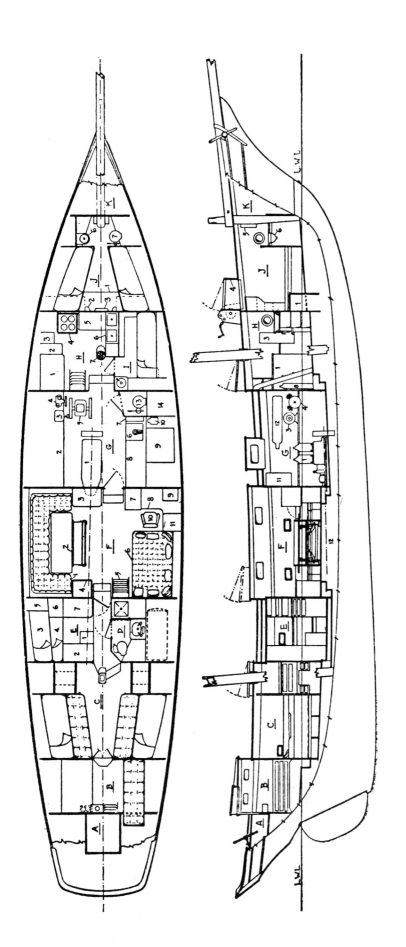

The Varua has an unusual arrangement with lots of living space for the small crew necessary to handle her. (Fore and Aft Sailing Craft by Douglas Phillips-Birt)

A bow view of the **Varua** *showing some of the details of her unusual rig. (Warren R. Roll)*

The Varua *under sail off Tahiti in 1952. (William A. Robinson)*

1945, impatient to start for Tahiti, she had her ketch rig as designed by Mr. Burgess. During the voyage, however, Mr. Robinson gradually converted her to a somewhat makeshift brigantine. A lower squaresail was added in Trinidad, a square topsail in Panama, and the staysails between the masts were worked out in the Galápagos Islands.

It is interesting when studying the lines of the *Varau,* drawn by the son of Edward Burgess, to compare her with a vessel she brings to mind, the great fishing schooner *Fredonia,* designed by the elder Burgess (see Chapter 17). The *Varua* could be considered a fuller, shoaler version of the *Fredonia* in which speed has been sacrificed for an easy motion and dryness in rough water.

At any rate, she has a long, narrow, very easily driven hull. The bow and buttock lines are long and easy, and she has a very long run. Her waterlines are fine. There is considerable depth to the hull for carrying capacity and the easy motion.

The *Varua* is 70 feet long on deck, with a waterline length of 60 feet, a beam of only 16 feet 3 inches, and a draft, at average loading, of only 7½ feet. At this draft, she displaces 43 tons. Her lead keel weighs 15 tons. And the shape of her transom, developed in the "following seas" of the tow tank, is handsome and practical.

If the *Varua's* long, narrow, rather shoal hull is a bit different, her rig is certainly unusual. Mr. Robinson is a great experimenter with rigs. When the *Svaap* set out on her second cruise, she had one of the earliest wishbone ketch rigs seen, which Mr. Robinson had worked out independently. He came to believe in square rig for an ocean cruising vessel, and the concept of the *Varua*'s brigantine rig was one he worked out over a long period of time.

She has the long, low sail plan that is best for ease of handling at sea. She is designed to reach and run safely and comfortably in blowing weather.

The rig, being so broken up, is most versatile. You don't often see a sail plan with an area as large as 2,700 square feet with no sail bigger than 500 square feet, yet that is what has been achieved in the *Varua.*

Her mainsail has 500 square feet; foresail, 470; fore topsail, 340; jib, 300; forestaysail, 205; lower main staysail, 235; middle main staysail, 330; and upper main staysail, 320. The mainsail has a single reef, but it is seldom used. She has a storm mainsail of 300 square feet, and a storm forestaysail and storm main staysail of 110 square feet each. Her sails are tanbarked the color of sienna.

The rig may be seen to be exceptionally well stayed, although she has no runners. The bobstay is a solid Monel bar. Her stern davits are heavily built of steel to take a pair of permanent main backstays.

All the sheets are kept up off the deck so there is nothing to trip over and so you can easily put your weight into pulling on them. The fore and lower main staysail sheets have an interesting arrangement: there is a double cringle at the clew of the sail; the sheet leads from the upper cringle around an overhead pipe traveler, back through the lower cringle, and to the deck. The result is a three-part sheet with nothing to bang around when the sail slats.

Each jib sheet leads from a forward cathead through a cringle at the clew of the sail, aft through a lead block on an after cathead and on aft.

The upper main staysails have combined downhauls and brails so they may be smothered quickly. When setting or handing these staysails, it is customary to run the *Varua* off the wind to blanket them with the mainsail.

The gear for the squaresails is well worked out. The braces are flexible wire rove through lead blocks on pennants held out from the side of the vessel to eliminate chafe by a heavy outrigger that crosses the stern davits just above the top of the transom. The outrigger can telescope in when not needed. The braces have manila hauling parts on

deck. The foresail tacks are lead to the forward catheads.

The lower yard is fixed, while the upper yard may be lowered to just above the lower yard. The foresail furls vertically on the mast, and is set with outhauls to the yardarms. Fixed brails on the topsail gather the sail under the yard as the yard is lowered. Then the sail is brought in to the mast, as is the lower sail, and can be furled in a bundle on the fore top.

There are mast ladders up each side of the foremast and an aperture on each side of the fore top, so you can climb up the weather side of something relatively steady and wedge yourself in securely on the weather side of the mast to furl the squaresails. The ladders also make convenient places to pass lashings when furling the foresail down the forward side of the mast or when furling the upper staysails. Then, too, they provide a convenient way to get aloft to inspect the rig or to conn the vessel between coral heads.

One of the best features of the *Varua*'s rig is that it virtually eliminates that persistent enemy of the offshore sailor, chafe. Mr. Robinson wrote, "After long experience with it, I can think of no improvement to the rig."

The *Varua*'s auxiliary power is a Deutz diesel made in Germany. It's a two-cylinder, two-cycle engine that develops 47 h.p. at 600 r.p.m. It's fitted with air starting and turns a Hyde, two-bladed, feathering wheel, 30 inches by 18 inches. The shaft is off center to port to cancel the torque of the right-hand-turning wheel. She makes a little better than seven knots under power in a calm.

The vessel has a Lister, one-cylinder diesel of 5 h.p. turning a 1.5 kw generator to provide juice for a 32-volt DC system. There's a converter for 110-volt AC. Five or six hours of charging twice a week keeps the batteries up when living on board. She carries 800 gallons of diesel oil and 625 gallons of water.

Mr. Robinson likes Danforth anchors. The *Varua* carries four of them, each of 200 pounds. The catheads make them relatively easy to handle, but it is the ground tackle that limits the minimum number in the crew needed to run her. It takes three people to get her underway under power from an anchor. Two are on the windlass and one is below seeing that the chain stows properly as it comes down. When the anchor is aweigh, the hand

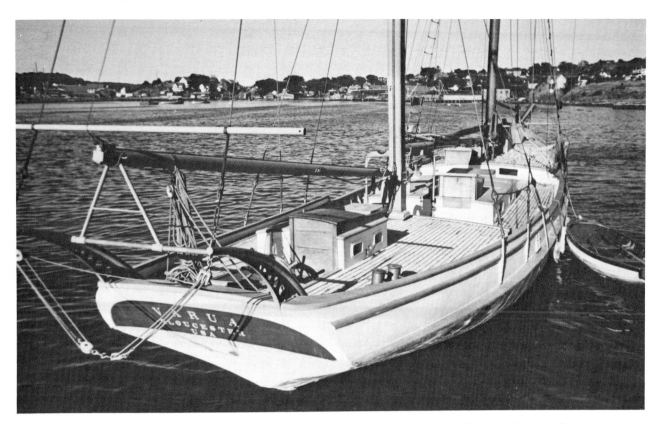

This view shows her interesting stern and her spacious, clear decks. (William A. Robinson)

below goes to the wheel, while the two forward get the anchor cleaned off and on board.

The boat stowed upside down on the midships house is a 13½-foot rowing and sailing tender. Beside it is a ten-person balsa life raft.

The *Varua* has double lifelines three feet high running around her decks. When at sea, she also carries boat booms lashed between the fore and main rigging at waist height. Her bowsprit is flat on top and is ten inches wide. Beneath it are footropes and a netting.

The *Varua*'s deck arrangement tries to get plenty of air and light below when she is lying in a harbor in the tropics, yet keep heavy water where it belongs if a sea should break aboard during an ocean passage. She has two breaks in the deck, making a waist between the masts, and there are rectangular ports in the breaks.

Her self-draining steering well is small, so it won't hold much water if she is boarded by the top of a sea. The binnacle is just inside the chart house on the after bulkhead; the well-protected compass is viewed through a six-inch port.

Mr. Robinson says the only substantive change he would make to the design of the vessel if he were doing it again would be to eliminate the tumblehome of the cabin house sides, so the cabin windows wouldn't drip if left open in a light rain. That statement goes a long way toward showing how well the details were worked out in the design of this complex craft.

Below, the *Varua* has berths for from five to eight people without anyone sleeping in the big saloon. The saloon has windows in the house to look out when you are standing and windows in the hull to look out when you are sitting. There is a big swinging table, a huge divan to starboard, and an "office" in the forward starboard corner.

In the big after stateroom, there is a port in the hull at the head of each berth. This would be pleasant enough in port, but might be looked upon with mixed feelings in heavy weather, especially just after being awakened for the next watch.

The after head has a small shower bath.

The separate companionway to the galley is very convenient. The galley range is a Shipmate diesel.

The upper half of her transom is convex, while the lower half (top plank only in place in this view) is concave. This photo shows the Varua *being rebuilt at Pago Pago, Samoa, in 1977. (Paul Rollins)*

The compartment to starboard of the galley can be used either as a stateroom or as a storeroom.

The engine room is nine feet long and has full headroom. Along its starboard side is a photo lab, and there is a head in its forward starboard corner.

The vessel has a steel collision bulkhead between the galley and the fo'c's'le.

The *Varua*'s performance at sea has been impressive. She has made long, successful, accident-free voyages with very small crews for a vessel of her size. She generally averages 150 miles a day at sea. She takes heavy weather very well. Mr. Robinson wrote of reaching in a hard breeze and rough sea under jib, forestaysail, and the storm mainsail crossing the China Sea in December, 1956, on the way to Bangkok:

"Racing now, even though the steep beam seas broke and crested across us, we drove through and made a day's run of 216 miles. Our speed increased to 10 knots, which we maintained hour after hour."

And down in the Roaring Forties on the way to Patagonia from Tahiti, Mr. Robinson and his *Varua* met a gale that gave them that ultimate test of survival. There is no way to measure the force of such elements when in their midst in a small vessel. After the worst of the gale had passed, Mr. Robinson measured the height of the seas at 40 feet. He estimates that during the worst of the storm, they were perhaps 50 feet in height. Having built up against a heavy, left-over swell, the seas were much closer together and much steeper than normal or expected. He knows the wind force was well beyond Force 10, and surmises from the wave action that it may have blown as hard as 100 m.p.h.

Normally, in a gale at sea, Mr. Robinson would heave to in the *Varua* under fore and main staysails with the wheel lashed. She would then make across the wind and slightly to windward and cover something like 100 miles in 24 hours. In extremely heavy weather, he would back the forestaysail with this same combination to slow her down more. That was the situation at the start of this ultimate storm, but then as the gale continued to increase, the crests of the seas began to blow off and solid water was coming across the deck into the sails. Mr. Robinson then took all the sail off her and lay ahull with the helm lashed down. The *Varua* lay with the wind on the quarter, a bit farther aft than with many vessels, due to the windage of the yards on her foremast. Mr. Robinson and his crew began using oil, to some moderate effect apparently, and the vessel lay comfortably for some time.

But the gale and the seas continued to increase. Whereas the seas had been breaking by spilling their tops to foam and tumble noisily down their slopes, now they became higher and steeper and broke with the sound of thunder, their huge tops plunging tons of water downward. Mr. Robinson figured the *Varua*'s best chance for survival if one of these plunging breakers caught her was to take it end on. So he ran her off before it. Her speed increased to six or seven knots, which was dangerously fast, but she still steered well. Mr. Robinson and his crew put out drags until they had slowed her to about three knots; she was still sensitive to the helm. To cut her speed by that much took 75 fathoms of two-inch-diameter manila

line, let out in a big bight; four 75-foot mooring lines of the same size; and 100 fathoms of assorted smaller lines. Such drags are much easier to handle than any sea anchor and can be added to or subtracted from to control the speed of the vessel. They continued to use oil, apparently still with some helpful effect.

Although the *Varua*'s average speed had been slowed to three or four knots, she went a good deal faster than that down the crests of the seas: "When a 50-ton, 70-foot vessel surfboards shudderingly down the face of a great sea on its breaking crest, you have experienced something," Mr. Robinson wrote.

One big plunging breaker did catch them. Mr. Robinson, lashed to the wheel securely, met the monster with her stern squarely to it, and although it broke over the whole after half of the vessel, it did no damage.

Mr. Robinson and the *Varua* passed the ultimate test. The next day he drove his vessel with the subsiding gale on the quarter 240 miles in 24 hours. In thousands of miles of ocean sailing, it was the greatest day's run for the man who had dreamed on Brooklyn's wharves and for the great vessel he had created to fulfill those dreams.

22/ The *Marco Polo*

> Length on deck: 55 feet
> Length on waterline: 48 feet 9 inches
> Beam: 10 feet
> Draft: 5 feet 6 inches
> Sail area: 812 square feet
> Displacement: 19 tons
> Designer: L. Francis Herreshoff

One of L. Francis Herreshoff's early designs, drawn in 1922, was that of a lifeboat-like, three-masted, auxiliary-powered ocean cruiser 100 feet long. Her outboard profile and sail plan make a most interesting study.

Nine years later, in 1931, Mr. Herreshoff expanded the idea for the design up to a length of 130 feet. The 130-footer, in particular, might make a good passenger cruising vessel for today, if ocean cruises could be made to pay.

Both these designs turned out to be dream ships only, for neither was built.

But then during the latter part of World War II, Francis Herreshoff brought this idea for the design of a safe, fast, simple auxiliary ocean cruiser down to a length of 55 feet. He figured that during the War a lot of Americans were being introduced to ocean voyaging and that after the War some of them might want to return to the out-of-the-way corners of the world they had seen, but on their own terms. What better way than in their own able vessel, one that could make long, fast passages under sail and power? He even designed the craft with a set of hoisting eyes for the world cruiser whose time was more limited than his wallet.

Mr. Herreshoff named his 55-foot world cruiser the *Marco Polo,* saying of the great explorer, "Comfort and show were not the main objects of

his life, but to get onward and visit strange places was more to be desired."

The *Marco Polo* is 48 feet 9 inches long on the waterline, has a beam of only 10 feet, and a draft of only 5 feet 6 inches.

She displaces about 19 tons depending on her loading. The load waterline is drawn in on her lines as if the vessel were light, with her tanks and lockers empty. Loading for a long cruise could bring her down in the water as much as ten inches, according to her designer, and one of the objectives of the design was that the vessel not change her stability characteristics much with changes in loading. This was achieved in part by making her topsides somewhat "slab-sided," and I hasten to add that that is Mr. Herreshoff's expression, not mine.

The *Marco Polo*'s sail area is 812 square feet, divided as follows: jib, 142 square feet; foresail, 201 square feet; mainsail, 261 square feet; and mizzen, 208 square feet.

Her lines show a hull that is extremely buoyant and dry. The turtlebacks in the ends of her provide extra reserve buoyancy, as well as an unusual amount of interior space in the bow and stern. The after turtleback gives the cockpit a bit of extra protection from a following sea.

She has very long, easy buttock lines and, in

L. Francis Herreshoff. (Muriel Vaughn)

fact, the very fine lines throughout of a long, narrow hull. The *Marco Polo* is very easily driven, which satisfies one of the primary requirements for the design—that she be easily and thus economically driven under power.

Yet this design is an unusual combination in that, though she is long and easy, she is also very powerful, with her nearly 15,000 pounds of lead outside ballast and her high, straight sections above the waterline. She could be driven very hard under sail without putting the rail under. And Francis Herreshoff wrote of her, "It is believed this model of vessel can be driven very hard in a following sea as she has a small midship section, an easy run, and a cutaway forefoot—all of great importance in running." Mr. Herreshoff envisioned her being driven under sail and power 24 hours a day at ten knots, though she would probably be far more comfortable at something between eight and nine, which of course would be a remarkable sustained speed for a vessel of her displacement.

Complete construction details of the *Marco Polo* were presented by Mr. Herreshoff in a series of articles in the *Rudder,* reprinted in his book *Sensible Cruising Designs.* Here are just a few highlights: her wood keel is 3¼ inches deep by a varying width from 5 to 14 inches; her floors are 2 inches thick; the frames are molded 2½ inches and sided 2 inches, being sawn in the ends of her and bent throughout the midships stations; deck beams are molded 2¾ inches and sided from 1⅜ inches to 3 inches; shelf, 2½ inches square; clamp, 5 inches

by 1½ inches; planking, 1½ inches; and deck, 1¼ inches.

Her three-masted rig is both intriguing and practical. There is something about a three-master: when she rolls a bit, you really have a lot to watch happening. The three-masted rig keeps the center of effort low on her narrow hull, gives considerable versatility in the way of sail combinations, and allows a big shift in the center of effort fore and aft depending on what you want to do with her. The masts are raked progressively aft, with the foremast having a rake of two degrees; the main, 3½ degrees; and the mizzen, five degrees. Mr. Herreshoff did this purely for aesthetic reasons, as far as I know.

Note the running backstays on the foremast. The one *Marco Polo* I've been aboard, the *Morning Star* of Cohasset, Massachusetts, nicely built of wood-core fiberglass by her owner Arthur Rowe, Jr., had runners fitted on the mizzen also.

For the rig of the *Marco Polo,* Francis Herreshoff used turnbuckles, sail track, wire halyards, one-of-a-kind masthead fittings, and so forth, all of which he engineered and designed for extra strength without great weight. Doubtless all of this gear would work very well indeed, its one drawback being that none of it is reparable without fairly sophisticated skills and equipment. When something does carry away in a far corner of the world, that is when gear like the deadeyes and lanyards that Mr. Herreshoff showed for the fore and mizzen rigging of his 1922 design comes into its own.

The *Marco Polo*'s rig is designed primarily for ease of handling in a fresh breeze and in heavy weather. Yet she does have a couple of light sails, a balloon jib set flying to a portable nose pole, and an overlapping, light-weather foresail. It would be a great temptation for me to fit the vessel with a permanent bowsprit to carry the ballooner and also to help in handling anchors.

In thinking about light sails for the *Marco Polo,* no one should be tempted to add main or mizzen staysails; these, in my opinion, would be more trouble than they would be worth.

Mr. Herreshoff designed this rig so that the largest sail, the mainsail, would be a light and moderate weather sail and would be the first to be taken in when shortening down. The sail is cross-cut and its spars and rigging are of lighter weight

Francis Herreshoff's drawing of life on the beach after the great gale suggests the reward that might accrue to a sailor with a Marco Polo. (The Rudder, *1945)*

than those for the foresail and mizzen. You will note, too, that while the mainsail is cross-cut, the foresail and mizzen are vertically cut for greater strength, giving up in return a bit of performance when close-hauled, but giving up nothing when off the wind. She would run or reach nicely in a gale under foresail alone.

L. Francis gave considerable attention to the rig for running before the wind. He shows boom guys on all three booms for holding them forward when she's rolling along before it and coasting down the seas. He describes a bifurcated trysail set on a track on the forward side of the foremast with the slides running up the middle of the sail. This sail would be like twin spinnakers all in one piece. Mr. Herreshoff wrote with some hesitancy, "It is believed she will be partly self-steering with this rig in heavy weather." Nor was he much more sanguine about the squaresail shown. The yard goes up the track on the forward side of the foremast, the sail is laced to the yard, and the problem comes when sail and yard must be taken down as the breeze grows too strong for it. There are no brails, and Mr. Herreshoff admitted it would be a rather ticklish, all-hands evolution. Brails and clew lines would probably pay their way.

Though Mr. Herreshoff shows the *Marco Polo* as a single-screw vessel, he also envisioned that she could be built with twin screws or even in a triple-screw configuration. He specified a folding propeller for minimum drag when sailing. I think the *Marco Polo* would be an ideal application for the variable pitch wheel, since she would often be propelled by both sail and power.

Another objective of the *Marco Polo* design was very long range under power; she has two big fuel tanks reaching from sole to deck amidships, each holding 507 gallons.

On deck, there is space for a dinghy between the

fore and main masts. L. Francis designed a very nice 11½-foot rowing and sailing pram especially for the *Marco Polo*. So she will fit down over two hatches on deck, she has a removable midships rowing seat, removable mast partners, and leeboards instead of a centerboard. In all but heavy weather, the hatches can be left open under her protection.

The *Marco Polo* has stout, high, lifelines and no bulwarks so that should a sea come aboard, it will be the crew and not the water that is retained on deck.

She is designed to be handled by one person on watch; all halyards lead to the cockpit, and all sails have downhauls.

Mr. Herreshoff suggested four anchors for the *Marco Polo*, of 100 pounds, 90 pounds, 75 pounds, and 40 pounds. He allowed as how the Herreshoff pattern would do. He gave her a stout anchor windlass just abaft the turtleback on the foredeck.

The dotted lines shown above the cockpit in the profile construction drawing show that the helmsman when seated can see over the deckhouse and can also see the compass mounted inside the after bulkhead of the house without shifting his line of vision greatly.

The *Marco Polo* steers like a sports car; one revolution of the steering wheel turns the rudder 45 degrees. This is reminiscent of the Herreshoff steering gear that Francis' father designed and built for boats like the Newport 29's. They took some getting used to, but once you have the feel of such a steering gear, you can control the boat like a dinghy. Of course such a high steering gear ratio will only work if the boat is well balanced and light on her helm.

It might be nice to add a second steering position, perhaps a horizontal wheel atop the after end of the deckhouse, similar to the arrangement

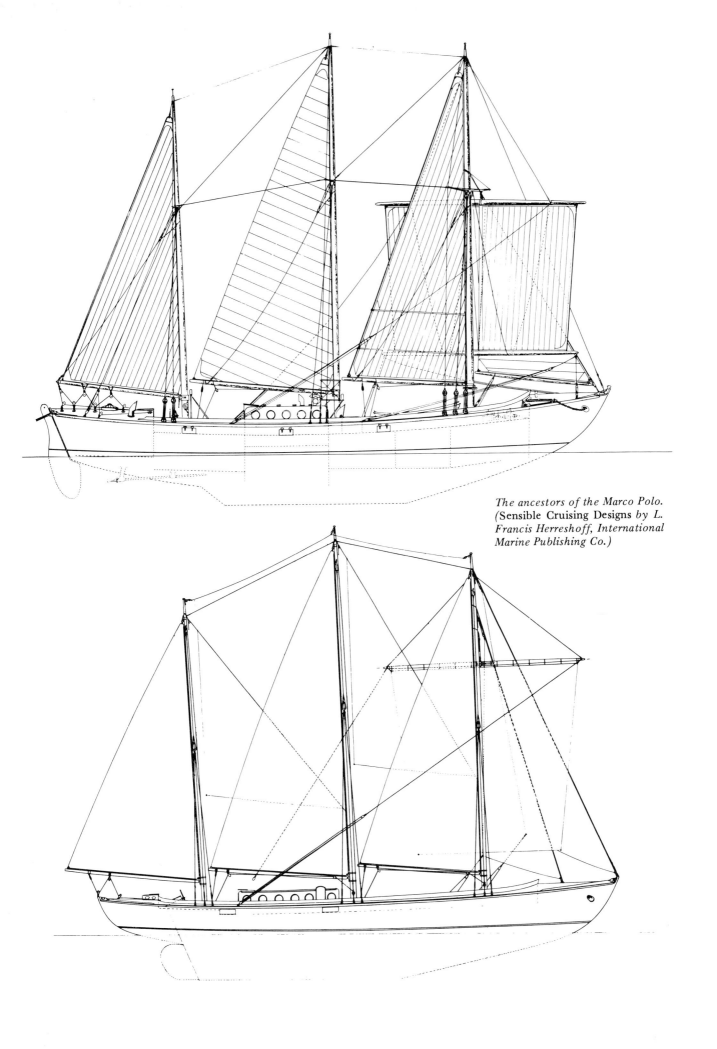

*The ancestors of the Marco Polo.
(Sensible Cruising Designs by L.
Francis Herreshoff, International
Marine Publishing Co.)*

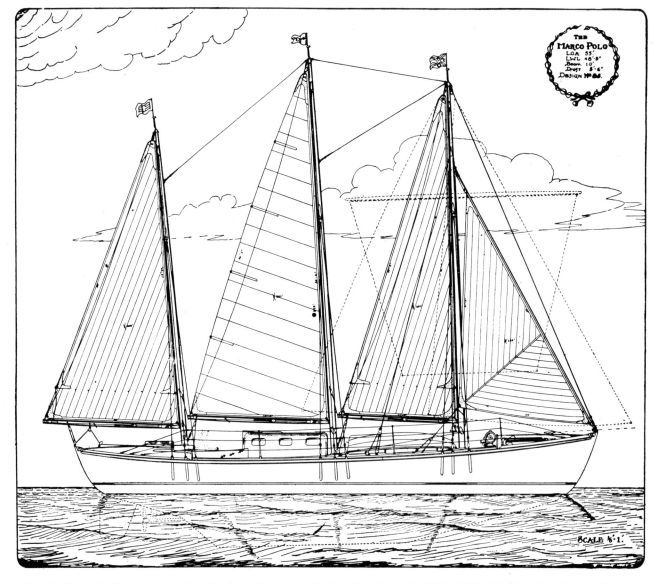

Francis Herreshoff's concept of an ideal world cruiser, designed at the end of World War II. (Sensible Cruising Designs by L. Francis Herreshoff, International Marine Publishing Co.)

L. Francis designed for his big ketch, the *Landfall.* You could even add a dodger that could fold up over the after end of the deckhouse to protect its companionway and this second steering position.

The *Marco Polo*'s balanced rudder is interesting. Mr. Herreshoff claimed it could stand as much abuse as a deadwood. In any case, it is high enough so that it shouldn't hit anything if the vessel should take the ground. The *Marco Polo*'s rudder and wheel do look a bit exposed to me, however.

The three-master's accommodations are divided into three completely separate compartments, each of which must be entered through its own hatch from the deck. Modern sailors seem to love to be able to walk from stem to stern of their vessels without even having to duck, but I would gladly

trade that feature off for the remarkable amount of privacy—perhaps quite important on a long cruise—that L. Francis has achieved with his arrangement for the *Marco Polo.*

In a way, she is arranged like a destroyer. Mr. Herreshoff gave top priority to the spaces for the engine and fuel that would be responsible for driving the vessel thousands of miles and then devoted what was left over in the ends of the boat to the crew. And he clearly wanted his engine room to be a well-frequented and joyful place, not a dark hole to be avoided. He wrote, "A large engine room makes a good workshop and a safe retreat away from the ladies. This engine room could have a workbench on one side and a leather covered transom seat on the other." With such an

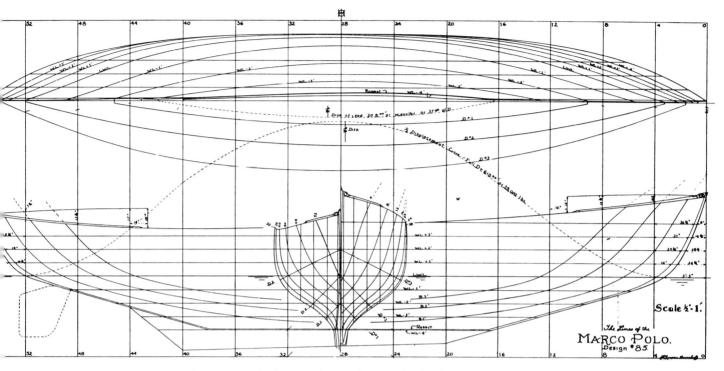

Above: *Her lines show a vessel that combines the speed of a long, narrow hull with the extreme seaworthiness of a lifeboat. (Sensible Cruising Designs by L. Francis Herreshoff, International Marine Publishing Co.)*

Below: *The construction drawing shows many features of a vessel that looks as if she just plain wants to go to sea. (Sensible Cruising Designs by L. Francis Herreshoff, International Marine Publishing Co.)*

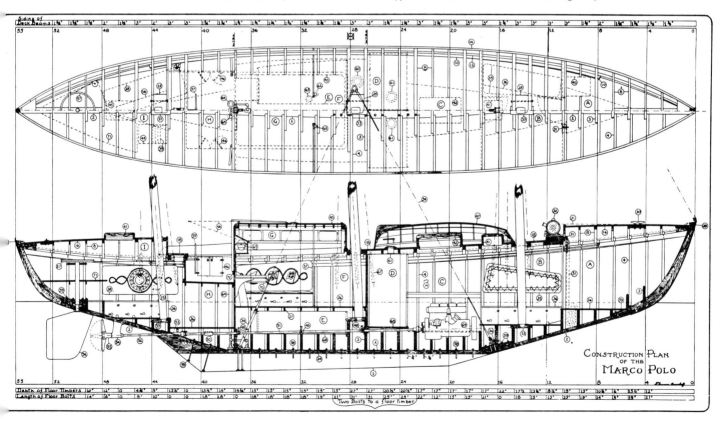

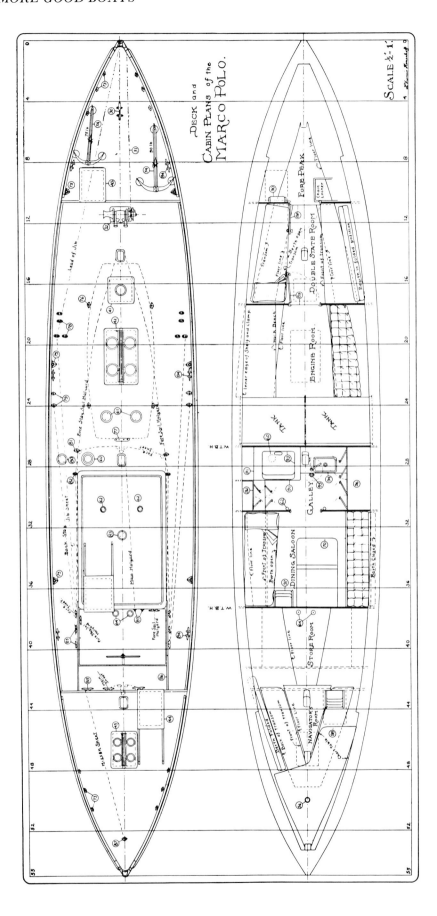

*The **Marco Polo** is arranged with a well-protected cockpit, a good place to stow her dinghy out of harm's way, a big engine room, plenty of fuel tank space amidships, and accommodations for up to five people in three well-separated compartments. (Sensible Cruising Designs by L. Francis Herreshoff, International Marine Publishing Co.)*

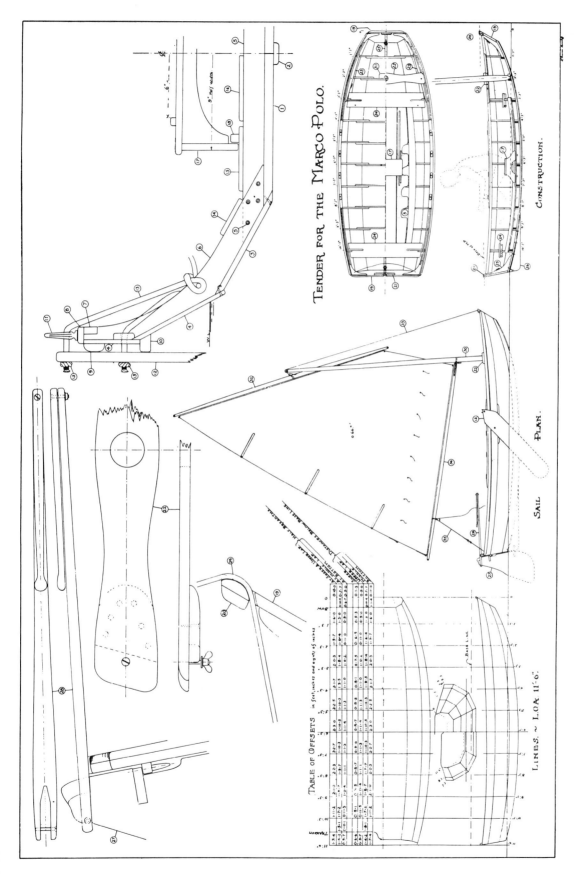

TENDER FOR THE MARCO POLO.

The plans of the 11½-foot pram that Mr. Herreshoff designed especially to be the tender for the Marco Polo. (Sensible Cruising Designs by L. Francis Herreshoff, International Marine Publishing Co.)

A Marco Polo, the Talaria, under sail. Note that her deckhouse has been extended forward of the mainmast. (Sensible Cruising Designs *by L. Francis Herreshoff, International Marine Publishing Co.*)

arrangement, you could hardly help but take good care of the engine.

L. Francis was well known for his predilection for the cedar bucket. He wrote: "The forepeak has enough space for a pump water closet for those who are fond of this mechanical contrivance." And again, "On a long cruise, nature needs every encouragement and if one can retire to the place of his choosing—bucket in hand—the whole business is simplified. And if by coincidence nature should call all of the crew at the same instant, then if there is a whole nest of buckets all can be accommodated."

L. Francis believed in simplicity in the cabin, and he told his readers why:

Although I do not like either water closets or ice boxes, I do not want to force my peculiarities on anyone even if I do know that it will save them from much expense and disagreeable drudgery. I should like to impress on the minds of contemplated owners of *Marco Polos* that extreme simplicity is the only practical way to reduce the cost of a boat of this kind. On many yachts of this size the hull costs thirty percent, the spars, sails and rig thirty percent, and the interior thirty percent. It is very doubtful if saving in cost of the first two mentioned is economical, but, if one sticks to extreme simplicity in the cabin arrangements, he can save several thousand dollars and, strange to say, have the best time in the end for such arrangements are so much easier to take care of. In fact the principal art of cruising is to learn how to take care of yourself easily and quickly so you will have time left over for enjoyment.

The saloon in the deckhouse is a light and airy place. L. Francis suggested sliding glass windows. The table folds out from the after bulkhead of the house.

The galley has much locker space and there is a huge storage area in addition beneath the cockpit. There are two 172-gallon water tanks beneath the galley.

The navigator has his own cabin in the stern with a chart table to envy. Here he can practice his magic without anyone looking over his shoulder, exulting in his pinpoints or wondering about his triangles, as the case may be.

L. Francis designed folding wooden berths for the *Marco Polo*. There are narrower transoms under them, and the bottoms of the berths—for which he showed handsome decorations—become the seat backrests when the berths are folded away.

Mr. Herreshoff suggested that if someone wanted a *Marco Polo* for short-range cruising, one of the water tanks could be converted to fuel, a smaller engine could be installed beneath the cockpit, and you would then have the space taken up by the big engine and the big fuel tanks for more accommodations, such as a head and another stateroom. (This is the way the first *Marco Polo* built, the *Talaria,* was, in fact, arranged.)

The *Marco Polo* would be a wonderful vessel in which to cruise offshore. She could be sailed nicely singlehanded, or comfortably with up to five on board. And true luxury at sea is to have several watch-standers and the need for only one to be on watch at a time. I remember one submarine cruise when we had six qualified officers-of-the-deck on board. Instead of complaining that it couldn't be your turn again already, you looked forward to the rare privilege of being allowed up on the bridge for four hours out of the twenty-four.

Captain Robert P. Beebe, U.S. Navy, made a passage from New York to the Bahamas in the *Talaria,* Josiah Newcombe's *Marco Polo,* in November, 1957, and described the trip in detail in an article for the *Rudder.* With his kind permission, I quote the parts of the article that pertain to *Talaria*'s performance:

Saturday. Beginning to get some sea and learn *Talaria*'s ways in such going. Decks wet but not much spray. Navigator finds the motion in the after cabin too much for him and moves his gear into the main cabin. Sea legs not all that might be desired. Barnegat light vessel at 1950. 7.8 knots.

By this time we were getting offshore and the seas were building up. Reaching right across them gave the ship a very quick motion and made the helmsman's task difficult. We are learning that she steers easily, but must be steered all the time.... *Talaria*'s short and taut rigging gives off a peculiarly high pitched moan that sounds much worse below than it does on deck. We are gradually realizing that the boat is by no means being pressed and is ready to handle much bigger things than this.

Sunday. By dawn we were well offshore, with the seas getting impressively high. Helmsman told to keep her moving at maximum speed. Is a fast reach in a beam sea the worst course for motion? It seemed that way....

With the wind drawing aft, and everyone's spirits reviving after a rugged first night, it was agreed the sooner we got across the Gulf Stream the better. So we hoisted the main and made her jump. She registered twenty miles in two hours on the log once and was not far from it the rest of the day. Glorious sailing, though life below was far from comfortable unless one was in a bunk....

Past Norfolk by sunset. Time to gybe over and commence the run through the Gulf Stream. Seas steadily building up, wind still thirty knots with higher gusts. At 2100 lowered jib and main to snug down for anticipated squalls in the Stream. Wind still well aft. Several violent gybes as the boat ran off course and hit wind shifts in the lee of the seas.

Top batten of the foresail caught under shroud several times and had to be freed by luffing. Rigged a preventer on boom. This did not keep the head of the sail from gybing and catching the batten again. The mizzen caught similarly, but in this case tore before it

could be freed. Herreshoff was right in leaving the battens off. Tremendous struggle to lower and secure the mizzen due to precarious footing on aft turtle-back and no way to keep the boom from flogging from side to side when held by sheet and topping lift only. Joe [Newcombe] finally did it while well belayed with a heavy safety line.

Sailing under fore only, quite sufficient considering the heavy Gulf Stream squalls building up. It appears we were in the Stream from about 2200 on the tenth to 0800 the eleventh. Wind from the north northeast varying from gusts of forty knots to quiet periods of about fifteen. Typical Gulf Stream weather, only more so, with the northerly blowing against it. Black squalls bearing down, sea confused from the shifting of the wind, and building up towering crests against the current. Motion below quite violent. On deck it is a different story. *Talaria* can be seen by the light of the moon to be making her way through the seas in tremendous fashion. We are learning to love the hull and the way she rides over the biggest breaking combers with no apparent effort. The ones we think will come aboard, great towering giants with breaking crests, never do so. There has been no solid water on deck throughout the voyage. The lee rail has never been under.

Monday. The log showed an average of nine knots since previous noon. Much rejoicing at our getting across the Gulf Stream and south of Hatteras in less than two days from New York....

Tuesday. Wind moderates and continues to veer toward east. Sea much reduced. Joe suggests that now is the time to try out the squaresail. Navigator all for it, but points out we may be sorry later.

We turned to on the gear. The exact arrangement shown on the plans was not quite finished, notably the blocks at the masthead for the topping lifts. Solved this by hoisting blocks on fore halliard. When lifts, braces and sheets were ready and everything led properly to be on the correct side when hoisted, we raised the yard alone to see how it went. No strain. Hoisting the crane and handling lifts to bring the yard nearly vertical to swing by the shrouds and out is very easy to do. Lowered yard to bend squaresail in stops. It swings up and out with ease. Man sheets and braces and break her out. A perfect break. The sail sets beautifully and off we go before the wind, making about five knots in a twelve to fifteen knot breeze. Beer for all hands. A half spoke is all the steering she needs....

Sailed all night under squaresail at about six knots. It was a comfortable night and the first real sleep for some of us....

Wednesday. At 1115 we lowered squaresail. It came down with the greatest of ease, with the yard held just off the lifelines under perfect control while lashings were passed as far out as could be reached. Then hoist again, top up one end and back through on deck.

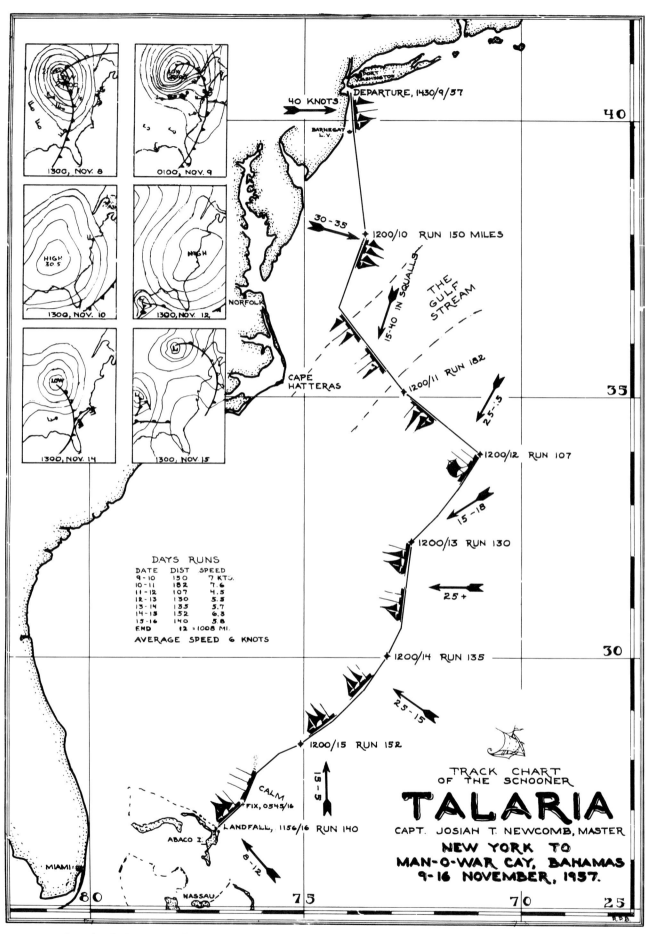

Captain Robert Beebe's chart of the Talaria's passage south. (Captain Robert P. Beebe, U.S. Navy, Retired)

Although twenty-four hours cannot be considered an all-out test of the squaresail rig we were all most pleased with it and the way the gear performed. No signs of strain anywhere. The yard made a perceptible difference in the roll, causing it to be slower and deeper. However this was not objectionable. . . .

After sunset, squalls clear off. Wind continues to increase, reaching about twenty-five knots, more in gusts. Why is this? Navigator at the helm, reluctant to bear off and lose precious southing, holds her to it. The ship is going faster and faster until finally the shocks and rolls become excessive as she leaps over the swells like a live thing. Loud complaints from the watch below holding an after dinner kaffeklatsch in the cabin. Decide we had better get the main off her as this wind seems sure to hold steady and is no squall. All hands require oilskins and safety belts. It takes fifteen minutes to get ready and for eyes to become adjusted to the dark. Then the main comes down with no trouble and is secured. This was our only rugged night sail drill of the whole trip. The 251 square foot sail posed no difficulties compared to the tales one hears of struggles with really big sloop and ketch rigs. Score another point for *Talaria.*

Thursday. At dawn the wind is southeast, twenty-five knots, sea somewhat confused due to veering of the wind. I suddenly realize what it looks like—the sea in Winslow Homer's *Gulf Stream,* a big copy of which hangs in my office. She steers easily with jib and fore at about six knots, which is enough in this sea. We are cruising, not racing.

At 1530 hoist main and increase speed to seven knots or a bit better. . . .

Friday. Joe breaks out the loose footed overlapping foresail which is rigged with ease and sets well. Adds about a knot to our speed. Not now laying Man-o-War, but on such a perfect day who cares? Could sail around like this for a week. Speed about five knots. Would like to try reaching jib also, but gear is not installed to rig it. Some talk of firing up the engine and making like a motor sailer as Herreshoff suggests. Conclude this would not prove anything. Things are nice the way they are.

Saturday. Pass northern tip of Man-o-War Cay at 1345, six days twenty-three hours and fifteen minutes from Sandy Hook, 1008 miles. Average speed six knots. . . .

The hull. The hull is terrific. The action of the boat in a seaway was a joy to behold. At night, by the light of the moon, it was easy to imagine that she was picking her way through the waves with intelligence, never making a wrong move. This may not be a very scientific description, but I have known boats that seemed determined to hit waves just the wrong way whenever possible, banging about and throwing spray all over in an impressive, but essentially futile, display. *Talaria* never did this.

There was no wake at all at any speed to affect the breaking of the seas. She never took solid water on deck. When Joe was securing the mizzen the second night, and we were running off slowly under fore alone, a sea came up astern and barely topped the rail with about a bucket of water that immediately slid off the turtleback. The bow never did get down into a wave or even close. For this trip the turtlebacks were unnecessary. But the sea can get a lot tougher than we had it and I would not venture an opinion as to whether it would be a good thing to leave them off. If they were absent sail handling would be easier of course.

The motion was described in the log several times as violent. However I am sure it was no worse than other types would have displayed in the seas and on the courses we followed. There is no doubt in my mind that *Talaria* can be driven much harder than more conventional vessels of the same weight. It is the crew that will cry for mercy, not the hull. We were quite content with six knots whenever the sea built up. This is a speed well below the potential of the hull though excellent by most standards for heavy weather. She rolls deeply and easily. Our thoughts were inconclusive as to whether more stability with the risk of a sharper snap-back would be worth while. Personally I would say no, for the really vicious rolls that caused havoc below were the result of climbing over big waves that came in on the beam. We spent over half the trip on courses that met the seas in this way. The confusing combination of convex, concave, hyperbolic and parabolic curves such a gray-beard can offer made contemplation of stability as expressed on a nice flat piece of buff drawing paper seem somewhat remote. But I was ready to agree with Herreshoff that the waves seemed quite "helical." It did seem that the idea that a narrow beam will reduce the "pitch-out" at the top of one of these mountains was demonstrated.

Steering. The unusual rudder is a *Marco Polo* feature. There is no doubt that she steers easily. Furthermore it did not seem to make any difference what combination of sails she carried. The amount of helm required stayed about the same. On the other hand, she had to be steered constantly. There was no leaving the wheel to get a cup of coffee or fiddle with the sheets. If you let go of the wheel she was sure to run off in short order to one side or the other. Is this a drawback? We never did agree. My own feeling is that the ease of steering makes a watch a pleasure compared to some boats and the attention required is hardly a chore. After all, that is what you are on watch for.

[But recently Captain Beebe wrote me, "On reflection it seems to me essential that she have an autopilot for occasional use. In this way the single watchstander can take care of all the little things during his watch without calling a relief."]

The Vivienne of Struan *is a school ship operated by the government of Western Australia.* (Sailing, *March, 1978)*

Sail and battens. The sail battens were heartily cursed. The sails were bought with them to give the best performance in light summer airs. They proved just a nuisance at sea, as has been related, particularly as the sails are rather narrow and the shrouds have an unusually wide angle which almost corresponds to that of the leech to the mast. The solution, of course, is two sets of sails. A rather expensive solution, I am afraid.

The jib was comparatively easy to muzzle and there was good support for the man who did it on the forward turtleback. The fore and main gave no trouble. But something must be done about the mizzen. My own solution would be to install a rather small inconspicuous (on such a large hull) patent stern. The lifelines could then be led farther aft and a permanent gallows installed to rest the boom upon while working the sail. The other booms have securing straps, but the mizzen does not. Consequently the boom swayed from side to side, putting a big strain on the mast and the topping lift at every roll during the five days when there was no sail spread on it. The patent stern would also allow spread for a kicking strap. The fore boom is well held down by the way it is sheeted. On the main we used a strap to one of the cockpit cleats and it improved performance perceptibly. There is no way to rig one on the mizzen at present. As it is sheeted to centerline blocks, the boom rise is excessive on a reach and probably one cause of catching the battens and tearing this sail.

General gear. Except for the torn mizzen, which took a day to repair, every piece of gear functioned perfectly throughout the voyage. There was no chafe. No seizing, no repairs were necessary. She was ready to return or to go on around the world the day we arrived. This certainly shows the hand of a master designer. . . .

The *Marco Polo*, as represented by *Talaria*, can do everything claimed for her. She is a tremendous sea boat, easy to work, quite suited to a one-man watch. She has all the room and more to make a real working oceangoing accommodation. She even exudes an impressive feeling of power while lying at anchor. What more could one ask?

Thanks to L. Francis Herreshoff for designing such a vessel.

Captain Beebe and L. Francis corresponded about the *Talaria*'s performance on the passage south, and I quote a few pertinent comments by L. Francis:

I am much surprised that she has a quick or sharp roll and think the seas at times must have coincided with her period of roll. Also I can't help thinking the seas were unusually steep for their length, and this condition may not often occur. If the crew of *Talaria* were more accustomed to her I think they would have carried more sail which would have had a great dampening effect. Of course if *Talaria*'s center of weight were higher she would have a slower period of roll, and this would have been the case if she had had a heavy motor near the water line, and large fuel tanks whose centers were above the LWL.

The desired amount of stability has always been a moot question on an ocean liner, but if you are close to dangers when struck with a squall, then a vessel that will remain manageable is desirable, and I think an H-55 can carry all sail and be manageable (or steer well) in a strong squall. With less stability, perhaps not, so the answer may be that bilge keels should be used on a vessel with light and low spars, but the added surface of bilge keels will reduce the cruising radius under power. . . .

As to the quick steering or unsteadiness of *Talaria*, I will say that all nautical designs have to be a compromise. If I had designed the H-55s with a deadwood and long run aft then they would have held their course much steadier, but it would then be very difficult to lay them to with the bow well to windward. Few people today realize how delightful it is to lay-to in disagreeable weather, and few of

today's yachtsmen have done it for the simple reason that it cannot be done with most of the modern yachts. But on a vessel like the H-55 if you lay-to say from 1200 to 1600, again from 2300 to 2400, the voyage will be ever so much pleasanter and sometimes seasickness done away with altogether. Sometimes I think the days' runs are nearly as much with these stops for then the crew will carry on and drive her harder when sailing.

However, to me a vessel that cannot easily be made to lay-to is no ocean cruiser, but don't forget that a light headed sail boat is easier to be made to steer herself than a long keeled vessel, and I believe *Talaria* can be made to steer herself much of the time when it is not rough. Also the quick steering vessel can be made to hold her course with proper helmsmanship while the long keeled types are apt to take wild yaws that cannot be quickly corrected. So we can't have both—both a quick and a slow turning craft, but there will be times when you will bless the quick turning vessel for its ability to avoid dangers and tack ship positively under all reasonable circumstances.

You have spoken of *Talaria*'s ability to "pick her way through the waves with intelligence, never making a wrong move." This is mostly because she does not have a deep forefoot and long deadwood aft which would allow the center of lateral resistance to jump from way forward to far aft when crossing the crest of a wave. However, if *Talaria* does require constant attention at the helm this has the advantage of keeping the helmsman awake in the dog watches, and to me a much pleasanter pastime than trying to correct a slow turning, deep yawing, vessel which, as you say, is prone to pick the bad spots.

As for the leech of the mizzen catching under the shrouds, I must say emphatically that the mizzen should not be set when there is a sea and the wind aft of wind-on-the-quarter. The principal reason for this is that the mizzen sail has a very bad effect on the forward sails for it causes the wind under its lee to draw in from one side then the other in a distressing way that causes bad steering, and causes the forward sails to want to jibe. Of course in light weather and no sea the mizzen can be carried running before it.

I think the mizzen boom, as all the booms, was designed with a strong boom bail to take a forward guy or cross tackle, for with high, narrow leg-o'-mutton sails when running freer than wind-abeam, (particularly if there is a sea), the boom must be held down and out, to prevent the sail from pressing so hard against the shrouds and spreaders.

Perhaps the mizzen boom should carry port and starboard boom forward guys always attached which lead to strong cleats just inside the mizzen rigging. But you must always remember to cast these off when tacking ship. You will ask why I didn't show these cleats on the design, and I will say that he who makes no mistakes does nothing. I think if the mizzen

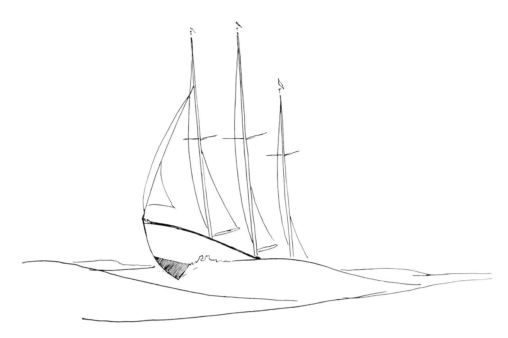

A sketch of the Marco Polo *drawn by her designer. (Muriel Vaughn)*

is never carried when running before it in a sea and wind, and the booms' forward guys are properly tended, then there will be no need of one going out on the after turtle deck, but if desired a stanchion each side, as there is forward, could be erected to carry the life rails further aft.

As for the turtle decks at both ends—these were adopted to give head room in the ends of the vessel, but I suppose some sort of a fiddly deck house could have been built on the after deck instead. To my knowledge there have been three H-55s built in various parts of the world without the turtle decks so apparently others do not approve of them, so I don't know. One way is better when below deck, the other better above deck, but I happen to like the looks of them.

And, from a later letter:

I got the idea of the sharp rolling not so much from your article as from conversing with Mr. Fisk, and I think the trouble is not with the model or the height of the center of weight but rather that the masts, although very strong, are light because they are pretty scientific. On account of there being three masts, the center of weight of the mast is lower than usual.

The way to heave *Marco Polo* to is to simply take in all sail excepting the mizzen, and have the main sheets about close hauled, and the rudder turned in whatever direction it wants to go. Under those conditions she will neither forge ahead nor go backward but will lay with her head about 45 degrees from the wind, making a dead set to leeward of 90 degrees from her center line. Under these conditions the boat can be in a very rough sea and the motion seem very slight.

Years later, Mr. Herreshoff wrote to an inquirer about the *Marco Polo* design:

There have been very few *Marco Polos* built, and as far as I know, only four or five rigged as planned. There have been ones with no rigging, some with sloop rigs, and some with staysail schooner rigs. Only God knows why. One with sloop rigging has been up in the Arctic Circle three different years, and one rigged as designed was sailed across the Atlantic by a man crippled below the waist, a woman, and a man who had had no previous sailing experience.

I would conclude that if the *Marco Polo* has any basic fault, it may be a rather lively motion in a seaway. Captain Beebe's account and, apparently, Mr. Fisk's remarks to Mr. Herreshoff, indicate that the *Talaria*'s motion could be a bit quick and uncomfortable. If this be true, it is probably a trade-off for extreme seaworthiness, buoyancy, and dryness on deck.

L. Francis Herreshoff wrote of the *Marco Polo,* "Though some auxiliaries in the past have been called 50-50 boats, we hope and expect the *Marco Polo* will be better than that. She should really sail well in moderate and heavy weather with her modern scientific sails, spars, and rigging. Under power she should go further and faster than many straight-power boats, so perhaps it would be safe to call her a 90-90 boat."

I ain't going to argue with him.

23/ The *Vigilant*

Length on deck: 100 feet 6 inches
Length on waterline: 93 feet 10 inches
Beam: 21 feet
Draft: 9 feet
Sail area: 2,507 square feet
Displacement: 130 tons
Designer: Eldredge-McInnis, Inc.

One of the handsomest workboat types on the coast of Maine is the sardine carrier. These long, lithe double-enders are a lovely sight as they make knots for a cove that has just been successfully "stopped off," or, with the fish aboard, head for market. Whether light or loaded, they disturb the water but little.

Sardine carriers have been put to many other purposes, for they are remarkably versatile little vessels. You could even rig one up for a motorsailer.

The big *Vigilant,* designed by the Boston firm of Eldredge-McInnis for Drayton Cochran, is in many ways reminiscent of a carrier boat and is, to my way of thinking, a fine motorsailer. She was heavily built of wood to commercial vessel scantlings at Shelburne Shipbuilders, Ltd., Shelburne, Nova Scotia, in 1939. Mr. Cochran wrote me that her construction was supervised by Jim Harding, "one of the best in Nova Scotia."

The *Vigilant* is really a power vessel with auxiliary sails. Though she would not do much to windward or in light weather under sail alone, her rig would give her the motion of a sailing vessel rather than that of a power craft, could often help her along considerably, saving on fuel, and could drive her many miles without the use of her engines in a fresh or stronger breeze that was not ahead. She would make an admirable world cruising boat, or a research vessel or charter craft. As a matter of fact, she was designed with research work in mind and was accordingly given much deck space.

The *Vigilant* is 100 feet 6 inches long on deck, with a waterline length of 93 feet 10 inches, a beam of 21 feet, and a draft of 9 feet. She displaces 130 tons and carries 15 tons of inside ballast. Her sail area is 2,507 square feet.

One thing about Walter McInnis' drawings of a vessel's lines is that you get plenty of them; with all those sections, buttocks, waterlines, and diagonals, you can really see the shape of her.

The *Vigilant* has the very easy buttocks, waterlines, and diagonals of the fairly large vessel. Her hull is easily driven. There is a slight hollow to the garboard. Her freeboard forward is 12 feet and there is a bit of flare high on the bow to help keep her dry in a head sea.

She has plenty of rudder area for maneuverability at slow speed and, in any event, when you needed to turn her in a tight corner you could put a twist on, with one screw going ahead and the other backing and the rudder hard over against the backing screw.

Walter J. McInnis. (Eldredge-McInnis, Inc.)

Her sail area is broken down into a big mainsail of 1,183 square feet, a mizzen with 591 square feet, staysail of 343 square feet, and jib of 390 square feet. You'd want a few people around to handle these sails in a breeze of wind.

The rig is all inboard, but how would it be to give her a bowsprit (equipped with a swordfishing pulpit, of course) and take the upper headstay to the end of it for setting a big jib for reaching in moderate weather? Such a sail would really pull her along and would keep her head off nicely when a big sea rolled in under her quarter. She could run off beautifully before a strong breeze with main and mizzen wung out with preventers and the staysail sheeted flat to dampen the rolling. You might even want a mizzen staysail to help the process.

She has an open crow's nest high on the mainmast; I'd want some rungs on the forward side of the mast to get up to it.

She is a big boat, and although she is moderately rigged, still the sizes of things are impressive. Her main boom is 36½ feet long and her mainmast head is 92 feet above the waterline.

The *Vigilant* is powered with two six-cylinder, 170-h.p. Superior diesels, Model MRD-6, with three-to-one reduction gears, each swinging a 42-inch-by-38-inch wheel. She carries 5,000 gallons of fuel in four tanks at the forward end of the engine room, enough to let her run for 2,500 miles at an easy ten knots.

She carries two Exide, 32-volt batteries. There is a separate generator set on the port side of the engine room and also a small generator located below the engine room floorplates between the engines that can be belt-driven from either engine.

Although she has such amenities as an electric anchor windlass on the foredeck and an Arcola heating plant in the after starboard corner of the engine room, she also has a three-inch hand bilge pump installed alongside the mizzenmast. Her rudder post runs right up through the main deck to take a big, emergency tiller.

There is a raised platform atop steel gallows

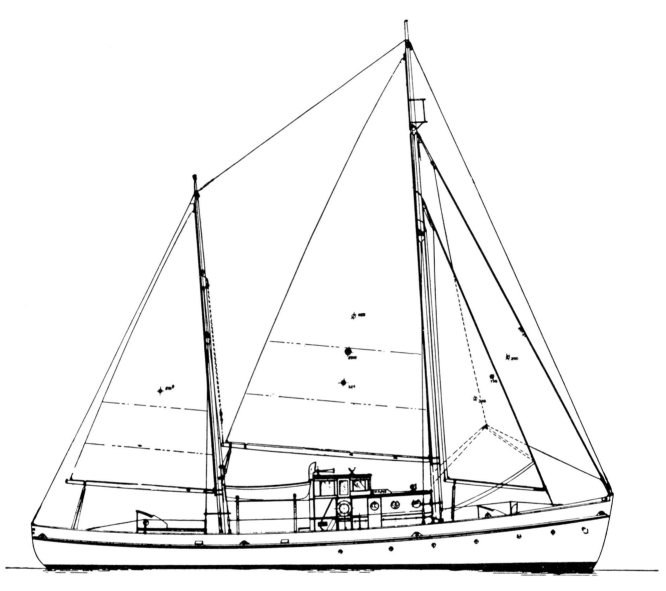

The Vigilant *is a grand, 100-foot motorsailer reminiscent in her good looks of the sardine carriers of the Maine coast. (*The Rudder, *December, 1939)*

frames abaft the pilothouse for stowing small boats and also for use as a perch, along with the tops of the houses, when loosing or furling the mainsail.

Her pilothouse has 360-degree visibility, except in way of her boats. There is one of those nice raised settees across its after side, the kind where you can spend a whole afternoon just watching the world go by.

In the deck saloon, just forward of the pilothouse, there is a small piano. Shucks, who wouldn't sell his farm and go to sea?

A stairway curves from the deckhouse down to the main saloon. And there is another one to take you from the deckhouse down into the galley, which contains a huge electric refrigerator to starboard and a six-burner, oil-fired Shipmate range, complete with hot water boiler, to port. She has a big roomy fo'c's'le, especially if the single stateroom in its after starboard corner were to be done away with.

Access to the engine room is through a deck hatch just abaft the pilothouse or, below, through

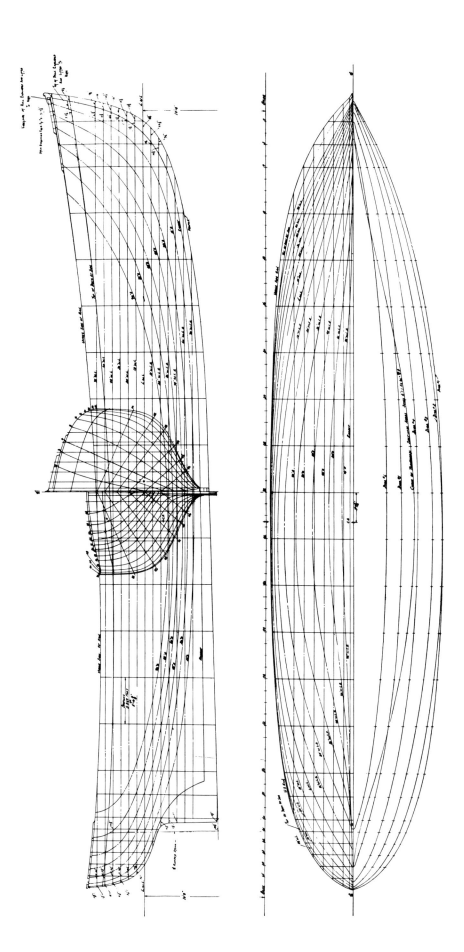

Walter McInnis gives you plenty of lines by which to judge the shape of her hull. (The Rudder, December, 1939)

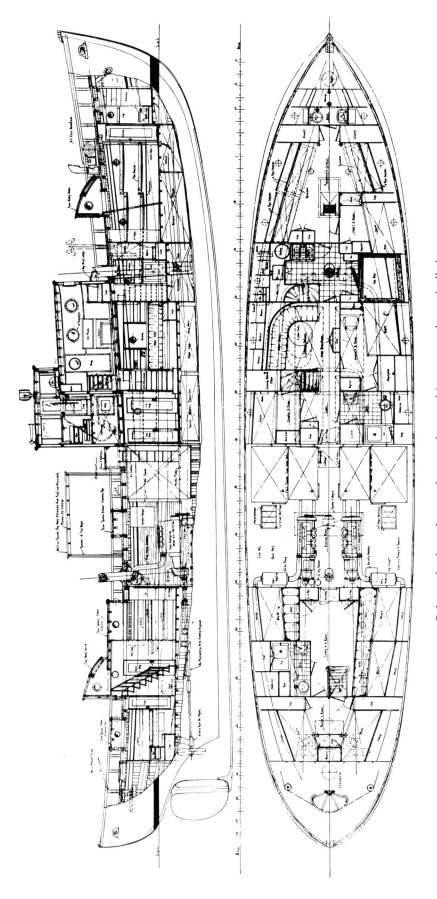

Below, she has plenty of room for machinery, people, and all the amenities. (The Rudder, December, 1939)

watertight doors at each end of the engine room.

This vessel is big enough to have a lot of space in her bilges. Beneath the fo'c's'le there is a chain locker and boatswain's locker. There is a stowage area under the galley sole. Beneath the midships living quarters are four freshwater tanks holding 1,200 gallons.

She has a good-sized forepeak and lazarette for stowage, and there is additional stowage space between the pilothouse floor and the main deck.

As arranged, besides her six-berth fo'c's'le, she has a triple cabin, two doubles, and two singles. There are what would be described by a realtor as 2½ baths.

All in all, the big motorsailer is a mighty handsome and able-looking craft.

24/ The *Glengour*

Length on deck: 39 feet 3 inches
Length on waterline: 35 feet
Beam: 10 feet
Draft: 4 feet 11 inches
Sail area: 671 square feet
Displacement: 12.3 tons
Designer: W. G. McBryde

Going through a secondhand bookstore with a good marine section is like going to a party in your hometown. You see lots of old friends and may make one or two interesting new acquaintances. Such was the case the day I discovered a slim, blue volume of at least middle age with "Forty Designs of Motor and Sailing Yachts by W. G. McBryde, M. I. N. A." stamped across its front cover in handsome gold lettering.

Flipping through this book was more like going to a party in a strange town. Among the vessels for which plans, dimensions, and brief commentary were given, there were many interesting new acquaintances, and there chanced to be one old friend.

The old friend was the *Glengour*, a motorsailer, plans and a photo of which I had long admired in Uffa Fox's book *Racing, Cruising and Design.*

Mr. McBryde, in his book, called the *Glengour* a "50-50 cruiser," as opposed to others of his designs that he called "motorsailers." The former term implied to him that the boat would perform quite well under sail alone. The *Glengour* had that reputation, and I agree that there is no reason why she shouldn't sail quite well. In any event, she would certainly be a most comfortable cruising boat for four people.

The *Glengour* was built, I believe in the mid-Thirties, by James Adam and Sons. She is 39 feet 3 inches long on deck, with a waterline length of 35 feet, a beam of 10 feet, and a draft of 4 feet 11 inches. Her sail area is 671 square feet, and her displacement is 12.3 tons. She is powered with two 15-h.p. engines, which give her a speed of 7¾ knots.

The *Glengour*'s hull is long and narrow, with very easy waterlines and buttocks. She would be an easily driven vessel. She has plenty of freeboard for dryness on deck in rough water.

Her short ends are nicely shaped and well balanced. Her hull looks especially handsome in the photo of her at anchor. Her sheered boot top adds greatly to her appearance, in my opinion.

The rig is well proportioned. She would balance nicely under jib and jigger in a strong breeze. Her mainsail has 377 square feet, the mizzen 138, and the jib 156.

She does need preventer backstays pulling aft against the forestay to keep the mast and forestay reasonably straight. I'd also be sorely tempted to pull my usual trick of giving her a bowsprit. That way you could move the "topmast" stay out onto the end of it for a big ballooner. And a bowsprit is an anchorman's best friend.

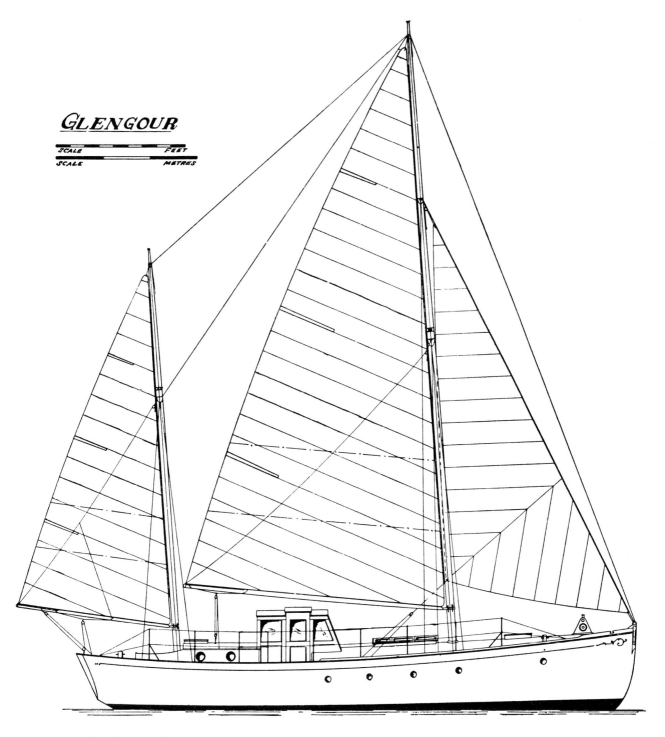

GLENGOUR

SCALE   FEET
SCALE   METRES

The Glengour *is a Scottish fifty-fifty cruising boat. (*Racing, Cruising* and *Design by Uffa Fox*)

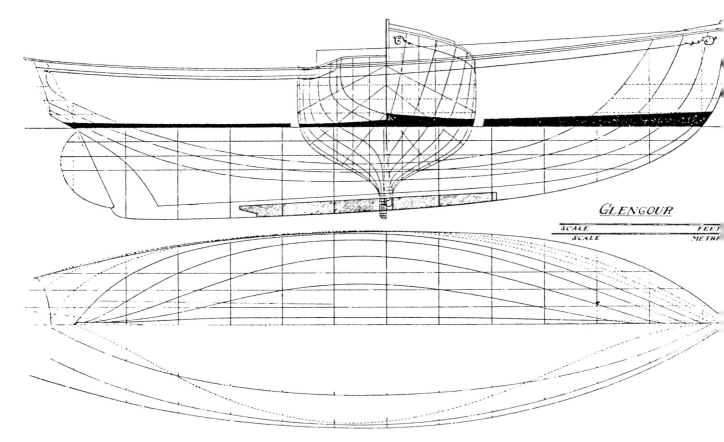

*Her waterlines and buttocks are long and easy, and her sections are powerful enough so she would stand up well to her sail. (*Racing, Cruising and Design *by Uffa Fox)*

In this day and age of extremely reliable marine engines, the increased reliability gained from having two engines instead of one is less important than it was when the *Glengour* was designed and built. Still, having a spare engine, so to speak, could be a mighty comforting thing if you had serious mechanical troubles a long way from an engine repair shop. And what could be more satisfactory when you have to turn her in a short space than to put a twist on—with one engine running ahead and the other astern—adjusting the throttles carefully so she stays in one place, and then just standing around nonchalantly while she turns herself?

The *Glengour*'s deckhouse adds to her looks, to my eye. It gives her a certain air of distinction. And there is something very different about a boat with a real wheelhouse. Standing and leaning in there looking out at the watery world through a glass window, you get the definite feeling that you

are involved with something that can be called a ship. Maybe that's the way to solve the old conundrum about what is a ship and what is a boat: a ship has a wheelhouse; a boat doesn't.

The ketch has a raised flush deck from the deckhouse forward to give her plenty of working space topside and plenty of living space below. There is a small cockpit just abaft the mizzen mast, where you can steer her with a tiller.

On-deck dinghy stowage would be something of a problem. She is fitted with davits on the starboard side, but with a dinghy either hung from them outboard in pleasant weather or swung in on deck in rough weather, the view from the wheel would be somewhat obstructed. A ten-foot boat on deck would reach from the middle of the forward hatch to the after end of the skylight.

The forward companionway from the wheelhouse comes down into the engine room, which has full headroom in its forward end. With the

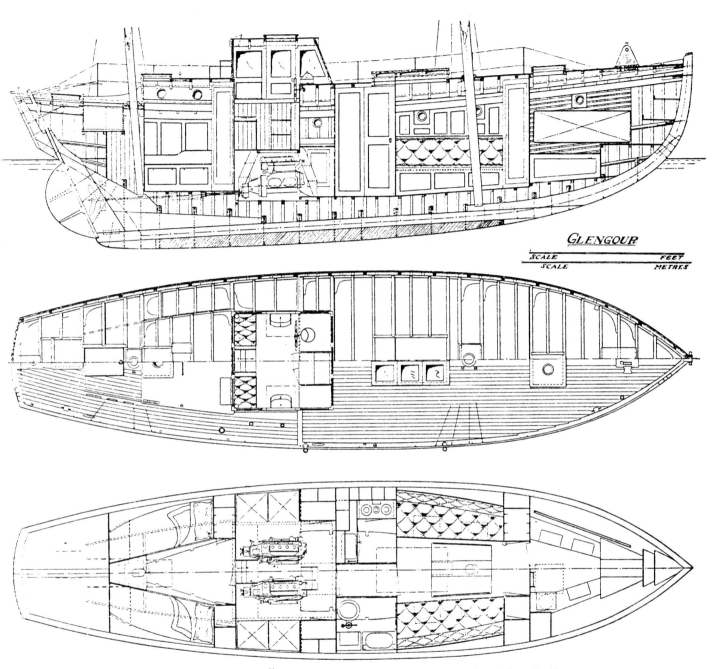

*She is laid out with plenty of space for four people and two engines. The wheelhouse would be a joy. (*Racing, Cruising and Design *by Uffa Fox)*

wheelhouse and engine room between the deck and the forward living quarters, little cold and wet should find their way below forward in bad weather. If this boat were to make serious passages offshore, the inside of the deckhouse should, of course, be strong, watertight, and self-draining, and the doors leading below forward and aft should be strong and watertight. When running under power,

you'd want to keep the forward companionway shut to keep the engine noise out of the wheelhouse.

All in all, the *Glengour* does seem to be a true 50-50 cruising boat. Of her performance under sail, her designer wrote, "She is able to go to windward, and remarkably fast for a vessel of this type." Uffa Fox wrote, "Though she is a full-powered motor-

The Glengour *anchored in a peaceful Scottish loch. (*Racing, Cruising *and* Design *by Uffa Fox)*

boat she is also very able under sail, and strangely enough is as fast as a 23-ton Bristol pilot cutter to windward in a good breeze." That is not to say that the *Glengour* is a fast boat under either sail or power, but she would certainly not be disappointing under either method of propulsion. She is the kind of boat in which it would be tempting to cheat a little, and sail merrily along with the lee engine just ticking over to give her a little extra push.

25/ A Motorsailer by Gordon Munro

```
Length on deck: 35 feet
Length on waterline: 31 feet 9 inches
Beam: 9 feet 4 inches
Draft: 2 feet 10 inches
Sail area: 542 square feet
Displacement: 7½ tons
Designer: Gordon Munro
```

All cruising boats may perhaps be divided into four basic types: sailing craft with no power; sailing craft with auxiliary engines; motorsailers; and powerboats with no sail. While there can be no confusion over cruisers that are propelled by either sail or power alone, the precise boundary between the auxiliary-powered sailing boat and the motorsailer may be—and often is—disputed.

When the internal-combustion engine first came into general use, many a boat owner thought it would be clever to put one in the bilge in order to be able to kick along into harbor when the afternoon breeze failed earlier than expected so as not to have to spend the night at sea. Then as horsepower-to-weight ratios increased, the typical little "iron breeze" became an "iron gale," fully capable of shoving the boat along at hull speed. Today, few sailing craft equipped with engines have any trouble getting up to hull speed under power. A few decades ago, such craft might have been called motorsailers, but the application of that term to today's high-powered sailing craft would be considered by most of their owners to be an insult. Yet the modern cruising auxiliary can usually power far and fast, and, if the wind is not just to her liking, often does. Thus, except for the absence of deckhouses with large glass windows, many modern cruising auxiliaries meet in full the old definition for motorsailer, and are used as such.

There is, of course, nothing wrong with this. These boats give their people a wide choice of speed and propulsion method. The danger in having the choice available, though, is that in the interest of "getting somewhere" one misses a great variety of good sailing.

Suffice it to say the combination of sail and power in a cruising boat has long intrigued yacht designers. There is always that dream of being able to design a boat that is both a good sailing boat and a good powerboat. What designer has not been tempted from time to time to push aside that old axiom about everything in boat design being a compromise and try to cheat a little? I'll bet Walter Mitty could have designed a Maine lobster boat with leeboards and a big gaff cutter rig that could win the Fastest-Lobster-Boat-in-the-World Race at Jonesport, Maine, on the Fourth of July with her sails furled, then throttle back to a nice easy cruising speed of something like 30 knots for the run to Marblehead, Massachusetts, and be just in time to shut down, make sail, and go roaring down to Halifax on the wings of a smoky sou'wester to win the biggest silver cup in the Marblehead-Halifax Race. At any rate, attempts by designers to

Gordon Munro.

produce cruising boats with strong capabilities under both sail and power are most interesting and instructive.

Gordon Munro became enamored with the problem and wrote of motorsailers in 1928, "I have come to regard the type as having more advantages than any other for small cruising craft." His 35-footer, designed at that time and shown here, was supposed to perform about equally well under sail or power. I believe she would and that she would be a fine cruising boat.

This power sloop is 35 feet long on deck, with a waterline length of 31 feet 9 inches, a beam of 9 feet 4 inches, and a draft of 2 feet 10 inches. The centerboard would add about 2 feet 6 inches to this draft. Her sail area is 542 square feet, with 422 in the mainsail and 120 in the jib. Her displacement is 7½ tons, with all her ballast being outside.

She is a very fine-lined boat with a long waterline for her displacement. She has very easy buttocks and waterlines fore and aft, and the only hardness in her sections comes near the middle of the boat.

She would be very easy to drive, power to carry

sail having been sacrificed to attain this slipperiness. She should have a good turn of speed, would not need a big engine to do her 7 knots, but would have to be shortened down in a breeze. One would expect her windward performance to suffer from lack of lateral resistance and from lack of power to carry sail in a hard breeze to drive her into a head sea.

It is interesting that the type of hull Munro developed for his shoal-draft motorsailer was quite similar to the *Presto*-type sharpie developed by his near namesake, Commodore Ralph M. Munroe forty years earlier. (The *Presto* was described in *Good Boats*.) By comparison with the *Presto*, the Gordon Munro motorsailer has less flare in the topsides, a harder bilge, finer waterlines aft, and less sail area. Of course the *Presto* had no engine.

Gordon Munro prepared an interesting comparison of his motorsailer with eight other specific designs, two of which appeared in *Good Boats*, the centerboard ketch *Alice* and the double-ended ketch *Tidal Wave*, and one of which is described in Chapter 7 of this book, the French pilot cutter *Jolie Brise*. In the table below, Coefficient A is a measure of plumpness, from displacement versus length; Coefficient B is a measure of sail area to bulk, from sail area versus volume in cubic feet; and Coefficient C is a measure of sail area to plumpness, from sail area proportioned to length versus a displacement-length ratio.

	Munro Motor-sailer	*Alice*	*Tidal Wave*	*Jolie Brise*
Length on Deck	35.00	52.	32.37	56.25
Length on Waterline	31.75	42.	31.00	48.00
Beam	9.30	13.6	11.00	15.75
Draft	2.85	4.0	4.75	10.25
Working Sail Area	542	1,120	654	2,400
Coefficient A	233	278	309	497
Coefficient B	13.31	13.9	13.91	15.51
Coefficient C	31.58	28.7	26.70	20.52

The power sloop's draft of less than three feet would allow her to wriggle into many a fascinating cove or creek. Her skeg has been rounded up slightly to protect the rudder. Note that her rudder is somewhat balanced, the post being 6½ inches abaft its leading edge.

Her gaff mainsail is peaked up parallel to the forestay, which looks good and lets the sail twist

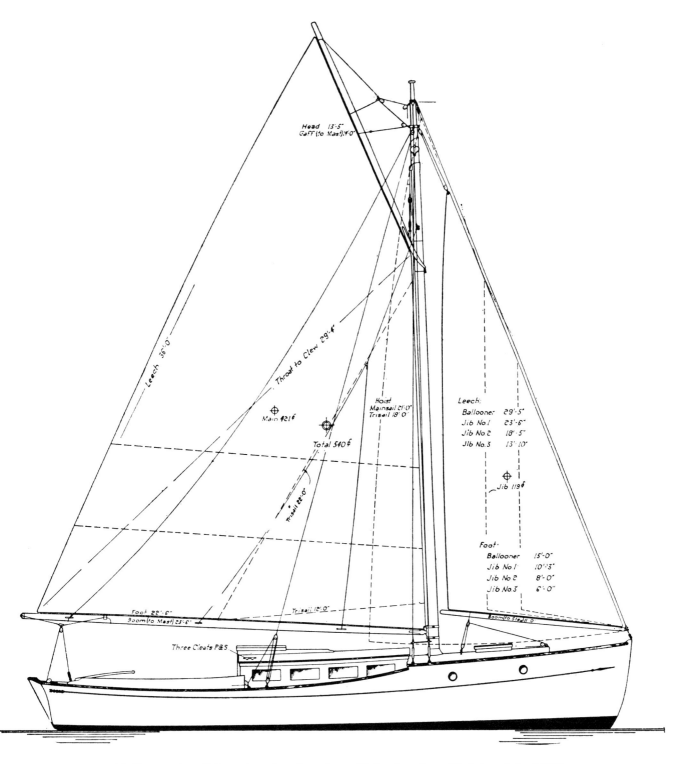

This "power sloop" draws less than three feet with her board up. (Yachting, *July, 1928*)

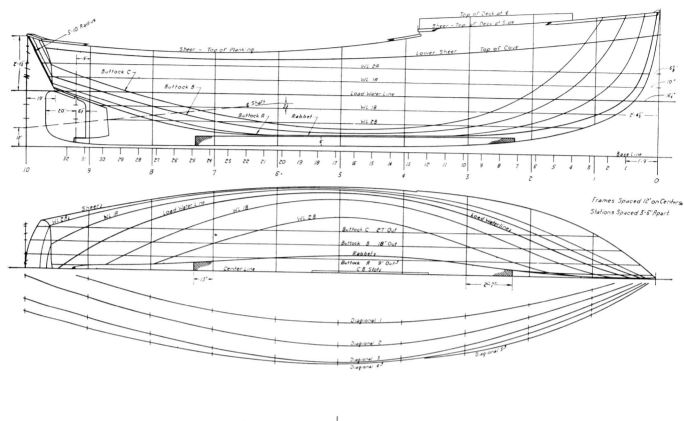

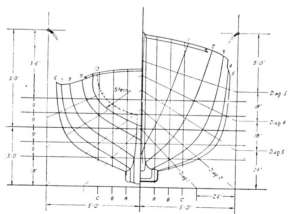

Her lines show her to be long, lean, and easily driven. What little horsepower she needs to make her seven knots can come from sails, engine, or a combination of the two. (Yachting, July, 1928)

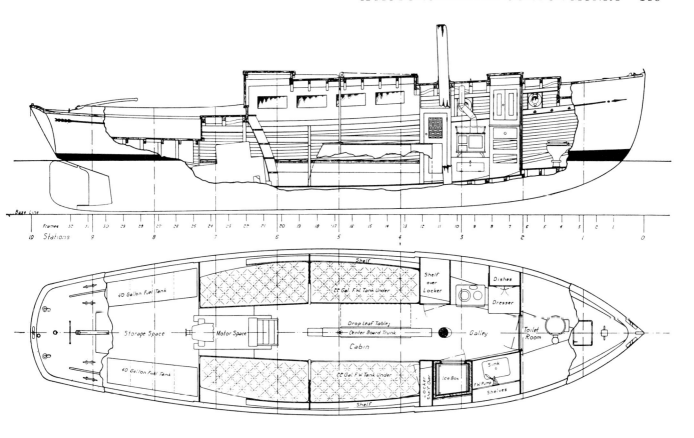

Above: *She is light and airy below. The cabin table doubles as centerboard trunk.* (Yachting, *July, 1928*)

Below: *The interior section drawings give a good idea of how things fit together. Note the width of the outside ballast at station 5.* (Yachting, *July, 1928*)

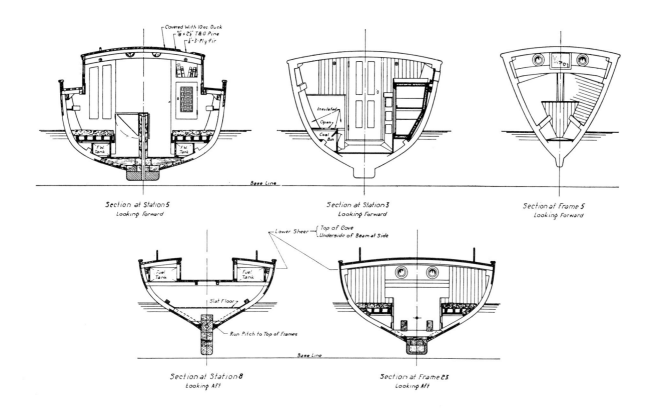

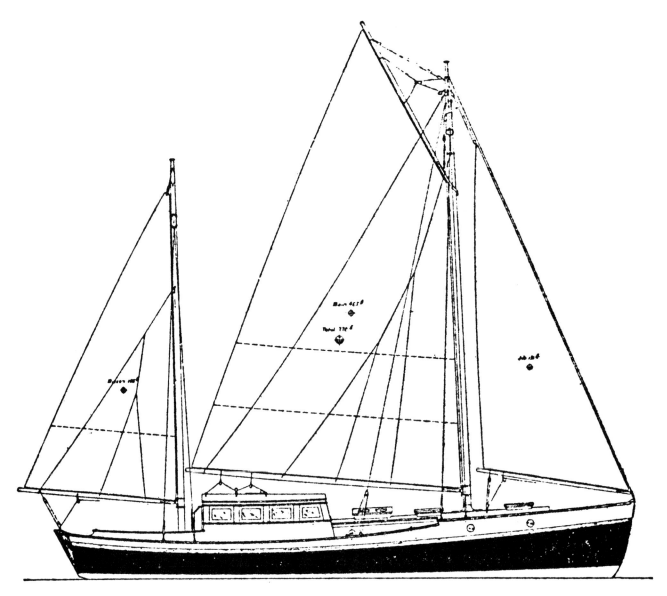

*Here is the same design, lengthened out to 47½ feet and given a deckhouse and a ketch
rig. Her sail area is 772 square feet. (*Fore An' Aft, *December 15, 1927)*

less. Between the high-peaked gaff and the long
boom, twist shouldn't be a problem for this sail.

She has two rather deep reefs in the mainsail,
and a trysail is also shown in the sail plan. As well
as having a big, overlapping jib, she has two jibs
smaller than the working jib. All of this is most
sensible, for it gives considerable versatility to her
simple jib-and-mainsail rig.

She'd be a handy boat for short tacking. The jib
is self-tending and the backstays are probably far
enough forward to be left standing on short tacks,
so all you would have to do is shove the tiller over.

The power plant of today undoubtedly would
be smaller in bulk and weight than the engine of

1928 outlined in the inboard profile plan. An ideal
propeller for this boat would be a variable-pitch
wheel, with its ability to adjust pitch to load and
speed and thus reduce cavitation and increase
efficiency when used together with sail. And it is
when power and sail are used to help each other
that a boat of this type can really come into her
own.

She has two 40-gallon fuel tanks, one under each
cockpit seat, and two 22-gallon water tanks, one
under each saloon transom.

There would be a feeling of real spaciousness on
the deck, for she has a big cockpit and a raised
deck forward. The combination of the short raised

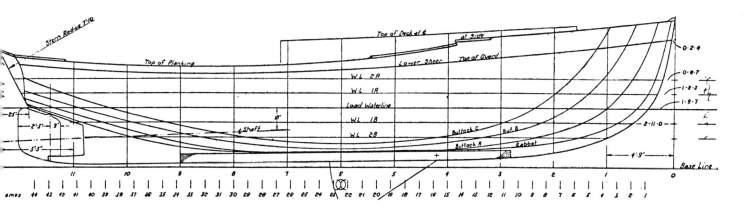

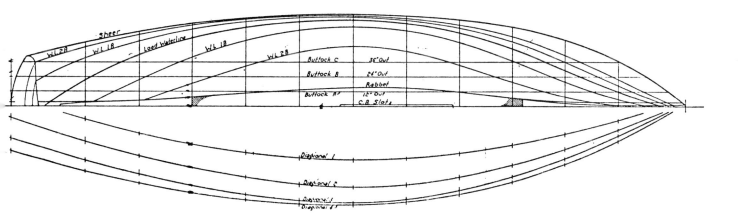

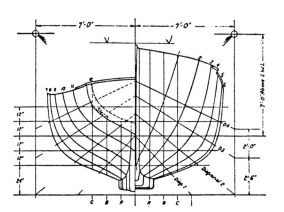

Her length on deck is 47 feet 6 inches, with a waterline length of 43 feet 3 inches, a beam of 12 feet 5 inches, and a draft of 3 feet 9 inches. Her outside iron shoe weighs 9,200 pounds. The ketch's layout is quite similar to that of the sloop, with the quarter berths moved to the deckhouse. She has a six-cylinder Sterling Petrel under the deckhouse floor, which will shove her along at ten knots in smooth water. (Fore An' Aft, December 15, 1927)

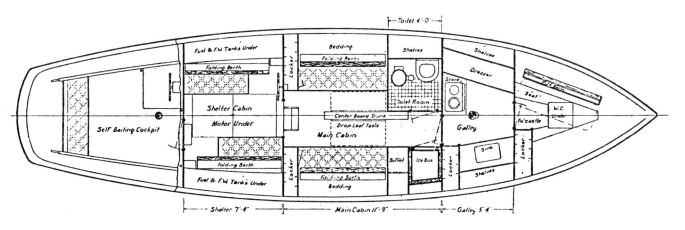

deck and trunk cabin looks good and gives space where it is needed most, both on deck and below. Note that the raised deck doesn't run all the way to the bow, leaving a well forward for storing ground tackle.

The generous, rectangular windows in the sides of the house make for a very light cabin. Such windows were a sort of trademark of Nathanael G. Herreshoff in some of his medium-sized class racing boats. I was at sea some time ago in one of these fine old thoroughbreds, a New York Yacht Club 30-footer, and noticed how pleasant it was when the boat was heeled a bit to sit on the weather transom and have a nice wide view of the horizon to leeward through this series of windows. One afternoon crossing the Bay of Fundy on a reach in thick weather I was thus watching the seas roll off to leeward when a big trawler lying to her net hove into view fairly close aboard. I went to the companionway to watch her as we slid by and was startled to find that the helmsman hadn't seen her! It turned out that the view off the lee bow was better from the cabin than it was from the cockpit, thanks to a low-cut Genoa jib we were carrying. That sail should either be outlawed or given a good long row of rectangular windows.

The centerboard trunk of this motorsailer doesn't interfere with her cabin layout at all; this is a good example of working the arrangement around the trunk.

The placement of the galley and head forward works out well, one big advantage being that it allows a very spacious saloon for this size of boat. The ventilation below would be from aft forward right out the galley hatch—as long as it could be left open. Perhaps it would be a good idea to have a Dorade vent in the galley or head.

She has not quite full headroom in the saloon, and it diminishes a bit as you go forward. You'd probably want a stool in the galley. I had one in my skipjack and it worked out fine. You get in the habit of making for the stool as soon as you duck below, so that instead of prowling around stooped over banging your head, you grab a seat, decide what you want to do, and just reach for it.

Call her what you will, this full-powered auxiliary, 50-50 cruiser, motorsailer, or power sloop would make a fine coastwise cruiser. She could take you to a wide choice of anchorages in comfort and style.

26/ A Forest Ranger's Patrol Boat

> Length on deck: 32 feet
> Length on waterline: 30 feet
> Beam: 8 feet 6 inches
> Draft: 3 feet 6 inches
> Designer: D.P. McMillan

I'm like the sailor in Darrell McClure's cartoon in *Yachting* some decades back who was down on his knees praying to God for forgiveness for having taken a cruise in a powerboat and liked it. As a matter of fact, I made two such trips and liked them both.

Once we went aways east in the old roly-poly *Penguin* to pick up and tow back a Herreshoff 15-footer. The other time we stacked four Blue Jays on the working deck of a big Novi, laid their masts across on top of everything, and headed up Long Island Sound in a vain quest for silverware.

Such shenanigans were hardly in the mind of D.P. McMillan of Vancouver, B.C., when he designed a 32-foot double-ended motorboat 60 years ago, for the project had been commissioned by the British Columbia Forest Branch (wonderful name for the outfit!), which wanted a one-man patrol boat for the Forest Rangers. The resulting boats, if given good sailing peapods to tow, would make admirable vessels in which a solitary soul could really soak up the qualities of a coastline. Powerboats seem always to be at their best when associated with smaller sailing craft.

The first boat built was launched in June, 1918, and was called the *Sitka Spruce*. Two sisterships were built the following year, the *Red Cedar* and the *Douglas Fir*. The boats proved successful for their intended purpose.

Mr. McMillan's creation (I'd love to see some more of his designs) makes quite a handsome vessel, in my opinion. The hull is deep enough to have six feet of headroom under the trunk cabin without having to build a skyscraper. Of course some of this height has been gained in the raised deck. This raised deck has just the slightest amount of sheer to keep it from being ugly. The appearance of the boat would have been improved if the top of the house had followed this same very gentle curve instead of being straight. The pilothouse—the focal point of visual interest on the boat—has just the right curved front, just the right crown to its roof, and just the right windows. Bow and stern profiles, sweep of rubbing strake, cabin house portholes, mast and standing rigging, and even such details as the samson post forward and the flagstaff aft, are all drawn with care and perception.

The boat is 32 feet long on deck, with a waterline length of 30 feet, a beam of 8 feet 6 inches, and a draft of 3 feet 6 inches. Note the flare high on the bow to keep her reasonably dry going into a head sea. She has fine waterlines (especially forward), easy sections, and a good run.

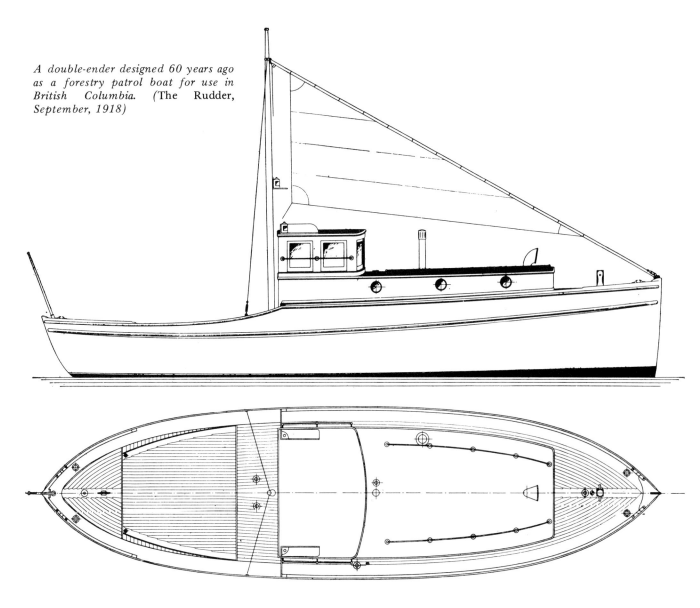

A double-ender designed 60 years ago as a forestry patrol boat for use in British Columbia. (The Rudder, September, 1918)

She should be easily driven at low speeds (one of the hot, new low-energy users?) and would be no bruisewater.

It may be that she needs another two or three inches depth of keel. It was written of her that in a small quartering sea, she would "roll considerably." It would also be desirable, in a boat of this type, to be sure to have enough lateral plane to be able to sail across the wind heading for harbor with a damaged or otherwise uncooperative engine.

While examining her hull shape, note that she has a metal strip supporting the bottom of the rudder and protecting it and the wheel. Does this strip have enough vertical dimension?

The boats were fairly heavily built. The keel, of Douglas fir, is five inches square. The false keel is of Australian gum. The stem is fashioned from a 5-inch square piece of white oak. Frames, also of white oak, are 1½ inches by 1½ inches, on 8-inch centers, but on 7-inch centers in way of the engine bed. Floors are white oak, 1½ inches thick. Longitudinals are all of Douglas fir: sheer clamps, 2½ inches by 5 inches; raised deck clamp, 2½ inches by 3 inches; and bilge stringers, 2½ inches by 4 inches. All of these were put in in one length. Planking is 1⅛-inch Douglas fir. Joinerwork is teak and red cedar. She carries a half ton of cement ballast in the bilge.

On deck, that low-angled headstay would be fine to lean on and hang onto when on the foredeck with the boat jumping into a sea. As a matter of fact, its angle may be just right so that you could use it to practice a bit of circus work, presumably with the boat in quiet water. Because of this shal-

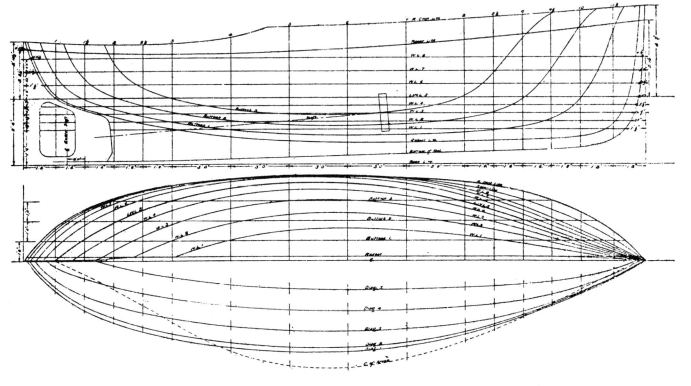

Her lines show a hull that is up to date, for she would be a consummate saver of energy.
(The Rudder, *September, 1918*)

low angle you'd certainly want a downhaul on the riding headsail, because otherwise you'd let go the halyard and nothing would happen.

I'd want to add another sail aft. It would be a trysail setting on a boom on the mast. I'd want the gooseneck quite high, about the level of the grab rail outside the pilothouse windows. The foot of this trysail would be parallel to the foot of the jib. It wouldn't be a big sail, but would help steady her, would really do some pushing with a strong breeze aft, and would help considerably on that sail to shelter with a dead propeller. The boom would double as a derrick for bringing the peapod into the cockpit in a hard chance.

I'd also be tempted to add a second pair of shrouds and give her some wooden "ratlines" and a spreader to stand on, maybe even with some swordfishing hoops. Maybe that's why I liked those powerboat runs. Both boats had A-frame masts with crow's nests. Even at a relatively low height above the vessel, it's a whole 'nother world up there.

You'd want a pair of heavy rope lifelines ready to set up from the shrouds to the stern for that wrong combination of seaway and passengers.

She needs a bowsprit to handle her anchors. The short plank variety—complete with swordfishing pulpit (and that's yet a third world)—would balance the main boom in appearance. These accoutrements wouldn't hurt her looks at all. She would use her anchors constantly, for she's not the kind of boat to lie at a dock longer than is necessary to fuel up, which wouldn't be all that often, given her camel-like efficiency.

The cockpit will take a low deck chair, or even a chaise longue, and it will be down out of the wind. You could also sleep out there, especially if you stuck your feet through the locker door and under the after deck. You could even put a tarp over the boom.

Her bridge deck keeps water from getting below through the pilothouse if she should be pooped; I'd want four big drains in the cockpit floor rather than the two small ones shown.

She cries out to have a big towing bitt amidships at the after end of the bridge deck.

This boat's engine is up in the middle of her to keep its weight amidships and make the engine and shaft fairly level. The thing is certainly accessible; you're living right with it, so it is impossible that it

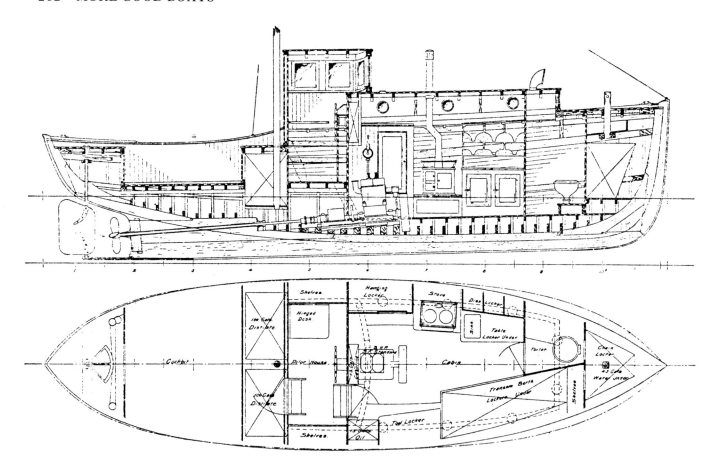

*Her slow-turning Union engine, right up in the middle of things, burns "distillate," which
Westy Farmer reveals is furnace oil. (*The Rudder, *September, 1918)*

will be neglected. The chances are quite good that, out of gratitude, it will run when you want it to.

The *Sitka Spruce* and the *Red Cedar* each had a 10-h.p. Union engine. They cruised at 6.5 knots and could make seven when all buttoned up. The *Douglas Fir* had a 12-h.p. Union; she averaged 7.6 knots for 132 miles on her trial trip and could make eight knots wide open.

The two 100-gallon fuel tanks are under the bridge deck; in Mr. McMillan's drawing, they are labeled to hold "distillate." There is also a little 15-gallon tank high against the bulkhead right above the engine for gasoline. This particular combination of fuels being beyond my tiny motorboating experience, I asked Weston Farmer what it was all about. Westy explained that the Union engine was a compression-ignition type, like the diesel, that burned furnace oil. He said that on the distillate chain, furnace oil lies somewhere between jet fuel and sludge. They're all distillates of the stuff that comes out of the ground; presumably

Mr. McMillan meant to be a bit vague to the Forest Rangers about the fuel they would be depending on. Westy explained that the gasoline was used to start her up and run her out of the harbor.

She has a 45-gallon water tank in the bow. This ought to be about a three-month supply for one person. It's too bad to have all that weight up there, but I suppose it could be used to give her just the right fore-and-aft trim.

She has a fine layout for the singlehander, though you might want a comfortable seat in place of the tool locker just aft of the berth on the starboard side. At the end of the day's run, you could relax and warm your toes on the very machinery that had given it to you.

The galley looks neat and adequate, and the head is up out of the way.

The pilothouse is not only a great place to run her from in comfort, but also adds greatly to her accommodations. It would be a fine spot, when anchored, in which to supervise harbor activities throughout 360 degrees. Of course it would need a stool placed so you could lean back against the after bulkhead. And I think you'd want a permanent chart table fixed across the whole length of the pilothouse in place of the hinged table shown.

All in all, one of these patrol boats from the Canadian northwest would make a fine little cruiser. Shucks, what are those ragmen after any-way? By the time they get through slatting around waiting for the afternoon sou'wester, we'll be in the cove, anchored, swum, fed, and setting out for an explore round the point to the island in our sprit-rigged peapod just in time to catch that breeze ourselves.

Oh God, what have I said . . . ?

27 / The *Eric*

Length on deck: 32 feet 1 inch
Length on waterline: 27 feet 6 inches
Beam: 11 feet
Draft: 5 feet
Sail area: 790 square feet
Displacement: 9¾ tons
Designer: William Atkin

If you asked the Old-Timer whether or not a boat without camel's humps could be designed by a committee, he'd probably reply, "It all depends."

"On what?"

"On who's on the committee!"

As usual, the Old-Timer is right. For instance, if you had on your committee William Washburn Nutting, Arthur Sturges Hildebrand, and William Atkin, there would be no humps in a boat design they created. Particularly if they used as a starting point one of Colin Archer's designs.

At any rate, it was this eminent group that was involved in the creation of the double-ended cutter *Eric*. Do you see any humps in her?

Colin Archer was the great designer and boatbuilder of Scottish descent who lived in Norway producing double-ended rescue boats, pilot boats, fishing boats, and yachts, all of which were modifications of the local types of craft of ancient lineage.

Bill Nutting was the editor of the now-long-gone *Motorboat* magazine, that delightful sheet of the Twenties with the light green border. Nutting got interested in Archer's boats and made a trip to Scandinavia in 1915 to become familiar with the double-enders at first hand. He liked what he saw.

Arthur Hildebrand was a cruising sailor who was

extremely sensitive to good boats, good shipmates, and good cruising waters. He was able to express these feelings; his book, *Blue Water*, published in 1923 by Harcourt-Brace, about a cruise in the Scottish yawl *Caltha*, from the Clyde through the Mediterranean, remains (in my opinion) one of the finest cruising yarns written.

Nutting and Hildebrand were friends, and one time in 1924 they got to musing over Colin Archer's plans of a redningsskoite, in E. Keble Chatterton's intriguing book, *Fore and Aft Craft and Their Story*.

Their musings led to the conclusion that an ideal cruising boat would be one of these redningsskoites scaled down from 47 feet long to 32 feet and rigged as a cutter instead of a ketch.

Nutting's and Hildebrand's good friend Billy Atkin, the cruising man's own boat designer, chanced to miss out on the initial wouldn't-it-be-great-to-have-a-miniature-redningsskoite gams, but the dreamers not only quickly brought him up to date, but also cajoled him (apparently not a task of extreme difficulty) into putting their dream ship on paper.

They thought the redningsskoite's forward waterlines were a bit full, so they asked Billy Atkin to fine up her entry a bit. The idea was to improve

Billy Atkin. (John Atkin)

her speed some going to windward in a seaway. Atkin did it, but he found that you couldn't tamper much with Colin Archer's lines without getting into deep trouble. The *Eric* is still quite full forward.

Other changes made to the redningsskoite in producing the *Eric* were to make her bilges harder, her garboard more hollow, her forefoot a little more cut away, and her sheer a bit bolder. And, of course, the ketch rig was changed to a cutter.

The resulting dimensions for the *Eric* worked out to a length on deck of 32 feet 1 inch, length on the waterline 27 feet 6 inches, beam 11 feet, draft 5 feet, and sail area 790 square feet. Her displacement is given as 19,545 pounds. She has an iron keel of 4,770 pounds and 1,200 pounds of inside ballast.

Nutting changed his mind about having this miniature and somewhat modified redningsskoite built, however, deciding instead to return to Norway, buy an original Scandinavian double-ender, and sail her home across the Atlantic. He got the *Leiv Eiriksson* and set out westward in her with companions, including Arthur Hildebrand. The *Eiriksson* never reached her final destination, and no trace of boat or crew was found. Billy Atkin wrote, "Never has man built *any* kind of vessel that will ride out *any* kind of sea."

Atkin published the design of the *Eric* and she excited much admiration and comment. Many folks said they'd like to see her as a ketch, so Atkin designed a snug ketch rig for her with only 588 square feet of sail. In the first three years after the *Eric*'s plans appeared in print, Atkin sold 175 full sets of drawings. He sold many more in succeeding years.

The first three boats built to the design were constructed by Richard B. Chute at his yard in Huntington, Long Island, all to the order of Henry D. Bixby. All three were to have the ketch rig. While they were under construction, the hulls were named the *Faith, Hope,* and *Charity,* but when they were launched, they were called the *Freya, Valgerda,* and *Eric.*

The design for the *Eric* produces a boat that is heavy and so would be comfortable in rough water. This business of an easy motion in rough water is something that seems to be somewhat misunderstood today. One can read claims, both of the advertising and editorial variety, that such and such a modern light-displacement or medium-displacement boat is very comfortable in a seaway, but I would suggest that the people making such claims in good faith have perhaps never been in rough water in a heavy-displacement boat and so have no experience of such a craft's truly easy motion in those conditions. If you want a boat that has an easy motion in rough water, the first thing to go for is heavy displacement. Of course heavy displacement has its cost, not only in terms of dollars to build the boat, but also in terms of the necessity for a big rig to drive her and a lack of that exhilarating feeling of quickness and ability to accelerate possessed by the light boat. You can't have it all at once. But the point is, you should take claims that light boats are comfortable in rough water with a healthy dash of skepticism. In any case (he said, climbing down off his soapbox), the *Eric* is a heavy boat.

She would be quite stiff for a double-ender, with her beam and ballast. And note how symmetrical is her hull.

The *Eric*'s construction is substantial. Her keel is sided 12 inches and molded 10 inches. Her frames are sawn out of oak and put in double, each sided 1½ inches, and molded from 2½ inches to 1¾ inches, on centers about 14 inches apart. Her planking is specified to be either 1¼-inch white cedar or yellow pine. The deck beams are of yellow

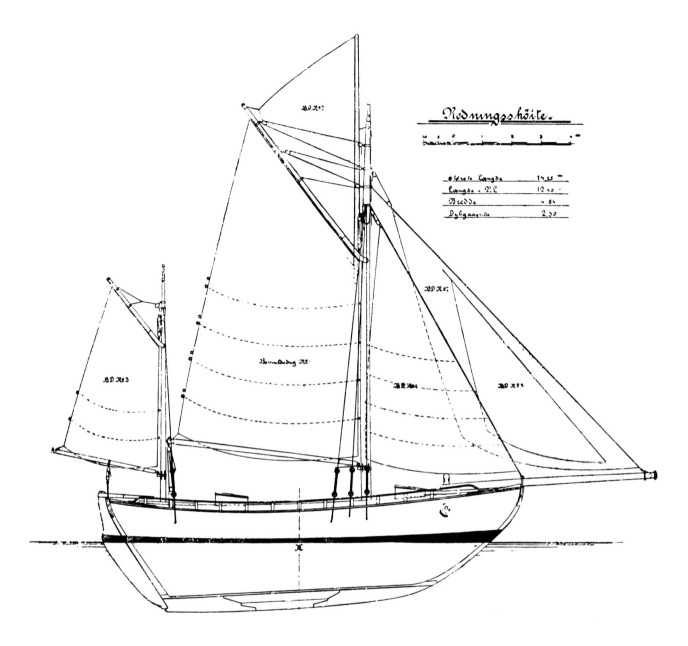

This is the Colin Archer redningsskoite that set the Eric's *committee to dreaming of a smaller version. (*Fore and Aft Craft and Their Story *by E. Keble Chatterton)*

pine, 1¾ inches by 2½ inches, and the deck is of 1⅛-inch white pine.

It is interesting to contrast the cutter rig against the ketch. I would prefer the cutter, except for passagemaking, because it would be a faster rig and spreads more sail. The cutter has 650 square feet in her three lower sails, while the ketch has 588 square feet in her four lowers. It wouldn't be long before I'd find it necessary to give the ketch a topmast on which to set main and jib topsails. With the cutter rig, the area of the mainsail is about 417 square feet; with the ketch, it is but 274 square feet. Yet the bigger mainsail should not be too much for one person to handle. In hard weather, which can hardly be avoided in offshore passagemaking, the ketch rig would come into its own, for it would be easier to shorten down, and you'd have more choices of sail combinations.

On the cutter, you'd want an alternate lead for the running backstays farther forward so they

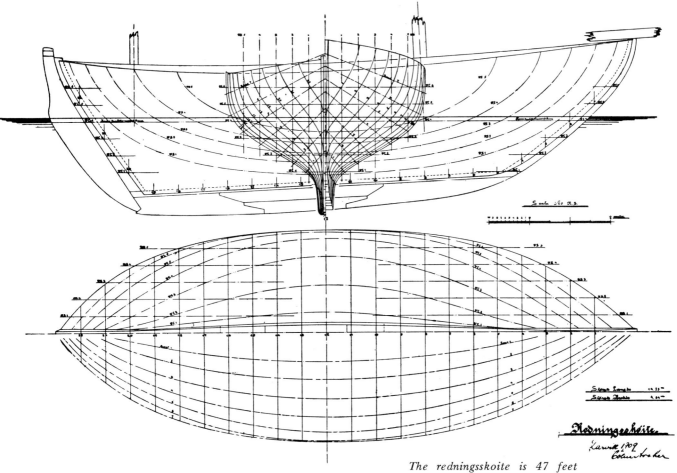

The redningsskoite is 47 feet long on deck, with a waterline length of 41 feet, a beam of 14 feet 6 inches, and a draft of 8 feet. (Fore and Aft Craft and Their Story by E. Keble Chatterton)

could be left set up when short tacking. On the ketch you'd want a piece of light line led from the end of the main gaff through a block in the mizzen masthead and to the deck. It does wonders for the _ _ _. Its name starts with a "V," I think.

The cockpit looks a bit small for normal coastwise day work, but would be fine for passage-making offshore.

The *Eric*'s deep stern sections allow the engine to be placed well aft in the boat and low enough so that the shaft may be level for maximum drive and the propeller still sufficiently submerged. This gets the engine back under the cockpit and allows considerable working area in the forward end of the engine room under the bridge deck. Atkin recommended a power plant of from 7 to 14 h.p. to drive her. She has two 30-gallon fuel tanks in the wings of the engine room.

There is full headroom under her house and nearly full headroom under her forward hatch, thanks to its rather high coaming. In the ketch-rigged version, Atkin allowed the forward end of the trunk cabin to move forward following the mainmast.

The *Eric*'s saloon is one of the most versatile I've seen. There is a good place to sit on either tack, you have your choice of a narrow seat or a wide seat, there are sleeping arrangements for two, or three in a pinch, and there is one berth tucked back out of the way far enough so that you could really get some sleep in it when off watch during the day.

Under the cabin sole, there is a big water tank and a coal bin. Her coal stove is set athwartships so the fire will stay in the firebox when it is being tended even though she takes a roll, a nicety that Atkin always tried to achieve in his designs. And the galley has a hinged seat so that the cook can sit down or stand up to his work, just as he pleases.

(continued on page 216)

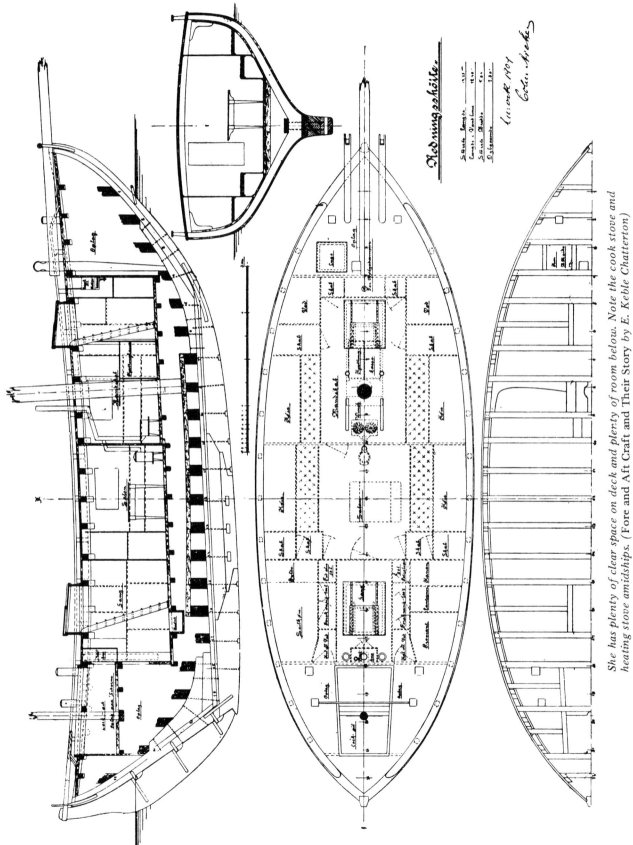

She has plenty of clear space on deck and plenty of room below. Note the cook stove and heating stove amidships. (Fore and Aft Craft and Their Story by E. Keble Chatterton)

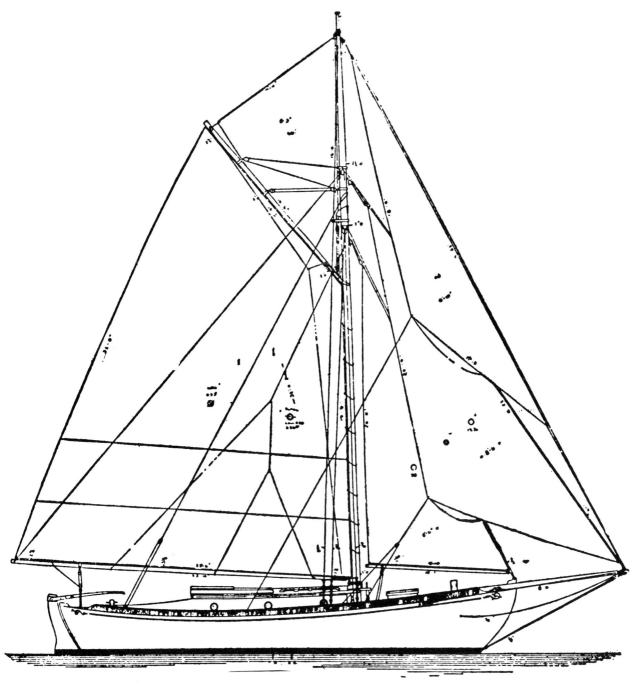

The Eric is a handsome little cutter-rigged version of a Colin Archer redningsskoite. (John Atkin)

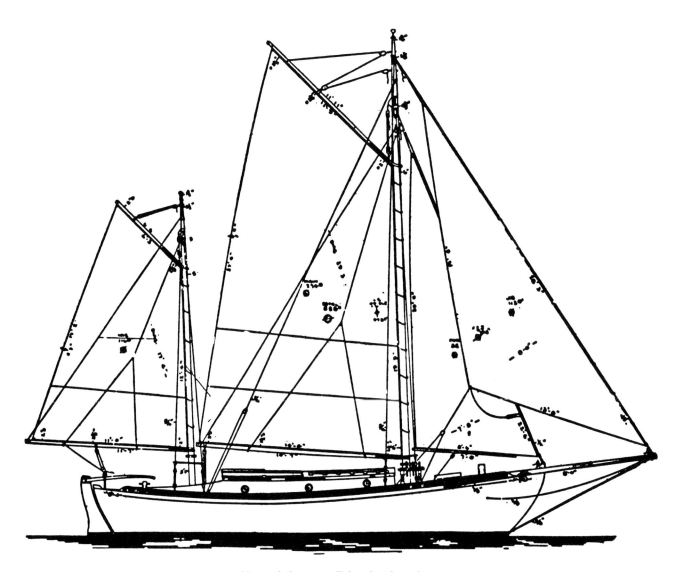

Most of the many Erics *that have been built have been rigged as ketches. (Of* Yachts and Men *by William Atkin)*

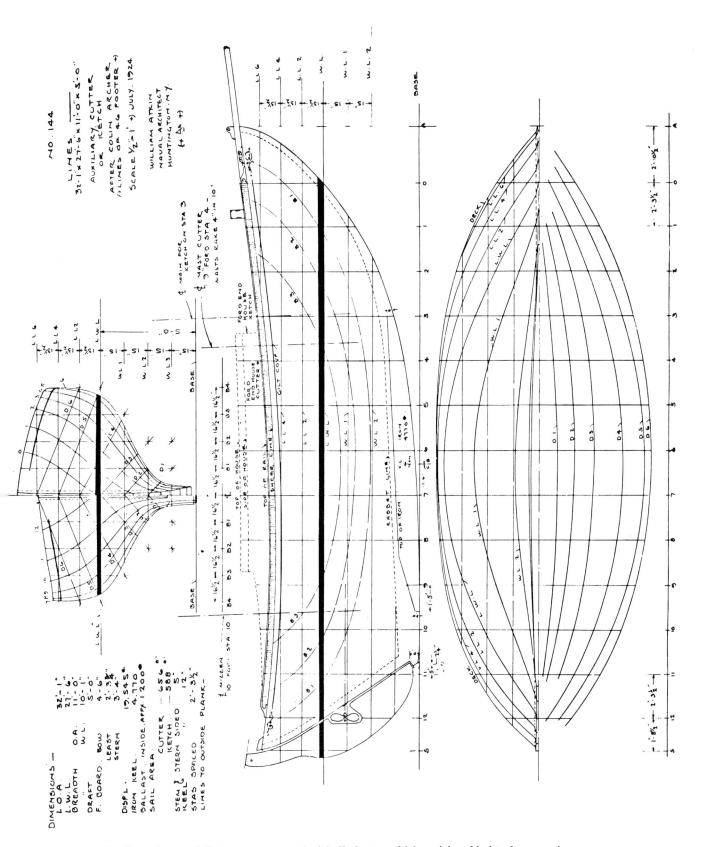

Her lines show a full, heavy, symmetrical hull that would be mighty kind to her crew in rough weather. (John Atkin)

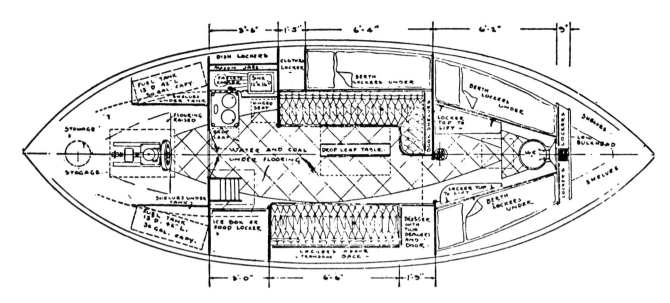

She is sensibly laid out for four people. Her deep stern lets the engine go way aft. (John Atkin)

The Freya *on a nice reach in Huntington Bay, Long Island. (Of Yachts and Men by William Atkin)*

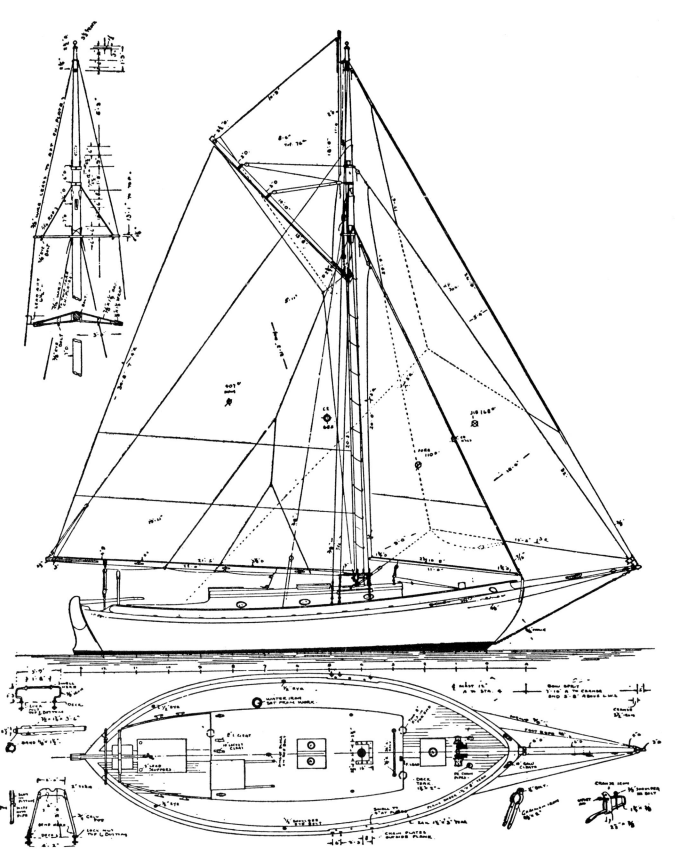

The *Dragon* *is a modified* Eric *that Mr. Atkin turned out a couple of years after he*
produced the original. (Of Yachts and Men *by William Atkin)*

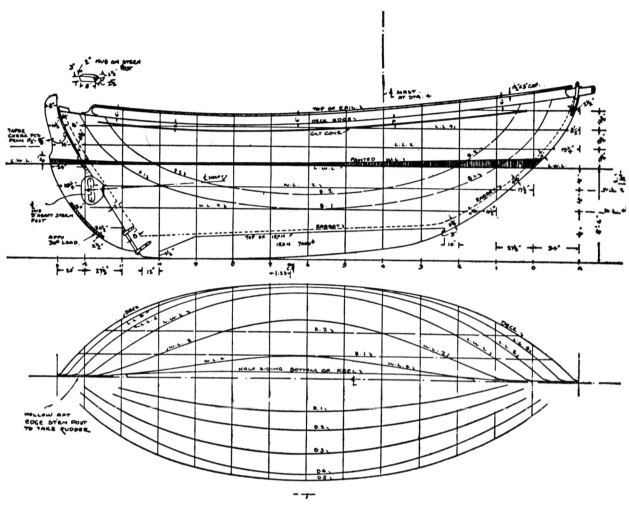

She is a bit closer to the Colin Archer redningsskoite that inspired these designs, for her waterlines are fuller. She draws six inches more than the Eric. *Otherwise, the dimensions of the* Dragon *and* Eric *are identical. (Of Yachts and Men by William Atkin)*

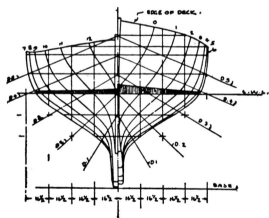

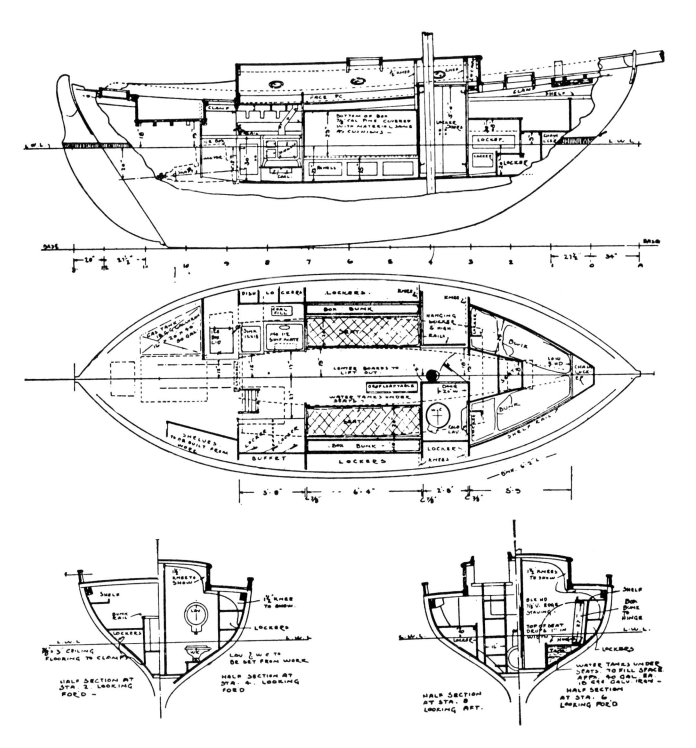

Her house has been extended forward of the mast and she has a separate head and a shorter saloon. (Of Yachts and Men *by William Atkin*)

The **Dragon** *reaching fast in smooth water with plenty of sail set. On this occasion, her speed was measured against that of the powerboat carrying the photographer as close to eight knots. (*Of Yachts and Men *by William Atkin)*

In the ketches, the head was moved from the fo'c's'le back to the after starboard corner of the cabin. If you must have a more elaborate sanitary system than a bucket in the engine room, moving the thing aft probably makes great good sense.

Before the first *Eric* was launched, William Atkin wrote, "Without doubt *Eric* will be a remarkable sea boat. She will carry on endlessly and comfortably, but she will not be fast." And without doubt, the designer of so many wonderful small cruising boats was right on all counts.

28/ The *Gaucho*

Length on deck: 50 feet
Length on waterline: 42 feet
Beam: 14 feet
Draft: 7 feet 5 inches
Sail area: 969 square feet
Displacement: 28 tons
Designer: Manuel Campos

One of my favorite cruising stories has long been the book *Seagoing Gaucho*, by Ernesto Uriburu, in which the author described sailing his 50-foot ketch, the *Gaucho*, on a 27,500-mile voyage, departing from Buenos Aires on July 28, 1946, and returning to Buenos Aires on August 22, 1948, after calling at 60 ports, including Dakar, Gibraltar, Alexandria, Cadiz, Nassau, Washington, D.C., New York City, Miami, Havana, and Rio de Janeiro.

It's not just that the log of the cruise makes a good yarn, but also that the book includes the plans of the *Gaucho,* and she is indeed a handsome and able-looking cruising vessel.

When I chanced upon a big, husky double-ender in a marina in Washington, D. C., some 15 or so years ago, I recognized her as the *Gaucho* long before reading her name on the stern. She looked just a little forlorn sitting there among the high-windowed powerboats. She had the unmistakable air of having been tied up in her berth for some time. She seemed to want somebody to come on board, open her hatches, bend her sails, and cast her off from the land. I would gladly have volunteered for such duty, but there was nobody around to volunteer to.

Ernesto Uriburu had the *Gaucho* built around an eight-inch compass he had acquired. Such a sub-

stantial compass obviously required a substantial boat to carry it, and the *Gaucho* is certainly that.

She was designed by the Argentinian naval architect Manuel Campos, who acknowledged freely that he was borrowing the ideas of Colin Archer.

Archer modified the form of existing Norwegian craft to produce the redningsskoite, a craft of great seaworthiness designed and built to patrol Norway's stormy, rocky coast as a rescue craft. These redningsskoites, mostly built just before the turn of the century, patrolled the waters frequented by the smaller, open, double-ended fishing boats, often picking men off the bottoms of overturned craft or towing them to harbor in single file if they were being forced offshore by a winter gale.

Archer also designed pilot cutters along the same general lines, though these craft were smaller and had somewhat finer lines than the redningsskoites. He designed Fridtjof Nansen's famous *Fram*.

In addition, Colin Archer designed yachts, and he said of them: "Those I have built for pleasure-sailing only are nearly all modifications of the same type [the Redningsskoite], being designed more for good sea-going qualities than for speed." Archer's influence was great, and many vessels have been designed and built along the lines he devel-

Manuel Campos in 1973 under the stern of the Lehg II, *a 31-foot 6-inch Colin Archer type double-ender that Campos designed and in which Vito Dumas circumnavigated in the southern oceans during World War II. She has since been restored and is in a museum in Argentina. Mr. Campos, now 84 years old, is still busily designing boats in Buenos Aires. (Mario R. Uriburu)*

oped, these often being acknowledged as Colin Archer types.

The *Gaucho* is an excellent example of these craft, I think; Manuel Campos did a fine job on her plans.

She was built in 1941-43 by the Parodi brothers, Lorenzo and Alfredo, 20 miles up the Parana River from Buenos Aires at the Tigre.

It is interesting to compare Colin Archer's redningsskoite design (see plans in the previous chapter) against Manuel Campos' design for the *Gaucho.* The redningsskoite is 47 feet long on deck, with a waterline length of 41 feet, a beam of 14 feet 6 inches, and a draft of 8 feet. She has two-thirds of her ballast inside and one-third outside, since an easy motion at sea was high on the list of requirements for this craft.

The *Gaucho* is 50 feet long on deck, with a waterline length of 42 feet, a beam of 14 feet, and a draft of 7 feet 5 inches. Her sail area is 969 square feet. Her displacement is 28 tons, with five tons of outside ballast and four tons of ballast inside.

The *Gaucho* has considerably less displacement than the redningsskoite. She is slightly more cut away forward and has a bit less drag to the keel. By comparison with the redningsskoite, the *Gaucho* has easier buttock lines, more deadrise, and finer waterlines. She would be faster than the redningsskoite but would have significantly less carrying capacity.

The heavy scantlings of the redningsskoite are apparent in her construction plan. Thomas C. Gillmer wrote of these craft more than 30 years ago:

In construction the strength built into them is amazing. Keel, stem, sternpost, and outer planking were of oak as well as some other principal parts. The frames were double, built of "grown" yellow pine. Between these doubled frames, steamed bent oak was alternated and riveted to the outer planking. The floors tying the keel and frames together were natural grown knees cut from the lower trunk and root of the tree. The fastenings of the outer planking to the frames were juniper tree nails. (A most superior fastening, but one requiring skill and tedious labor.)

Inside the frames a watertight inner skin was worked from gunwale to the cabin floor which was also watertight. This was a safety measure in case the outer hull was stove. The deck was two-inch pine.

Note that the redningsskoite's mizzen mast is stepped on her cockpit sole.

The *Gaucho* is built of Argentine woods, lapacho and viraro, both hard, durable, workable, and rot resistant; peteribi, a semi-hard wood; and cancharanda, a type of cedar that is similar to teak.

Her keel is of lapacho, 18 inches by 9 inches. Her frames are double and are of lapacho, 4½ inches by 3½ inches, 24 inches apart. She is planked with 1½-inch lapacho below the waterline and with viraro above the waterline. Her deck is 3-inch by 2-inch peteribi. The house is built of 1¾-inch viraro, tied down with 1¾-inch galvanized bolts.

The *Gaucho*'s mast is a 13-inch hollow spar built of Oregon spruce. Her leg-o'-mutton rig looks quite modest beside the gaff rig on the redningsskoite. Note the exceptionally deep reefs in the redningsskoite's mainsail and staysail. Both vessels would balance well under main and staysail or under staysail and mizzen. The characteristically big staysail and small mizzen of the redningsskoite have

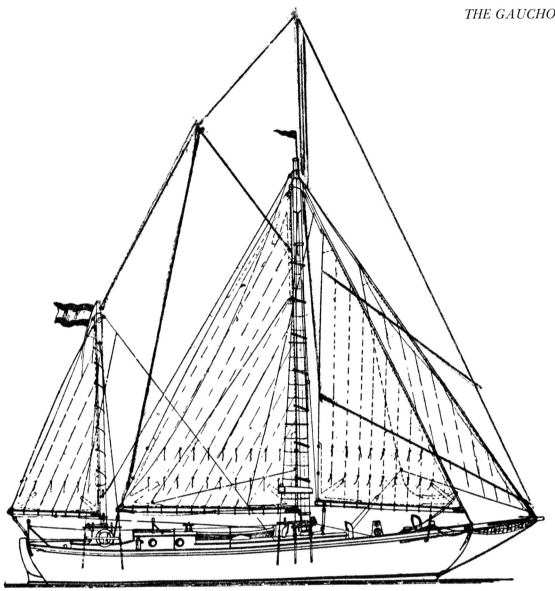

The Gaucho *seems a bit under-rigged, so some years ago I succumbed to giving her a gaff mainsail and a main topmast. (*Seagoing Gaucho *by Ernesto Uriburu)*

been retained in the *Gaucho*'s rig. Note that the redningsskoite's mainsail and mizzen are loosc-footed.

In the belief that the *Gaucho* really didn't have enough sail, I couldn't resist some years ago sketching in a gaff mainsail and adding a topmast with main and jib topsails. I even put in a big jib topsail tacking all the way down to the bowsprit. (I wonder who could have drawn in that vang leading to the mizzen masthead?)

Of course the *Gaucho*'s leg-o'-mutton mainsail would be a fine sail in hard weather. Maybe a good cruising rig would be to borrow the idea of the laced-on bonnet: have a leg-o'-mutton mainsail and then a big triangular bonnet that would lace to its leech and have its peak extended by a gaff. In light or moderate weather, you'd use the sail as a gaff mainsail, and when it breezed on you'd lower away, unlace the bonnet diagonally from throat to clew, take the gaff off the mast, roll the bonnet up on it, and sail her with the leg-o'-mutton mainsail. I suppose if the leg-o'-mutton sail had a normally taut leech, that would make a hard line down the middle of the gaff sail when the bonnet was laced on. It's probably all been tried somewhere in the past. This brainstorming should probably lead us back to the gaff mainsail with deep reefs, which is what the redningsskoite had in the first place. At

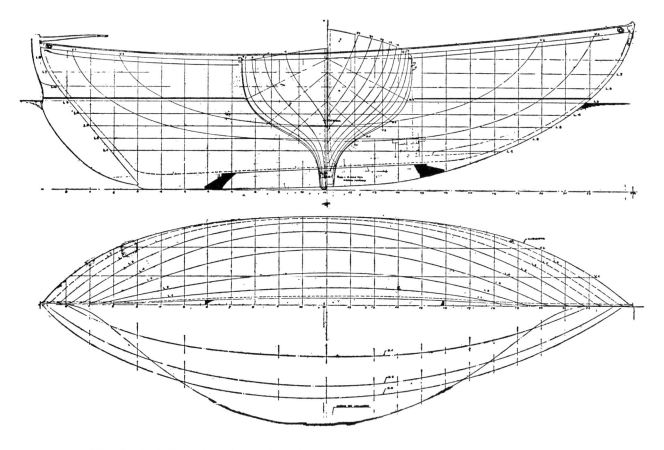

The Gaucho's *lines show her to be a lighter, finer, faster version of her redningsskoite ancestors. (*Seagoing Gaucho *by Ernesto Uriburu)*

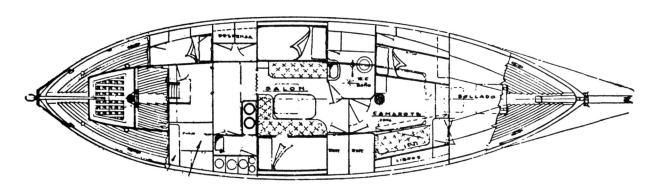

The Gaucho *has plenty of room for four people on a long cruise.* Seagoing Gaucho *by Ernesto Uriburu)*

The Gaucho *hustling along on the wind, with a big jib adding to her somewhat skimpy sail area. (Mario R. Uriburu)*

any rate, if anyone's interested, my gaff rig with topsails increases the *Gaucho*'s working sail area from 969 square feet to 1,521 square feet.

After reading all this palaver in the *National Fisherman* about enlarging the *Gaucho*'s sail area, Bobby Uriburu, Ernesto's brother, wrote me.

"After our first trip we enlarged the mast 10 feet and increased the sail area with big genoas and a big mainsail. With this change of sail area, the

condition of the yacht improved. However, we knew this originally—but with our close friend, Manuel Campos, designer of *Gaucho*, we decided on the smaller sail area for our first trip to assure very comfortable sailing. We were in no hurry—and wanted to stay at sea the longest time possible!"

The *Gaucho*'s power plant is an Ailsa Craig diesel of 30 h.p. that is capable of driving her at 6½ knots. She carries 125 gallons of water and 70 gallons of fuel, though Mr. Uriburu used to carry up to 600 extra gallons of fuel when starting on a long passage.

She has a heavy windlass on the foredeck and carries two 170-pound fisherman anchors and a 110-pound Danforth, along with 400 feet of galvanized, half-inch chain.

The *Gaucho*'s decks are given security by a lifeline three feet high. This ought to be the minimum height for any lifeline if it is to stop you from falling overboard instead of merely turning you upside down as you do so. On the rednings-skoites, they used a stout railing instead of a lifeline. This makes good sense, for it combines the strength and leanability of bulwarks with the openness of lifelines so that water won't be trapped on deck.

The *Gaucho*'s house is narrow, leaving plenty of room to work the vessel. She has a permanent shelter over the forward end of the cockpit just abaft the mizzen mast. This shelter protects the helmsman steering in the cockpit with his long tiller. It might be well to put in a second steering station with a wheel at the after end of the bridge deck, trading the protection of the tiller in the cockpit for the visibility from a wheel up on the bridge deck. The two steering stations would also bring some variety to a long trick at the helm.

Below, the *Gaucho*'s navigator has his own bailiwick aft. I would be tempted to relegate the W.C. to the fo'c's'le and make the space now taken up by the washroom into the best corner of the saloon. The *Gaucho*'s fo'c's'le is used for stowage, but it is plenty big enough for a couple of pipe berths if a big crew were on board.

The *Gaucho* left her marina slip at Washington, D.C., not long after I saw her, and I wondered what ever became of her. Bobby Uriburu supplied the answer:

"With respect to *Gaucho*, you may be interested to know that she is still sailing—but under new owners. We sold *Gaucho* in 1966 to an American engineer from California who sold her some months ago to a yachtsman from South Africa who currently [1976] is sailing her in the southern oceans."

29/ The *Amos Judd*

> Length on deck: 49 feet
> Length on waterline: 42 feet
> Beam: 14 feet
> Draft: 4 feet 8 inches
> Sail area: 1,200 square feet
> Designer: S.S. Crocker, Jr.

The astronomers tell us that there are billions upon billions of "solar systems" in the universe. Some few million planets probably exist that are somewhat similar to our watery one in terms of oceans, gravity, temperature, atmosphere, and chemical make-up. That intelligent life other than *Homo sapiens* (*sapiens?*) exists in the universe scarcely seems arguable any more. In speculating on who else may be around, there are many interesting unknown variables, not the least of which is the level of advancement that "they" may have achieved. Are the other chaps way behind or way ahead of us in their development? If way ahead, what kinds of boats and vessels have they created?

And what are the boats like on a planet where there is neither wind nor wave worth mentioning? Or where a 100-knot breeze is commonplace and 60-foot breaking seas are just average? Where the water is so salty that boats made of lead are regarded as light-displacement freaks? The possibilities for hull shape, construction materials, and method of propulsion are considerable.

How do standards of beauty in boat design differ around the universe?

And what would naval architects from the seas of space think of earth boats? Which would get higher universal marks, one of the Electric Boat Company's nuclear-powered submarines, or one of Henry Vaillancourt's birch bark canoes?

But 'vast heaving and belay all. This is supposed to be down-to-earth coverage of boats, so let's re-enter and take a look at a rugged ketch that is able to sail to any seaport in this particular world.

The *Amos Judd* was designed by S.S. Crocker, Jr. and was built in earth-year 1929 at the yard of W. J. Reid at Winthrop, Massachusetts, for S.K. Dimock of Hartford, Connecticut.

The most noticeable feature of the *Judd* is, of course, her big, square, glass deckhouse. Years ago I would have condemned such a structure out of hand and talked sarcastically about a seagoing greenhouse, but at this point in time I have to admit that the *Judd*'s wheelhouse looks mighty pleasant and comfortable and, while there are certainly a lot of shapes and sizes of deckhouses that would ruin the looks of this ketch, the very boldness of the *Judd*'s house looks fine to my eye.

The *Amos Judd* is clearly a motorsailer, not, of course, because of her big deckhouse, but because she would need her engine ticking over slowly to give her a reasonably good performance to windward under sail. She would sail just fine off the

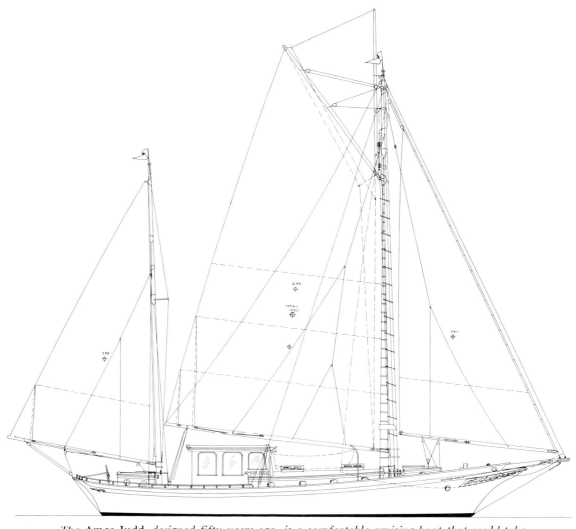

The Amos Judd, *designed fifty years ago, is a comfortable cruising boat that could take her crew to any port on earth. (S. Sturgis Crocker)*

wind, and she has enough sail area so that she'd still be fun to sail in a light breeze, unlike many motorsailers.

I'd be tempted to put in a long, narrow centerboard under the cabin floor to give her a bit more to hang on with when going to windward.

Now right here we have to back the jib, take all way off her, and check our position, because when John T. MacIsaac, Jr. of Marshallberg, North Carolina, who sailed on the *Judd* for four years, read the preceding two paragraphs in the *National Fisherman*, he took pen in hand and wrote me as follows:

> She was *not* a motorsailer; if Sam Crocker could hear that he would take off his pince-nez glasses, clean them, and say, "Aw shit." She was a sailing vessel

period. She had enough power to get home but carried only 120 gallons of fuel. (I have her last log: 'bought 100 gallons of fuel and 10 gallons lube oil $12.50.') She did in fact have an enormous centerboard [So that's where we are. Beautiful.] about 15 feet long and about 3 feet deep. The top of the centerboard trunk was the cabin sole; she drew 8 feet, 6 inches with the board down. The board pennant came up through the main cabin in a brass pipe which took a bit of polishing to keep in shape. The tackle was on top of the cabin and was double so it could be operated from either side.

There. Now that Mr. MacIsaac has kindly told us what's going on around here, we can let draw the jib and go on our merry way again. We'll be calling on him again for more interesting information about our vessel.

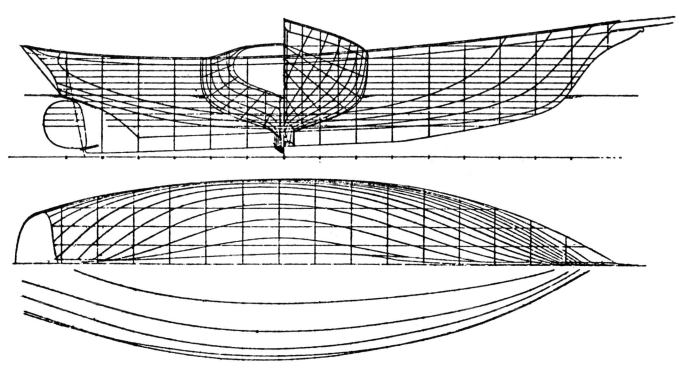

Above: *Though no centerboard appears in her plans, it turns out she had one. (S. Sturgis Crocker)*

Below: *The most popular place in the boat would undoubtedly be that nice big wheelhouse. (S. Sturgis Crocker)*

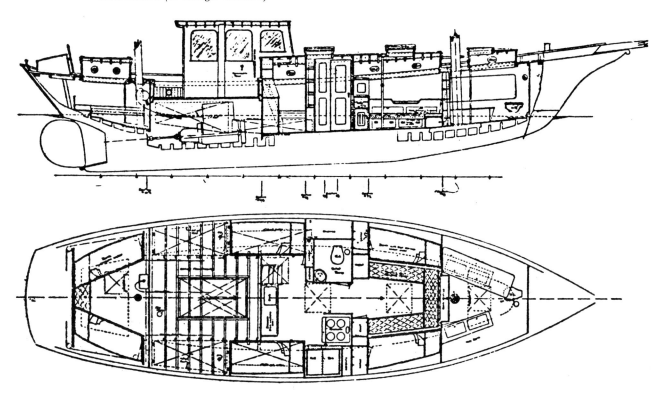

The Judd *stands in for her mooring. (S. Sturgis Crocker)*

When built, the *Judd* had a four-cylinder Cummins diesel that gave her a cruising speed of 8 knots.

The ketch is 49 feet long on deck, with a waterline length of 42 feet, a beam of 14 feet, and a draft of 4 feet 8 inches, with (now I can say) board up.

Her hull is quite flat-floored. She has a hollow entry forward and considerable flare above it; she should be quite dry when punching into a head sea under either sail or power. She has very easy bow and buttock lines, though her run is not quite as long and flat as you might expect in such a shoal-bodied boat. Her rather full quarters make for a roomy after cabin, but would keep her from being as fast a sailer as she might otherwise be.

Note that her rudder is slightly balanced.

There is just a bit of curvature to the transom; it would be worth considering a flat transom on her for simplicity of building.

The *Judd*'s construction is conventional for wooden boats of her size: frames, 2½ inches x 2½ inches of Eastern oak; clamp 1⅞ inches x 6 inches of Oregon or hard pine; shelf 2 inches x 4 inches Oregon or hard pine; bilge stringer 1½ inches x 6 inches; planking 1⅜ inches cedar; ceiling ½-inch pine. Her deck is 1½-inch pine; top of the trunk cabin 1⅛ inches tongue-and-groove pine; and sides and ends of the trunk cabin 1½-inch pine.

The *Judd*'s sail area is 1,200 square feet, with 630 square feet in the mainsail, 322 in the jib, and 248 in the mizzen. You can reef away over half of the mainsail in heavy going. The sail would, of course, be rigged with the usual vang to the mizzen masthead. The big jib is self-tending. She has plenty of lazy jacks and a separate topping lift on the main boom.

You'd probably want a topsail and a big ballooner to play around with on light days.

Mr. MacIsaac:

> She also had an enormous club topsail; the club was about 18 feet long and 4 inches in diameter, which was something to handle in a blow. As a matter of fact I still have a sore spot in my ribs as a result of getting it down when we were caught in a blow in the Moosabec Reach.*
>
> She also had a large jib which we called a "jumbo." This was loose-footed and came aft to just clear the boats on the davits.

The backstays are led far enough forward so they could both be left set up when short tacking. You wouldn't even have to leave the house; just roll her over onto the new tack. But don't forget to stick your nose out occasionally to see how hard it's really blowing.

The ketch would balance nicely under jib and jigger or mainsail alone.

Mr. MacIsaac:

> We never tied in a reef as she was perfectly balanced under main alone or with the main down and the others left standing.

It's nice to see rigging rattled down, and it's practical too. Occasionally you see a schooner with the fore rigging rattled down on one side and the main rigging on the other, but you can't very well go up the lee rigging, so that arrangement limits which mast you can climb on a given tack. That's all right if you just want to go up to take a look around the horizon, but not if you need to get aloft on the other mast for repairs or for reeving off gear. I suppose you can always tack. The practice always makes a schooner look lopsided, though; might as well rattle down everything and be done with it.

When the *Judd* is being steered from the outdoor wheel aft, passengers who want to converse

with the helmsman have a little trunk cabin to sit on. Such conversation is permitted on most yachts except in time of fancy maneuvering, but it should always be understood that the helmsman has the absolute power to interrupt any conversation and gain silence when need be. The windows in the deckhouse are big enough so that the structure wouldn't obstruct vision unduly from the wheel aft.

The house would have to be considered dispensable in terms of the watertight integrity of the deck and companionway, but until it gets washed away by a freak sea, you could enjoy its many comforts. It's high enough to give the woman at the wheel good visibility. Of course, you'd have to climb up on top of it to furl the mainsail, but once you get there, everything is easy to reach.

Why do oval ports in the side of a cabin house always look better to me than round ones? Maybe simply because I was brought up with them? And why (on earth) did Sam Crocker shift to round ones for the little house aft?

You'd want a hatch in the overhead of the deckhouse above the wheel so you could open it up and see the luff of the mainsail, and you'd want a deadlight in the hatch so you could watch the sail rain or shine.

There is room between the house and mainmast for a couple of 12-foot boats, maybe a nice lapstrake sailing dinghy on the starboard side, and a peapod to port. You don't see boat davits much these days, but they make great good sense. You can keep the boats swung out or you can swing them in when circumstances, such as rough water or docking, don't suit their being carried outboard. A well-shaped boat looks especially nice hung on davits where you can really admire her.

Mr. MacIsaac:

> She had davits on both sides; port side a 16-foot dory which had the midship section of a Swampscott dory and the stern of a banks dory. The starboard boat was a 14-foot, round-bottom, clinker-built dinghy. These boats were carried swung out except in bad weather or when coming alongside a dock.

The almost extinct boat boom ought to be rejuvenated too. Why not keep a handsome dinghy out alongside where you can appreciate her (and

---

*By "club," I think Mr. MacIsaac means a spar to extend the head of the topsail above the masthead. That's what I used to call it too, until I was corrected by L. Francis Herreshoff. He called that spar a "yard" and the sail so rigged a "jackyard topsail." If the topsail also had a spar to extend its clew beyond the end of the gaff, he called that a "club" and the sail a "club topsail." Mr. Herreshoff is, of course, right on this, for on all other sails, yards extend heads and clubs extend clews. I'm not trying to nitpick Mr. MacIsaac, the pilot of this chapter, whose local knowledge has already saved us from stranding, but just wanted to mention the point because yards and clubs appear elsewhere in the book.

And she lies quietly, all put away. (S. Sturgis Crocker)

where she will be less vulnerable to collision in today's crowded anchorages)? With the dinghy on a boat boom, she won't go bump in the night when the tide turns. We old folks use a haul-off on the boat boom, but youngsters always seem to prefer to climb out after the boat.

Speaking of admiring dinghies, that's a good reason to tow one occasionally—just to watch her go through the water.

The *Amos Judd* has a big engine room with lots of space around the engine and big hatches in the deckhouse floor to open up to get at things. The engine is low enough so that the shaft is nearly level.

Below, she has a flexible arrangement. Eight people can sleep aboard with reasonable space, and four would have considerable elbow room and privacy.

She has a solid bulkhead right across the boat just abaft the mainmast, giving a separate fo'c's'le and a snug, dead-end saloon with a nice U-shaped settee around the table.

Again, the deckhouse is the unusual and versatile feature of her accommodation. It's a great pleasure to get out of the weather yet be handy to the deck and be able to see almost as well as from an open cockpit. It makes a fine mudroom to keep the wet out of the cabin. And what a luxury it is to be able to keep a chart by the wheel and not have to worry about it blowing overboard.

Now Mr. MacIsaac tells us more about this fine vessel:

The *Amos Judd* was purchased by my uncle Luther W. (Pop) Turner from Mr. Dimock in the fall of 1929. Mr. Dimock took one look at that mainmast and, according to his paid captain, said, "Not for me." So she was sold after being taken from Bill Reid's yard at Winthrop, Massachusetts, to Connecticut for delivery. If I recall correctly the contract price for building her was $21,000 and she was sold for $12,000—this just before the stock market crash. I sailed on her as crew and in the last year as captain from 1929 until the fall of 1933. Coast of Maine, New Brunswick, Nova Scotia, and Newfoundland and Labrador. She was sold in Florida in March of 1937—to whom I do not know.

She was the best sailer I ever saw and would hold her own course for hours. I remember leaving Seguin Island [Maine] for Thatchers Island [Massachusetts] on a close reach and going the whole distance without touching the wheel. She would self-steer on any course if you took the time to trim the sails properly (by hand—no winches).

She was fairly fast; Sam Crocker, Bill Reid, Pop Turner and I raced her in the Jeffries Ledge Race and came in fourth, if I remember correctly. Pop Turner and I raced her in one of the Boston Yacht Club Cruise races and placed second (I sure would like to have the cup to look at).

All in all, I think Sam Crocker's *Amos Judd* makes a fine sailing vessel—at least for this planet. And I do thank John MacIsaac for his expert pilotage.

30/ The *Poseidon*

Length on deck: 42 feet
Length on waterline: 32 feet 8 inches
Beam: 12 feet
Draft: 5 feet 9 inches
Sail area: 754 square feet
Displacement: 11 tons
Designer: Francis E. Fredette

One of the many interesting pieces of mail that has come to us as publishers of the *Mariner's Catalog* series is some correspondence from a college in the northwestern United States that was setting up an experimental program with faculty and students to study the whys and wherefores of commercial fishing under sail. This program didn't come under the history department; these folks wanted to go out and do it today.

One of the things they did, with the help of a naval architect, was to come up with a contemporary design for a small sailing fishing vessel. They sent us study plans of the boat, and we had to laugh. The influence, albeit indirect, of the International Offshore Rule for racing yachts was all too evident.

Here is a design for a 42-foot ketch that might better meet the requirements of that college study project. She was designed to be a combination work and pleasure boat, the idea being that the owner would troll for salmon in summer and sail her south and live on board in winter. Not a bad life, eh what?

The ketch is named the *Poseidon,* after the Greek god of water, earthquakes, and horses. (I thought that an odd combination of responsibilities to assign to a Greek god, too, until I realized that all Poseidon had to master to do his job well was dealing with the unpredictable, perhaps not too tall an order for a Greek god.)

The ketch was designed in 1957 by Francis E. Fredette of Victoria, British Columbia. She was built in Victoria by her owner, Fergus Walker, and was launched in 1959.

She is indeed an able-looking boat. She would not be fast under sail, but would certainly be seakindly and easily handled. She is the kind of boat that might often need a bit of help from her engine to do her work.

The *Poseidon* is 42 feet long on deck, with a waterline length of 32 feet 8 inches, a beam of 12 feet, and a draft of 5 feet 9 inches. She displaces 11 tons. Her sail area is 754 square feet, with 380 square feet in the mainsail, 160 in the mizzen, and 214 in the working jib.

Her power plant is a British diesel, a Parsons Pike of 35 brake horsepower, with 2:1 reduction gear. She cruises under power at 6½ knots.

The ketch's backbone and planking are of fir, and her frames are bent oak.

Her bow is well shaped to deal with a head sea; she has about five feet of freeboard forward. She has fine, high shoulders, a strong sheer, a fairly

Francis E. Fredette. (Bernadette Mertens, National Fisherman)

deep forefoot, and moderate drag to the keel, giving her moderate draft. Her rudder is big and is well aft. Her propeller is well submerged.

Her bilges are firm, but not hard, and she has considerable hollow to her garboards. Her stern sections are flat enough above the waterline to allow her to pick up good bearing aft as she heels. As a matter of fact, she is one of those boats with a bit of flare all around her waterline, so she picks up a little bearing everywhere. That shape also makes a boat look light on her feet.

The *Poseidon*'s ketch rig is well proportioned. She would balance well under mainsail alone or under jib and jigger. There are practical, deep reefs in her mainsail and mizzen, and a small jib is shown.

Whenever I see a pair of headstays meeting at the stemhead, I want to separate them so each can be used for setting a headsail. I think this boat cries out for a bowsprit so that the upper headstay may be taken out to the end of it and then be used to

Mr. Fredette in his sealing boat replica. (Bill Garden wouldn't send me a picture of himself, saying he preferred to stay out of sight, but he kindly provided this photo by Bernadette Mertens of Mr. Fredette.)

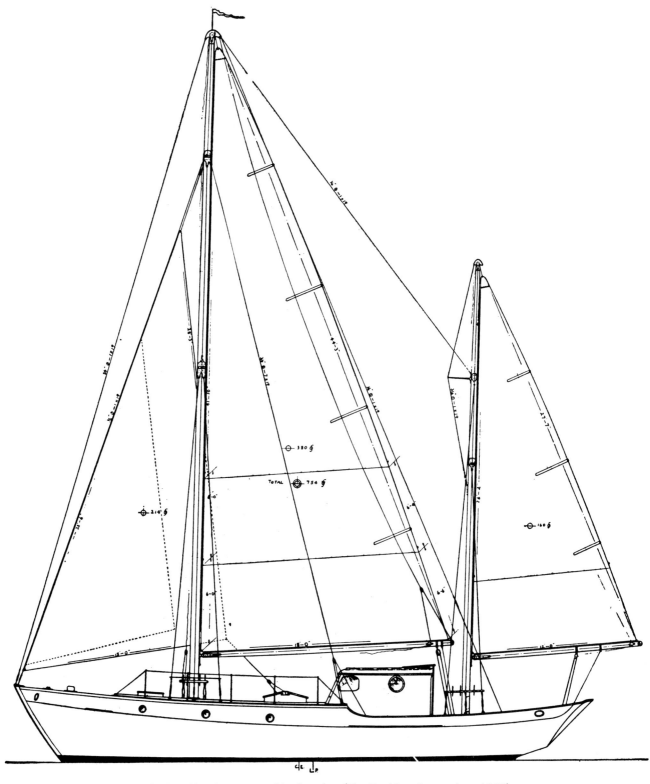

The Poseidon *has a rugged look to her.* (The Rudder, *September, 1959)*

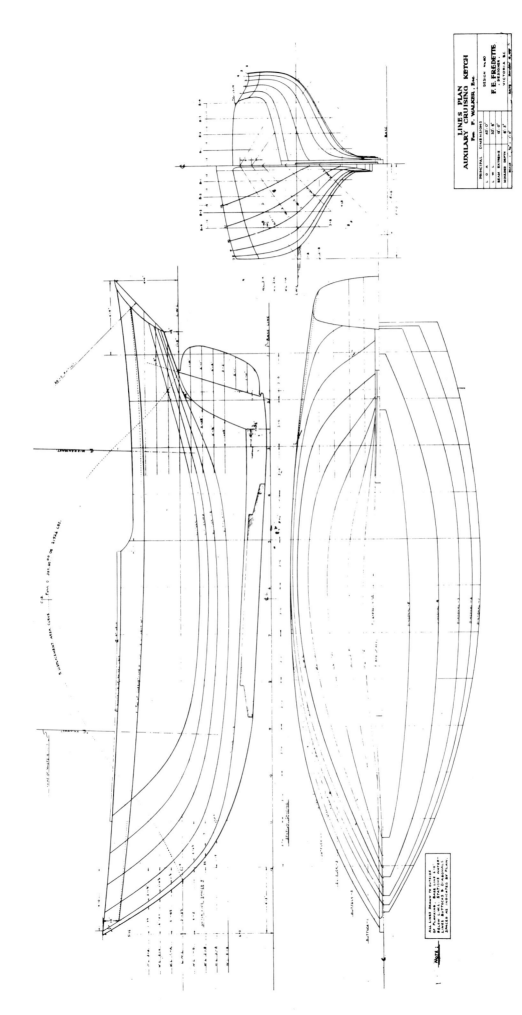

LINES PLAN
AUXILIARY CRUISING KETCH
For F. WALKER, Esq.

DESIGN No.80
F. E. FREDETTE
- DESIGNER -
VICTORIA, B.C.

PRINCIPAL	DIMENSIONS
L. O. A.	42'-0"
L. W. L.	32'-6"
BEAM EXTREME	12'-0"
MOULDED DEPTH	6'-3"
SCALE	½" = 1'-0"

DATE: December 9, 1957

Her lines show a hull that is seakindly, dry, and powerful. (Francis E. Fredette)

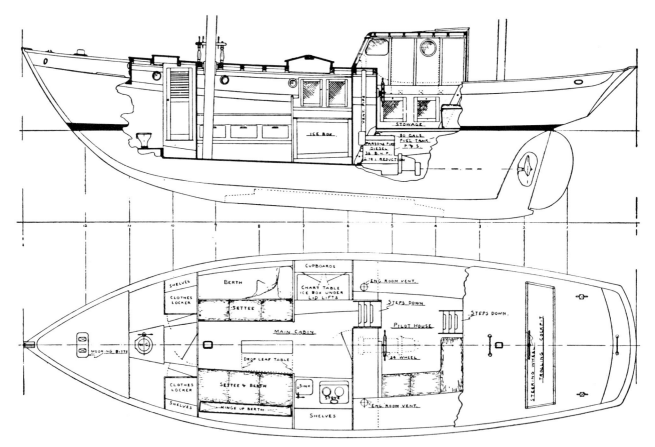

*Two people could live in her quite comfortably. (*The Rudder, September, 1959*)*

carry a big, light, reaching jib. She might also have a big jib for the lower headstay that would overlap the mainsail considerably to add area for working to windward in light and moderate weather and to pole out as a running sail. Such a sail ought to be high-cut along the foot, though, so as not to present the helmsman with a large blind spot on his lee bow.

I suppose you'd want to carry a mizzen staysail in the sail locker, though such a sail seems seldom to be really useful. And you'd probably want twin running headsails for any serious ocean work.

Her raised deck gives the *Poseidon* strength and dryness on deck and looks good, being nicely balanced by the deckhouse. Either the raised deck or the house could be an ugly feature of this design by itself, but taken together, they work out all right to my eye. I do wish, though, that the designer had made up his mind about a pilothouse window shape and then had stuck with it. I think a row of four windows on each side with the forward ones as shown and the after three being rectangles

with rounded corners would have improved the general appearance of the boat considerably.

She has a well deck forward, but I would still continue the lifelines to a bow pulpit at the stem or on the bowsprit end if a bowsprit were added. And why not run the lifelines aft to the stern as well, or at least to the mizzen rigging?

There is room to stow a nine-foot dinghy on the raised deck over the skylight between the mast and the house, though she'd interfere some with visibility from the wheelhouse.

The wide trolling cockpit gets you out to the sides of the vessel where you can see around the house or work overboard. She has a wheel amidships in this cockpit. What about a wheel at each end of it, so you could steer from right out at the side of the boat?

She has plenty of places for people aft. There is the trolling cockpit, the nicely raked transom for a backrest, and even the perfect place for a chair on deck on the port side up against the after end of the pilothouse.

I think it would make sense from a safety standpoint to consider the *Poseidon*'s wheelhouse to be dispensable. Raise the floor slightly, and make the enclosure into a self-draining, watertight cockpit that just happens to have a house built around it for shelter. Then if that house should be washed away by a freak sea, you'd still have a watertight cockpit. The wheelhouse is a most worthwhile addition to the vessel, however, for it would be a tremendous comfort in bad weather.

The engine was installed farther aft than it is shown in the inboard profile plan, being shoved all the way back under the wheelhouse floor. I prefer the design shown, for an area of full headroom in the engine room is not a luxury to be discarded lightly in return for mere cabin space. There are two 80-gallon fuel tanks in the engine room wings.

She has both a wide and a narrow settee in the saloon and both a built-in and a hinged berth above them. This arrangement gives a lot of versatility for sitting down, lying around, or sleeping. She has a head and a couple of big clothes lockers in the forepeak, just where they should be.

A second craft was built to this design, the *Roebuck Bay*. She was built in Australia of hardwood and is now owned in Victoria by a man who has done extensive ocean cruising in her and likes her very much.

The *Poseidon* was not so fortunate. On a cruise in the Caribbean, she was run down at sea by a freighter and lost. But for anyone who wants a handy little vessel for fishing, cruising, or as a home afloat, whether he is studying in or out of college, this design is well worth considering.

31/ A Bugeye by Rhodes

> Length on deck: 55 feet
> Length on waterline: 45 feet
> Beam: 16 feet
> Draft: 4 feet
> Sail area: 1,335 square feet
> Designer: Philip L. Rhodes

Chesapeake Bay watermen developed the bugeye for and with their oyster industry as a dredgeboat. The craft was long, low, and shoal, usually had a pointed stern, and usually had a two-masted, leg-o'-mutton rig with a single large headsail set on a bowsprit of moderate length. As in other craft of the Chesapeake Bay, the masts were well raked and the longhead at the stem had a nicely shaped concave profile.

The hull was constructed of big, shaped logs laid longitudinally and pinned together athwartships.

The bugeye was the last generation in a distinguished family that began with the log canoe; grew in size to the coasting canoe; developed to the still bigger, decked brogan; and finally came forth in its own typical length of 50 to 60 feet.

The bugeye generation of the family came into being as a distinct type soon after the Civil War ended and the oyster business boomed again on the Bay. Two major changes in the industry, as well as its general success, caused the watermen to go to bigger boats. Oyster beds in shallow water had been pretty well tonged out, rich beds in deeper water had been discovered, the dredge had been developed to take the oysters from the deeper beds, and now, with a heavy demand for the succulent shellfish, dredging was again legalized on

the Bay despite some fears that the method was so efficient it would deplete the beds permanently. The change from tonging to dredging required more sail area to tow the dredge, and so, of course, a bigger boat.

The second change was the development of big packing centers to serve the new, hungry, more widespread market. It was more profitable to haul a large catch directly to these packers than it was to sell it to the buy-boat middle man or try to sell in local villages. Carrying the catch to a relatively distant market also meant a larger boat was needed.

Though the bugeye's direct family lineage is straightforward, the cousinly characteristics she borrowed from other Bay craft made her heritage a bit more complex. Marion V. Brewington wrote: "If any watercraft can be said to be a hybrid, taking from many other types features best adapted to its own specific use, it is the bugeye. From the canoe came the principal elements: the basic design, the dugout log hull, and the sail plan; all admirably developed for economy, durability, and ease of handling with a minimum of trained hands. From the pungy came the combination knight-heads and hawse-pieces, the sweeping sheer, the low freeboard, and the log rail which allowed the

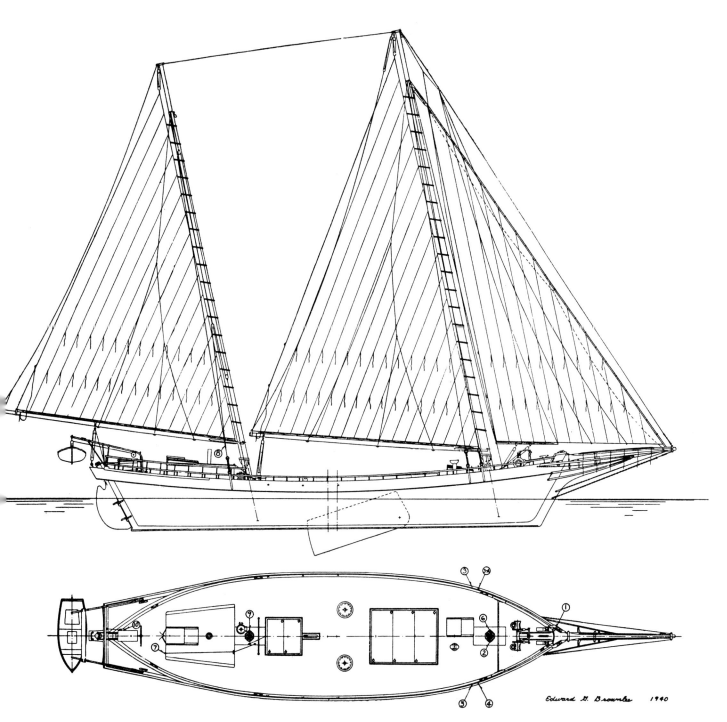

The Lizzie J. Cox *represents the full development of the bugeye type. She was built by John Branford at Fishing Island, Maryland, in 1905. (Drawing by Edward G. Brownlee,* Chesapeake Bay Log Canoes and Bugeyes *by M. V. Brewington, Cornell Maritime Press, Centreville, Maryland)*

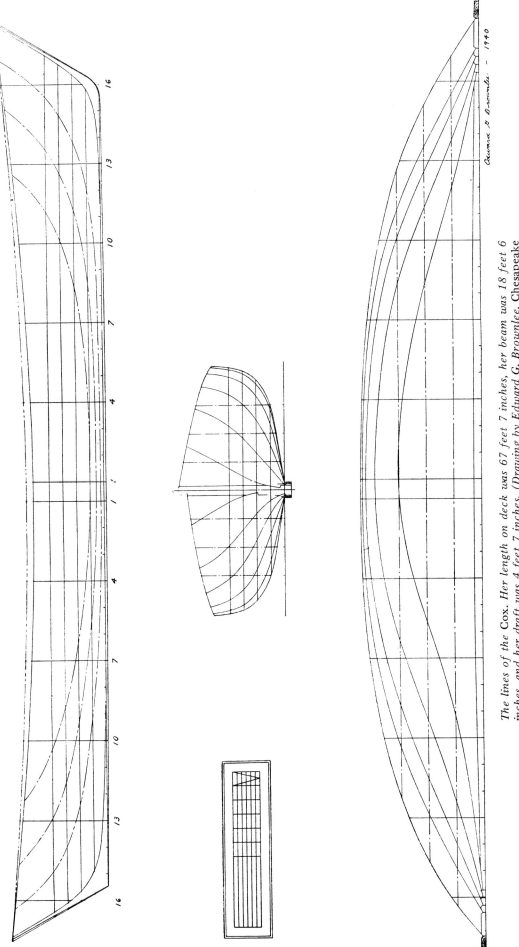

The lines of the Cox. Her length on deck was 67 feet 7 inches, her beam was 18 feet 6 inches, and her draft was 4 feet 7 inches. (Drawing by Edward G. Brownlee, Chesapeake Bay Log Canoes and Bugeyes by M. V. Brewington, Cornell Maritime Press, Centreville, Maryland)

Edward G Brownlee — 1940

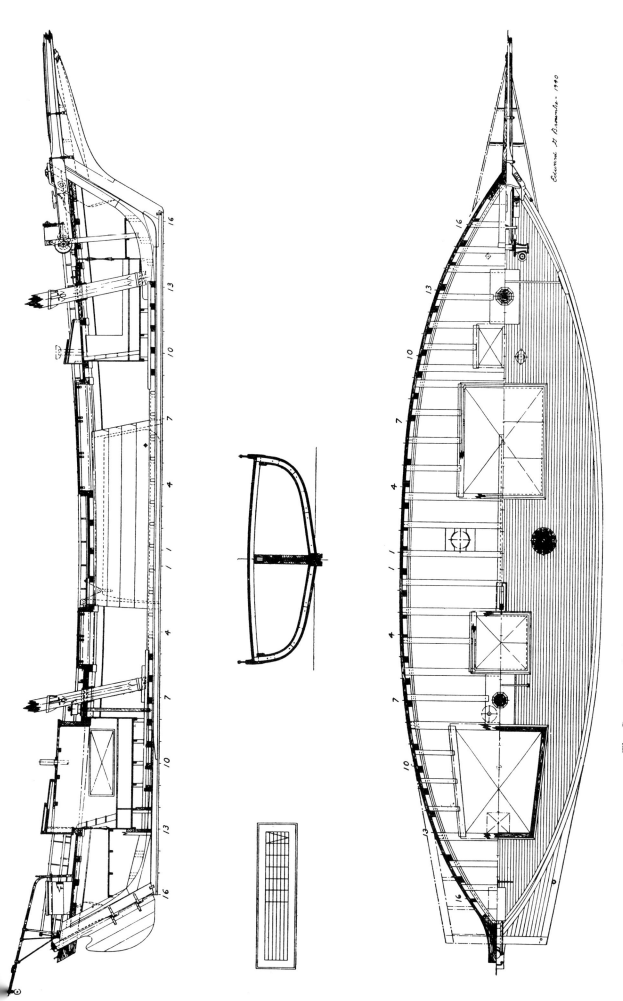

The Cox was a plank-and-frame bugeye. Her deck plan shows the planked-out platform at the stern to support the pushboat davits and gain deck space, but the Cox's owner probably escaped paying a royalty to the inventor of this structure for the stern was not patented until 1908. (Drawing by Edward G. Brownlee, Chesapeake Bay Log Canoes and Bugeyes by M. V. Brewington, Cornell Maritime Press, Centreville, Maryland)

oyster dredge to be hoisted on deck easily and quickly. From the Bay schooner came the shoal draft, the broad beam, the unobstructed deck layout, and the graceful longhead with its decorated trail-boards."

No one really knows why the bugeye was called the bugeye. When the name was first used (1878), it was buckeye, but apparently was pronounced bugeye and was later so spelled. Many have been the explanations for the appellation, some serious and some hilarious. The theory that strikes me as being the most plausible is the one that has Scottish immigrants to the Bay conferring the name buckeye to the new, big dredgeboats either from Buckie, their east coast fishing port, or from the same word which means oyster shell in Scottish, or from both.

Most of the bugeyes were built on the Bay between 1880 and 1900. The biggest one built was 85 feet long, the *A. Von Nyvenheim,* put overboard in 1906.

When big logs became scarce, some bugeyes were built with a log bottom but with planked-up topsides. Later plank-and-frame bugeyes were built.

Though the after mast was always a bit shorter than the forward one, the two masts were always called foremast and mainmast, not main and mizzen.

One of the drawbacks to the design was the lack of deck space aft allowed by the pointed stern. Some round-sterned bugeyes were built to solve the problem, but most watermen felt the extra expense was not justified. In 1908, Captain Joseph E. Robbins came up with his patent stern, which was simply a platform built out over the water at the deck level to square off the stern in plan view to gain deck space and provide support for stern davits to carry a pushboat. Captain Robbins' royalty each time one of his sterns was installed on a bugeye was 25 dollars.

The bugeyes suited their purpose admirably, working the oyster bars of the Bay throughout the winter dredging season with a small crew. They also served well as freighters in a time when remote waterways were a boon, not a barrier, to transportation.

As oyster dredgeboats, the bugeyes lost their place of pre-eminence to the V-bottomed skipjacks soon after the turn of the century. The skipjacks were cheaper to build with available materials. There is still a handful of them dredging under sail on the Bay.

But the bugeyes lasted quite a while. Bob Burgess wrote that in 1925 there were still 125 bugeyes working on the Bay under sail. Of course when engines came along, many bugeyes were converted to power vessels. A pilothouse would be installed aft, the mainmast and bowsprit would be removed, and, gradually, the foremast would be shortened so that it no longer could carry even an auxiliary sail, but merely a boom for working cargo.

There was a bugeye in Annapolis up into the 1960s that served a useful purpose even though she was no longer fit to leave the harbor. This was the *Anna Florence,* built in 1918. She stayed tied up at her appointed place in the city slip and served as a buy boat. The skipjacks would bring in their 100 bushels, unload them onto the decrepit deck of the *Anna Florence,* get their cash money, and depart for their berths 50 feet away. The oysters would then be transferred into a waiting truck backed up to the other side of the *Florence.* I never did discover the economics of the situation, but presumably the old bugeye was still earning a dollar for somebody.

The last few working bugeyes still dredged under sail up into the 1960s. The *Edna E. Lockwood* is preserved at the Chesapeake Bay Maritime Museum at St. Michaels and still goes sailing during the summer.

The best history and description of bugeyes is to be found in *Chesapeake Bay Log Canoes and Bugeyes* by Marion V. Brewington. The best collection of bugeye photos in a book is in *Chesapeake Sailing Craft, Part I,* by Robert H. Burgess.

A handful of bugeyes were converted to yachts, among them the *Dorothy A. Parsons.* She was built in 1901 and was converted about 1940. She was given to the Mystic Seaport and then transferred to the Harry Lundeberg School at Piney Point, Maryland, where she is preserved today.

As is the case with most American working craft, bugeyes have been copied by yacht designers in recognition of the value of considerable development of a craft to do a job of work on the water in any reasonable weather. Naturally, modifications creep in, and the trick is to prevent the modifica-

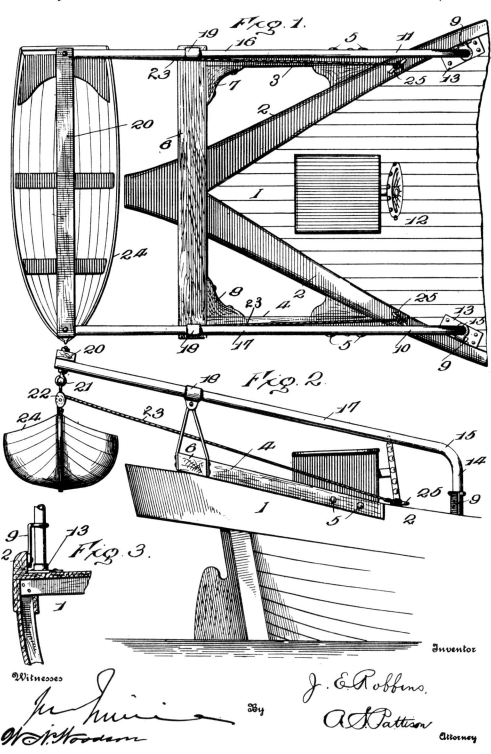

J. E. ROBBINS.
DAVIT SUPPORTING MEANS FOR SHARP STERN BOATS.
APPLICATION FILED FEB. 10, 1908.

902,452.

Patented Oct. 27, 1908.

The original patent drawing for Captain Robbins' patent stern. (Chesapeake Bay Log Canoes and Bugeyes *by M. V. Brewington, Cornell Maritime Press, Centreville, Maryland*)

The Cox's *patent stern as built. This photograph was taken in 1935 by Bob Burgess.*
(Chesapeake Sailing Craft, Part I, *by Robert H. Burgess, Cornell Maritime Press,*
Centreville, Maryland)

tions from destroying the valuable characteristics of the original craft being copied. I think Philip L. Rhodes accomplished this with his design for a 55-foot bugeye yacht, the best such design I know of.

This boat was built for F.H. Reagan of Baltimore in 1929 by M.M. Davis and Sons at Solomons, Maryland. Her length on the waterline is 45 feet; her beam, 16 feet; and her draft, 4 feet. Her sail area is 1,335 square feet.

It is interesting to compare the lines of the Rhodes bugeye with those of a working plank-and-frame bugeye, for example the *Lizzie J. Cox,* a 68-footer built by John Branford at Fishing Island, Maryland, in 1905. Of course the Rhodes bugeye is more akin to the round-sterned type, and, in fact, has been given a handsome counter and transom.

The Rhodes design has harder bilges, but less flare in the topsides, and has considerably greater freeboard, since, for her intended use, standing

upright below is more important than easing the task of bending over a heavy dredge to help the winder pry it up on deck. Neither vessel is overly stiff, yet neither needs to be driven hard to go fast.

Both craft have a fine, hollow entry. The counter stern gives the Rhodes bugeye a longer, flatter run.

The *Cox* has a straight stem, her curved longhead giving a nice shape to the bow profile; the Rhodes design has a well-formed clipper bow further enhanced by the traditional longhead and trailboards.

The Rhodes boat was heavily built for a yacht, but not as heavily built as a working bugeye.

As can be seen in the sail plan of the *Lizzie J. Cox,* the working bugeyes carried a bit more sail than Phil Rhodes gave to his design, for the *Cox* has a slightly longer bowsprit and her main boom overhangs the stern by upwards of 15 feet. The Rhodes design takes the bugeye rig toward the

The Cox *leaving Baltimore in July, 1933, with the help of her pushboat. She has discharged a cargo of wheat and is heading home for Cambridge. Photo by Bob Burgess.* (Chesapeake Sailing Craft, Part I, *by Robert H. Burgess, Cornell Maritime Press, Centreville, Maryland)*

conventional ketch with the after leg-o'-mutton sail being considerably smaller than the forward one. And both are small in relation to the jib, by comparison with the sails on the working bugeye. These changes give the Rhodes bugeye the ketch's ability to balance under jib and mizzen or mainsail alone. All this would have been heresy, of course, to the Bay waterman, who needed his big leg-o'-mutton sails to tow dredges in moderate weather and who, when it breezed on, reefed his sails with as much consternation as he tied his shoes.

All the wasted space between the leg-o'-mutton sails of a bugeye draws the attention of the man at the wheel, and sooner or later he begins devising ways to fill it with something that will pull in light going. The Bay watermen used to set a sail shaped like a schooner's fisherman staysail between their masts, with a short luff tied off to a couple of mast hoops on the foresail, the head of the thing hoisted to the main truck, with the sheet taken to the stern. They also occasionally put out a jib boom and set a flying jib on it, much as Joshua Slocum did on the *Spray.*

The Rhodes bugeye could also set such kites, or she could stick with the more conventional mizzen staysail and overlapping jib. In any case, she adheres to bugeye tradition by having deep reefs and lazy jacks all around, both most useful appurtenances.

At anchor in the Rhodes bugeye, you could leave her mizzen set on a moderate afternoon to keep her from sailing around her anchor too much. And on a wet day the mizzen boom would make a good ridgepole for a big tarp over the cockpit.

This boat's cockpit is about 14 feet long by about 10 feet wide at its forward end. It's a real outdoor palace! The cockpit is self-draining and has a big hatch for access to the engine, which can

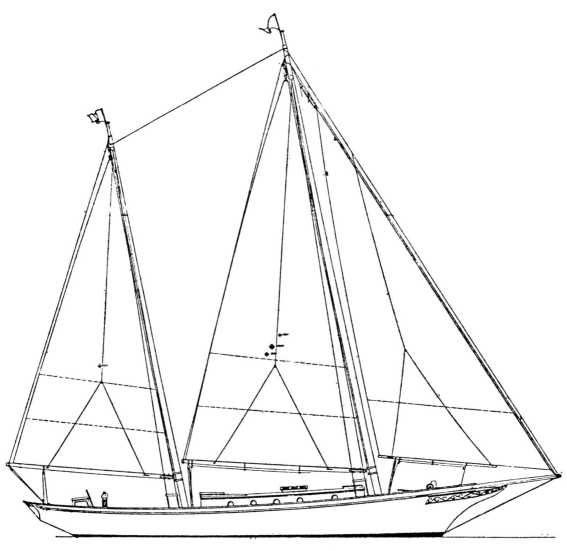

*Phil Rhodes designed this shoal-draft ketch
along the lines of a Chesapeake Bay bugeye
in 1929. (*The Rudder, *1929)*

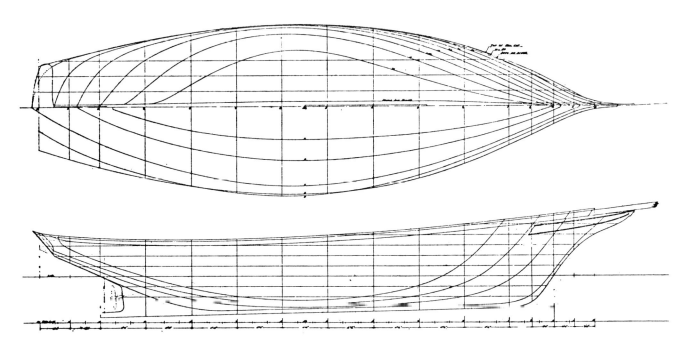

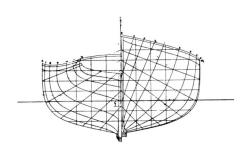

Once her big centerboard has been raised, the Rhodes bugeye draws but four feet on a waterline length of 45 feet. She has 6½ feet of headroom throughout most of her spacious layout. (The Rudder, *1929*)

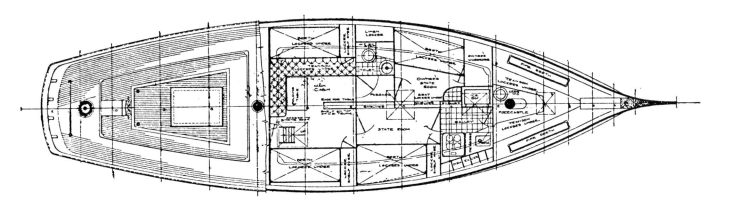

also be reached through a door behind the companion ladder. The machine is a 40-horsepower Lathrop.

She has a big saloon, and with her relatively high freeboard for a bugeye you get 6 feet 6 inches headroom under the house.

One drawback to her layout seems to be that the starboard stateroom also serves as a passageway between the saloon and the galley. Maybe the positions of this stateroom and the galley should be reversed. Or, if you didn't need the sixth bunk, that stateroom could be converted to a wardroom for eating, leaving the saloon clear of dirty plates. What a luxury to be able to eat without having to clear the chart off the table!

All in all, the bugeye is an interesting type for coastwise cruising, combining, as she does, ability, speed, ease of handling, and shoal draft. Phil Rhodes retained these characteristics in his design, added spacious accommodations for up to six people, and turned out a handsome vessel indeed.

32/ The Lemster-aakjacht

Length on deck: 45 feet
Length on waterline: 41 feet 4 inches
Beam: 15 feet 4 inches
Draft: 2 feet 8 inches
Sail area: 1,211 square feet
Designer: H. Kersken

The Dutch have for centuries enjoyed a most extensive system of protected waters, though in recent years they have been trading in large chunks of these admirable inland seas for mere land. They developed fine distinctive craft for their "zees" and estuaries, and, occasionally, one of these bluff-bowed Dutch vessels turns up in American waters, where it finds itself right at home on our bays, sounds, and rivers. Perhaps some of these Dutch vessels have even sailed on some of our large lakes, where they would be entirely suitable craft.

These Hollanders are heavy, shoal-draft boats designed for carrying bulky, heavy loads and for coping with short, steep seas. Much attention has been paid to the aesthetic side of these vessels, and the well-designed ones are handsome indeed, with their constantly changing curves everywhere.

This example of Dutch boat design is a Lemster-aakjacht. It is perhaps easiest to translate the term from aft forward. The "jacht" part obviously designates her as a boat used to give pleasure. (The Dutch, being an eminently sensible people, early gave themselves up to the pleasures of going to sea and gave us our word for that particular activity.) The "aak" means that the boat was developed from a fishing craft. "Lemster" means she was built at Lemmer, on the former Zuider Zee.

This Lemster-aakjacht is 45 feet long on deck, with a waterline length of 41 feet 4 inches, a beam of 15 feet 4 inches, and a draft of 2 feet 8 inches. Her sail area is 1,211 square feet.

She was designed some 70 years ago by Mr. H. Kersken of Amsterdam. This prolific naval architect was still designing boats for his country's sailors in 1963, at the age of 80. Mr. Kersken's more recent designs, based on the traditional Dutch types, may be seen and studied in his book, *Dutch Yachts in the Future,* published in Holland in 1963. None of the aakjacht or aakschip designs that appear in that book are as handsome, however, in my opinion, as this much older design from Mr. Kersken's board. For one thing, the run has been spoiled in many of the newer designs in order to make room for an engine under the cockpit.

The aakjacht, it seems to me, would make a most admirable houseboat. She has space and grace, two desirable attributes in any house, and could provide an all-around decent performance under sail, provided the owner of the house remembers that his craft was meant to travel in waters separated from the open sea by at least a sandspit. No one would accuse these craft of real speed, but they would be a bit faster than their design at first would indicate.

Shoal-draft burdensome vessels have a long tradition in Holland. This is a sketch of a model of the paviljoen-pom Prince of Orange *dating from 1784. (*Fore and Aft Craft and Their Story *by E. Keble Chatterton)*

The Dutch vessels are also designed with ease of handling in mind, meaning, among other things, that you could leave the helm lashed for a walk forward or a duck below without the vessel flying into a rage to get attention.

She has no engine, for everything about her seems in harmony with nature. She is designed to travel with wind and tide and in thin waters if need be. A man might learn patience in such a vessel.

As these Dutchmen march along, they always make a great fuss at the bow. She will look as if she is pushing half the ocean ahead of her, which makes her appear to be traveling faster than she really is. On the other hand, the wave-making characteristics of these craft shouldn't delude us into thinking they can't get out of their own way. They are designed to lift to a head sea and crash through its top, rather than slice through its body. Of course the huge bow wave is fun to watch and adds to the excitement. (I think one of Phil Bolger's cleverest designs is the one for a small sailing boat for a tiny pond. He designed her to make a great roaring bow wave as she struggled across her tiny dominion. That feature enlarged her

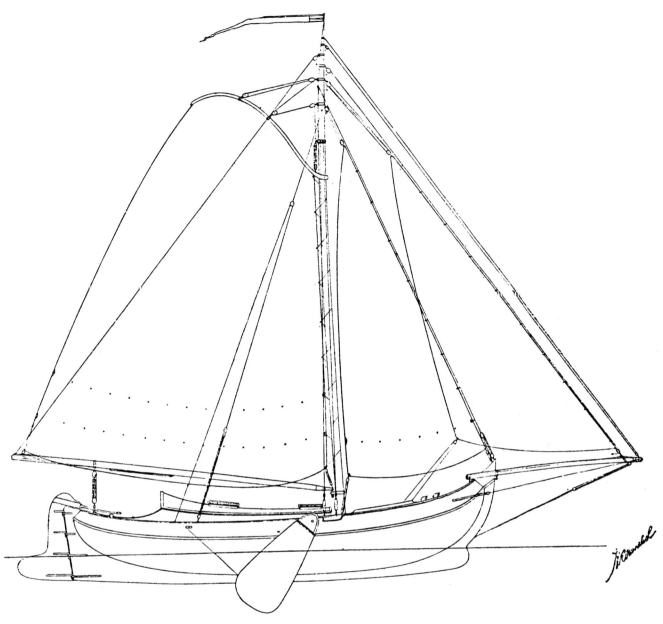

A fairly generous rig is necessary to drive the Lemster-aakjacht's heavy hull. (The Rudder)

skipper's watery world as surely as if he had scoured out extra acres of land for his pond to run into.)

The aakjacht has considerable stiffness due to her flare all around and the considerable beam carried well out into her ends. She also has considerable tendency to roll in a seaway due to her relatively slack bilges and oval sections. We once watched one of these craft tie up in Annapolis, Maryland, after a run across from Bermuda. The delivery crew was mighty impressed with the way she had rolled out in the ocean, and they explained that the reason they were about to have lunch off paper plates was that all the crockery was smashed to bits. I guess these vessels are reasonably safe at sea as long as you keep a good grip on something.

No one could quarrel with the admirable run on this vessel, an intrinsic advantage of this type of shoal hull. Her barn door rudder is somewhat reminiscent of that to be found on some American

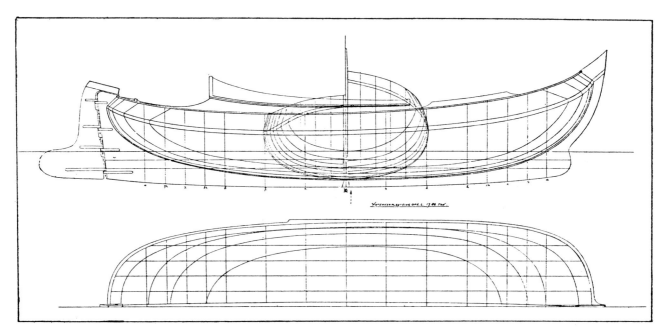

Her lines show a curvaceous barge-like hull, designed to smash over the tops of the waves, rather than slice through them. (The Rudder)

She has plenty of room below—enough to make her an admirable sailing houseboat. (The Rudder)

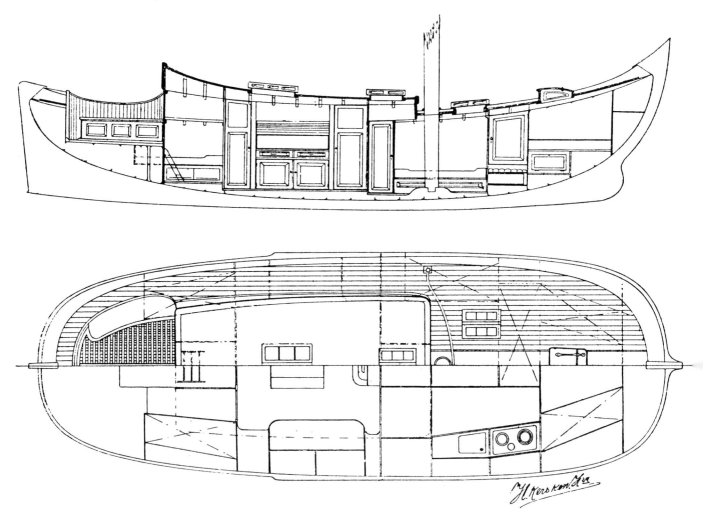

*An aakjacht pushing up a nice bow wave. (*The Rudder*)*

catboats, but it is shoaled up, trading somewhat reduced steering control for protection when the vessel takes the ground. The protrusion of the forefoot is to keep the high, shoal bow from blowing off. The Dutch call this "bow skeg" the "loefbijter," which translates literally into the delightful term "windward biter," so I am informed kindly by Mr. H.M. Kolstee. This "loefbijter," keel, and skeg aft are all fairly generous for increased lateral resistance, yet the draft is kept

very moderate indeed. Of course it is the leeboards that keep her from sliding off too much when working to windward.

The boat is built of one-quarter-inch steel plate. Her leeboards and rudder are of stout oak. The leeboards would not be troublesome to handle (generally there is a winch to wind them up), but they do give you one more thing to do when tacking.

The rig is fairly generous, as it must be to drive

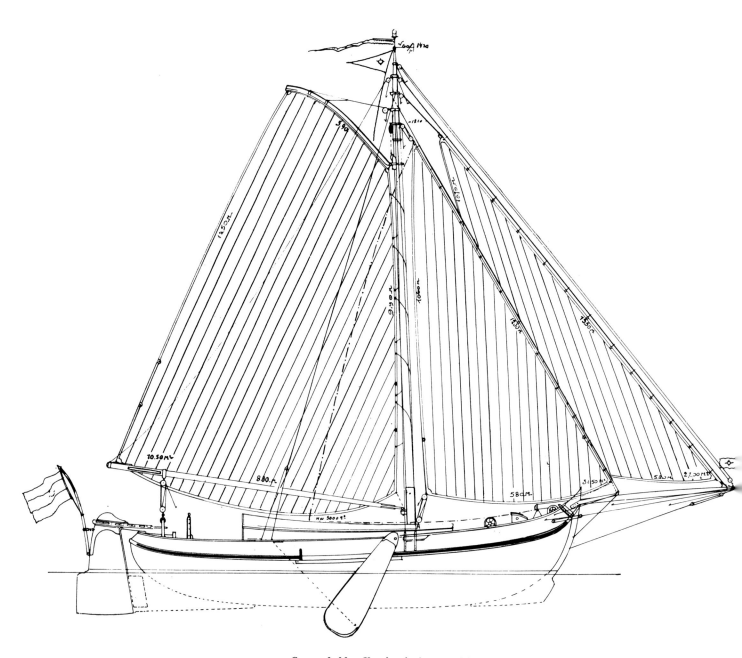

One of Mr. Kersken's later aakjacht designs. Her sail area is 1,360 square feet. Note the staysail set to its own boomkin. (Dutch Yachts in the Future by H. Kersken)

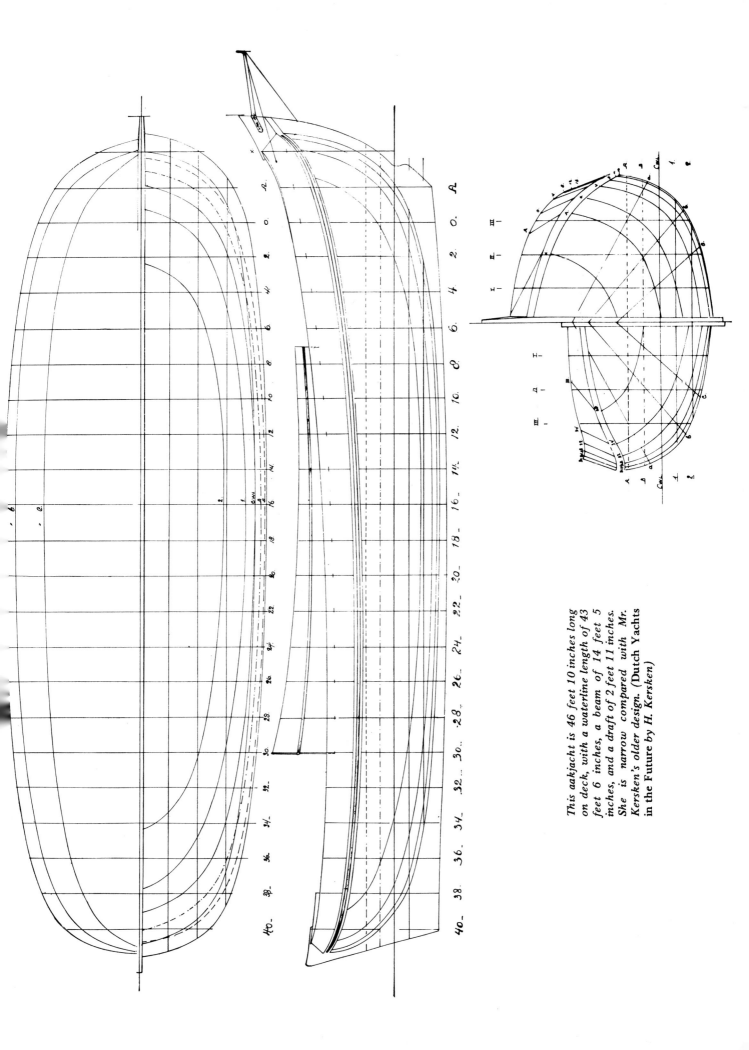

This aakjacht is 46 feet 10 inches long on deck, with a waterline length of 43 feet 6 inches, a beam of 14 feet 5 inches, and a draft of 2 feet 11 inches. She is narrow compared with Mr. Kersken's older design. (Dutch Yachts in the Future by H. Kersken)

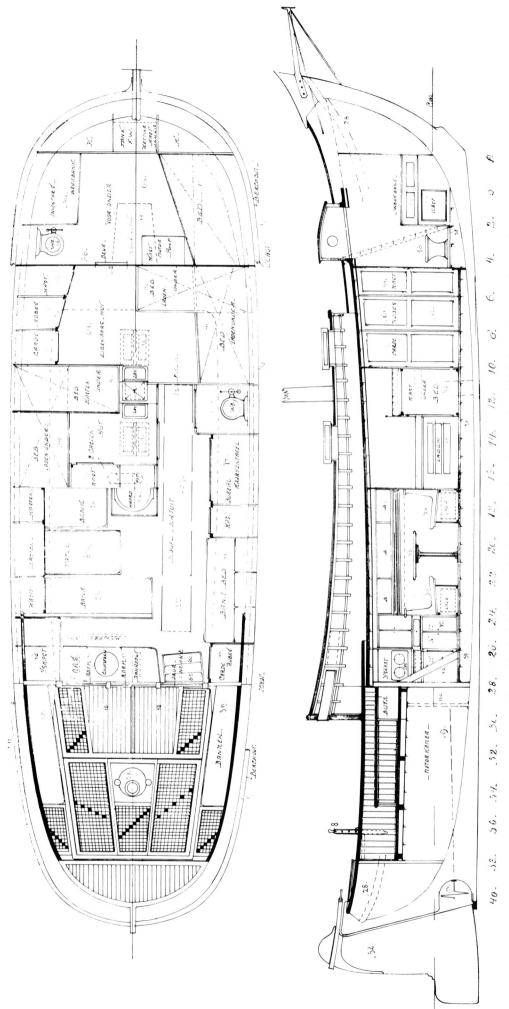

The aakjacht is laid out with her galley aft and two pairs of high-low, criss-crossing bunks.
(Dutch Yachts in the Future by H. Kersken)

An aakjacht smashing her way through the crest of a head sea.

her heavy hull. All the sails are loose-footed for ease of reefing and so that their draft may be controlled. Cutting the mainsail to set well to the shape of the curved gaff must be an art in itself. The sails were all cut on the full side; these boats are not close-winded. Note that the mainsail is laced to the mast.

All the head rigging on the aakjacht is adjustable with tackles so that the bowsprit, with its short "bury" on the stemhead, can be put where you want it. The forestay sets up on the stem with its own tackle. The jib has its own stay leading over a block near the masthead. (I was disappointed not to see a jib downhaul led aft to the stern to bear out the old adage: "Different nations, different customs, as the Dutchman said when he went aft to haul down the jib.") The headstay is, in effect, a long tackle, with its blocks widely separated at the masthead and bowsprit end.

One might ask why the upper blocks for the running backstays are so far aloft.

The long masthead fly looks good on this—or any—traditional vessel.

On deck, she has a long, curved horse for the foresheet. The curving bulwarks, with their marked tumblehome, would give a nice sense of security on deck. And the curving sheer to the top of the house is a joy to behold.

She has a big, deep, protected cockpit. These craft are nearly always steered with heavy tillers, and often the tiller and rudderhead are used as opportunities for considerable ornamentation.

Below, the aakjacht has plenty of space. There are two double and two single staterooms. Presumably the head might go in the compartment just abaft the galley on the starboard side.

But the really glorious thing about living in this aakjacht would be the enjoyment of her palatial saloon. There is a nice fireplace on the forward bulkhead, and of course it would have blue and white tiles, perhaps showing a variety of Dutch craft. There could be a boeier, a botter, a hoogaars, a pluut, a punter, and a tjalk, for instance.

To put a well-known American epithet into Hollandaise, "Who wouldn't sell his plot of reclaimed land, and move afloat?"

33/ A British Centerboard Cruiser

> Length on deck: 18 feet
> Length on waterline: 17 feet
> Beam: 7 feet
> Draft: 1 foot 8 inches
> Sail area: 200 square feet
> Designer: E.A. Stowe

The southern New England coast used to abound with small, wooden, centerboard daysailers. These were generally fairly heavily built, carvel-planked, half-decked boats. They had rounded stems and rounded bilges, flat floors, and broad, raking transoms. The rig was that of a leg-o'-mutton sloop, with a low aspect ratio.

Many of these boats belonged to one-design racing classes (such as the 15-foot Cape Cod Nimblets or the 18-foot Alden O boats), but most of them sailed fewer miles in pursuit of racing trophies than they did seeking other less competitive objectives. We used to race one of the 15-footers on a long salt pond just behind the beach, but then we moved her over to the river where she was put to all kinds of uses, including sailing people and gear back and forth across the flats to and from our little cruising yawl moored at some distance in a deep corner of the channel.

You don't see many of these serviceable knockabouts around today. I suppose they have been replaced by a combination of Boston Whalers and Lasers in the great search for speed. Well, there is no denying that it's fun to go fast on the water, but speed afloat is a funny thing. High speed can shrink an interesting bay, transforming it into a

boring puddle. On the other hand, a boat that averages a speed of three or four knots can be mighty exciting when she occasionally gives you six, seven, or even—momentarily—eight! I remember becoming extremely agitated the first time our 15-footer accidentally got up onto a plane. Doubtless your Whaler or Laser skipper would have been yawning.

At any rate, all those knockabouts were useful boats, and perhaps some of them deserve to be reincarnated. For instance, suppose an Alden O boat were reborn in Britain as the same basic daysailer, but with the added mission of cruising rather than racing. In the process, she might get a plumb bow, a gunter rig with a little bowsprit, and a small cabin house; of course she would be clinker built.

Now we just happen to have—by the merest coincidence, you understand—a design that is quite suggestive of such a transatlantic knockabout reincarnation. The boat was designed 70 years ago by one E. A. Stowe, of Messrs. Stowe & Son, for one J. J. Waddell. She was to cruise in Dublin Bay and was built specifically to be able to take the ground at her mooring every tide.

The sloop is 18 feet long on deck, with a

*This little centerboard cruiser of 70 years ago could be considered an Anglicized version of the little, open knockabouts once so popular along the southern shores of New England. (*The Yachting and Boating Monthly, *December, 1909)*

waterline length of 17 feet, a beam of 7 feet, and a draft of 1 foot 8 inches. Her sail area is 200 square feet.

She has, in my opinion, a very handsome profile. This type of hull can't stand a very strong sheer, and she has just enough, but not too much. Her plumb bow is relieved by a little turn just below the painted waterline. Her short bowsprit with a slight steeve is nicely balanced by the rake of her transom, the curve of her outboard rudder and the overhang of her boom. The little details in these matters are so important. Her bobstay, for instance, is attached at precisely the right point. I would prefer the head of the rudder to be horizontal.

The sloop is quite beamy and stiff. There is

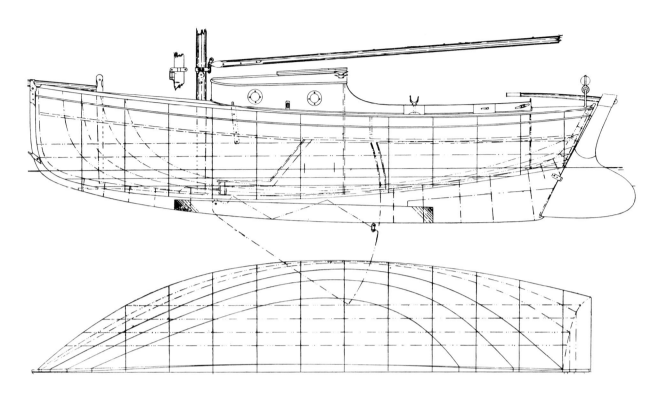

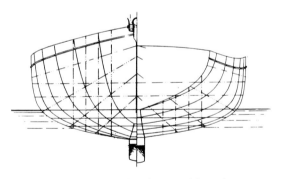

With her shoal draft, she would make an admirable daysailer and cruiser on inside waterways. (The Yachting and Boating Monthly, December, 1909)

some turn of the bilge above the waterline. The shape of her transom is a nice compromise between giving her bearing and yet not giving her too much drag as she heels. She has a sizable chunk of outside ballast in the keel.

This boat—true to her type—has a really clean run. Her belly, though wide, is flat rather than round; that's the secret of her ability to give a good turn of speed under a wide variety of conditions.

She has a low rig, which is sensible for a boat with low ultimate stability. If you tried to abuse her in a hard puff, she'd probably lift her rudder just enough to take things into her own hands, and, using her long main boom, spin herself into the wind and look you right in the eye.

Her rig is simple; there is just one shroud on each side and it is led far enough aft so that backstays are unnecessary.

The mast is short and the yard on the head of the mainsail reefs down with the sail. You'd want to be able to reef her down until the heel of the yard was just above the gooseneck. You'd also want plenty of lazy jacks on the mainsail led way up high on the mast to keep the long yard under control when hoisting and lowering sail, as well as to keep the sail up on the boom.

The mainsheet ought to be three or four parts with a small rope and big blocks.

The jib rolls up on a wooden roller. I have mixed emotions about such a rig. A sailor who doesn't, Denny Desoutter, editor of the British magazine *Practical Boat Owner*, wrote me as follows:

When I had headsails on a wooden luff spar, I used to reef them. As the roller jib was set inside the forestay it could be rolled up completely while a larger headsail was hanked on to the stay. In some circumstances one could deploy the hanked sail and the roller sail, goosewinged.

I still use roller headsails on my present boat, which has a bowsprit and is rigged as a cutter. The roller spars, of course, are of aluminium alloy nowadays, and they are set up permanently. The yankee jib at the bowsprit-end measures 300 square feet and I find that I can use it down to a size of about 80 square feet. After that it is rolled completely and the 180 square foot staysail carries on. At this stage one would be reefing the main so that the loss of the jib is reasonably well balanced. It is probably foolish to have the big yankee on the end of a bowsprit like mine, because it is not a proper walk-out affair. But I keep my fingers crossed.

I still maintain a fixed forestay to the stemhead, on which I can hank a storm jib, or spare jib should there be any need. But that has happened only once, when the leech of the roller staysail was torn in a gale, and I decided it was better to roll it up completely than to try and change it.

There are minor difficulties in maintaining a standing forestay alongside a roller headsail. In some circumstances one could roll the standing stay into the sail when reefing. But if that happens one simply has to unroll and start again. With about nine inches clearance between the two, I find that troubles are pretty rare on a luff length of about 36 feet.

The headsails are removed from the spars when the boat lies at her mooring, but while we are aboard they stay in place.

Boat handling is greatly eased and the gear is much appreciated by a middle-aged couple like ourselves. Before entering a harbour I usually hand the main and continue under headsails alone. The area of the big jib is steadily reduced and we sometimes finish up with just a small part of the staysail. But this can be used like an accelerator pedal and deployed again instantly if you have to go round again or change speed. And when you come to drop the anchor there are no sheets whipping your ears, and no sails to tidy up—they are already furled.

I think that cruising has been revolutionised by reliable engines and that the next step is the improvement of variable-area sails. They *have* always been *variable* of course, but it can now all be made so much easier for a small and weak crew. I had better stop—you have already had an earful.

I guess my question is, where on this sloop do you put a 15-foot window shade when you have to take it down?

At any rate, besides a roller jib, you'd want a small jib, a high-cut overlapping jib, and—if young at heart—a huge, gossamer balloomer hoisting to the head of the main yard and sheeting to the end of the boom.

The sloop's house is wide, but short, so it would not be too much of an obstacle to getting forward. Not that you'd need to very often, for she would be handled from her nice, big cockpit. Her halyards lead aft to cleats on top of the after end of the house. The string to roll and unroll the jib would lead aft. You'd keep a small anchor handy aft with its rode led forward through the bowsprit chock. In fact, you could become something of a hermit in that cockpit, only venturing forth to inspect the rest of the vessel on bright, moonlit nights.

She looks as if she could use a longer tiller to get more leverage on her long, catboat-like rudder and to let you sit farther forward if you want to.

You'd want a tarpaulin to go over the boom and you'd want to be able to raise the boom at the gooseneck (boom jaws would make sense) to get adequate headroom.

Her cuddy gives barely sitting headroom of 3 feet 4 inches, so you'd want low transom berths and no basketball players. With some shelves, net hammocks, and a hook to take the lanyard of the cedar bucket, all that would remain to make her a self-sufficient little cruiser would be to load stores.

You could explore some intricate and interesting inland waterways in a boat like this. She'd make an admirable little cruiser for bay, estuary, river, or creek. With a couple of minor modifications—her 16-foot mast counterweighted in a tabernacle and the carrying of a small outboard motor that could be clamped to a bracket mounted on her flat transom to keep the top of the motor below the level of the rail—she could negotiate the narrow confines of canals and canal locks. She could travel quite handily to her chosen network of waterways either over land on a trailer or over sea in a freighter. Not a bad second life for a little old reincarnated knockabout!

34/ A Hand Batwing Sloop

> Length on deck: 20 feet 3 inches
> Length on waterline: 17 feet 7 inches
> Beam: 7 feet 11 inches
> Draft: 2 feet
> Sail area: 367 square feet
> Displacement: 2 tons
> Designer: William H. Hand, Jr.

One of the little mysteries of the history of boat design is why French sailors, wanting a one-design racing class for the river Seine in 1907, turned for the design to William H. Hand, Jr., of New Bedford, Massachusetts, U.S.A. Whatever their reasons, they got a good boat for the purpose, in my opinion, and one that is worth looking at 70 years later as a fine daysailer and short-range cruiser for river, estuary, bay, or sound.

Her plans were published originally in *Forest and Stream;* I found them reprinted in the February, 1908, issue of *The Yachting and Boating Monthly,* the British fledgling still flying as *Yachting Monthly.*

The sloop is 20 feet 3 inches long on deck, with a waterline length of 17 feet 7 inches, a beam of 7 feet 11 inches, and a draft of 2 feet with the board up. Her displacement is given as 4,134 pounds, of which 850 pounds is in her lead keel. Her sail area is 367 square feet.

In general appearance, the hull looks a bit like a rakish version of the Cape Cod catboat, a type with which Bill Hand was thoroughly familiar. In any case, she has the great virtues—and the drawbacks—of the shoal, beamy vessel.

With her ample width and flare in the topsides,

she'd carry her big rig well. She has a good run for so short a boat. She could, of course, pound going into a steep chop.

The sloop has, to my eye, a pretty curve to her bow, and this is nicely balanced by considerable rake to her transom, whose shape gives her a handsome stern despite its flatness. (This last characteristic of the design would no doubt be appreciated by her builder.) The gentle, downward curve in her bowsprit and the shape of her simple, outboard rudder seem to complement the appearance of her ends. The cove, with its bit of scrollwork fore and aft, sets off her fair and gentle sheerline. And the single, oval port light in each side of the cuddy house looks just right. Bill Hand has paid attention to the details of this design and in so doing has made of what could have been a very ordinary and plain craft a handsome boat.

For planking, the designer specified ¾-inch Spanish cedar. This was to go on double oak frames, 1¹⁄₁₆ inches square, spaced on 8-inch centers. She has an oak clamp, 1¼ inches by 3 inches, and oak bilge stringers of the same dimensions. Mr. Hand specified oak ⅝ inch thick for the sides of the house and coaming. The centerboard trunk is of 1-inch white pine. There is a chunk of

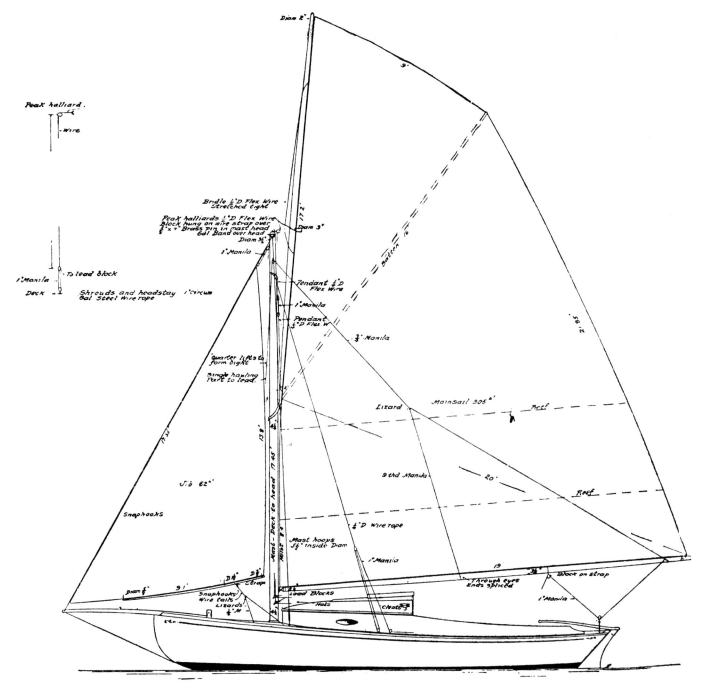

*Bill Hand designed this fast batwing gunter sloop 70 years ago for racing on the river Seine. (*The Yachting and Boating Monthly, *February, 1908)*

lead in the wooden board to sink it. Her bobstay is a rod that is bent and passed through the stem; it is of ⅜-inch galvanized steel.

The sail plan shows a big racing rig with 305 square feet in the mainsail and 62 in the jib. That mainsail is a sail of some interest. The British called it the Bembridge rig; in this country, sails like that on sailing canoes were called batwing sails. It's a gunter rig (which is really just a gaff rig arranged so that the spar at the head of the sail can come right up to nearly vertical) with a full-width, flexible batten to hold out the peak. Or, from another point of view, it's a jackyard topsail with a gaff mainsail hanging from its foot!

Whatever you call it, the sail looks exciting to use. Unwieldy? Well, perhaps a bit, but before

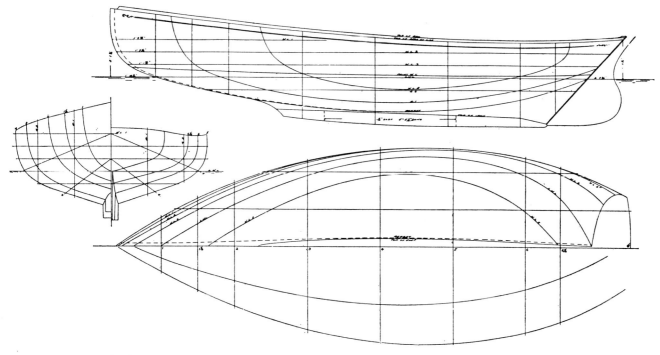

*She is a sort of rakish Cape Cod catboat. (*The Yachting and Boating Monthly, *February, 1908)*

*She has a triangular centerboard, a big, shallow, watertight cockpit, and a high-crowned house sheltering a snug cabin. (*The Yachting and Boating Monthly, *February, 1908)*

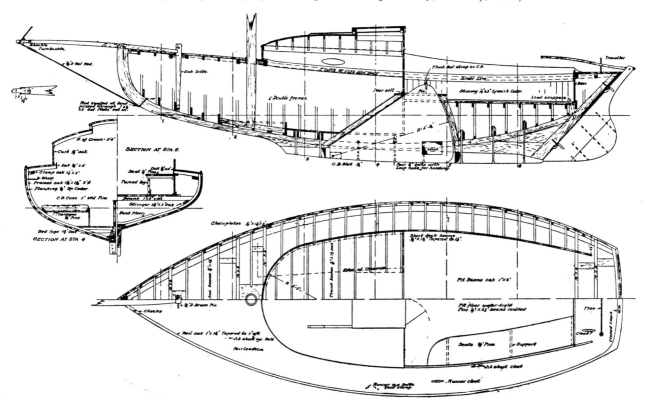

discarding the thing out of hand, think how much fun it would be to sail her with it in light weather. She could really do some fancy ghosting with all that high sail area.

Of course you'd want the first reef in much of the time. You'd leave all the reefing gear rove off, and pretty soon tucking in a reef would be no more of a chore than tying the children's shoes. And it wouldn't be long before they could tie in their own reefs.

It would make sense with a rig like this to have a hard-weather mainsail, a leg-o'-mutton sail setting to the masthead and the boom end, lacing to the mast, and with a loose foot. And you'd even want to be able to reef *that* sail, in case misjudgment or over-exuberance resulted in a hard chance.

Let's look at some of the details of the gunter rig:

The lower throat halyard block is attached to the yard at the jaws on a long wire pennant that puts the block high enough above the jaws so that the yard can lie close to the mast.

The peak halyard is two parts, of flexible wire. The upper peak halyard block is hung on a pin at the very top of the mast. The lower block slides on a taut wire bridle on the yard. The hauling part of the wire peak halyard leads to a rope jig tackle of three parts that makes down at the foot of the mast.

The bridle on the yard is long enough so that the first reef can be taken without touching the peak halyard; as the yard is lowered by the throat halyard, its bridle slides through a metal saddle on the peak halyard block. When taking in the second reef, however, the peak halyard would have to be slacked when the upper end of the bridle reached the saddle on the peak halyard block. Slacking the peak halyard would let the yard sag off from the mast a bit, which would let the boom droop, so the second reef really should be cocked up at the leech rather than being parallel to the foot of the sail. And by then you'd want to be thinking about taking down all that paraphernalia and putting up that nice little leg-o'-mutton sail.

Her mast stands only 17½ feet above the deck; it's 4½ inches in diameter, tapering to 3½ inches at the top. The boom is 19 feet long, 3½ inches in diameter, tapering to 2¼ inches at the ends. The yard is 17 feet 2 inches long, 3 inches in diameter, tapering to 2 inches at the ends.

Her running backstays are far enough forward so that they wouldn't need tending when short tacking. Her lazy jacks are far enough aft so that they would keep sail, batten, and yard under control and out of the helmsman's eyes when taking in the big sail. They also act as a topping lift for the boom. Are the three parts shown on the mainsheet enough? The jib is nicely rigged with a three-quarter-length club and two-part sheets. All the halyards lead aft on top of the house; this is a most sensible arrangement in a boat of this size, for it lets you work the halyards in the steadiness and security of the cockpit.

The cockpit is seven feet long by an average of five feet wide, and is watertight and self-bailing. The seat arrangement lets you go right into its forward corners to work her running gear.

On deck forward, the samson post would be a good friend; it beats a cleat nine ways to Sunday. Surge a heavily straining line on it, tow her with it, lash everything to it, use it to keep yourself from falling overboard, and, above all, know that when most you need it, it'll be there. It won't break or uproot.

Below, the sloop has room for a full-size transom on either side of the cuddy and space enough for the necessary gear to manage her and to live on board for short periods.

The headroom under the house is about four feet on average. It's hard to get much headroom, of course, in a shoal-draft, low-sided hull, and Bill Hand got this much by giving her a rather high house. Though the height of her house is greater than her least freeboard, the structure is not ugly, for its height has been won with a high-crowned roof that allows its sides to be kept relatively low.

One of the interesting things to work out in a boat of this type is what kind of gear to have on board and where to put it. Most of the things you can think of to take would be best left ashore, of course, but you would have to work out convenient stowage for the essentials. After ten years or so of sailing her, you'd probably have figured out where best to stow a heavy anchor and rode, charts, the bucket, a tarp to go over the boom in wet weather, a sounding pole, sculling oar, heavy weather mainsail, balloon jib, stove, wash basin, food box, binoculars, ditty bag, tool chest, spare rope, and so forth. It would be a great feeling of satisfaction when, after three years of struggling with a heavy anchor rode stowed way up in the bow, you suddenly realized that the right place for it was in a big coil lashed up under the port cockpit seat. All that is needed to carry out the idea is two or three stout screw eyes and as many lanyards. Then drag it all aft, coil it down, and tie it up under there. Now there's really room for folded tarp and bagged sails in the bow, the wasted space under the cockpit seat has been filled, and the anchor rode is much handier to get at. The time it takes to realize these little satisfactory changes is reason enough to keep a good boat long enough to get to know her well.

I can see this one—her simple gear well stowed quick to hand, her whole fabric scrubbed with use—stealing up some Chesapeake Bay creek at dusk, or reaching fast in bright New England sunlight across the flats behind some low sand beach on which her crew hears breakers.

35/ The *Nirwana*

Length on deck: 20 feet
Length on waterline: 16 feet 7 inches
Beam: 4 feet
Draft: 5 inches
Sail area: 142 square feet
Designer: F. Rehfeldt

When I learned that the creator of Horatio Hornblower, the great C.S. Forester, had written long ago a couple of books about small-boat cruising in the waterways of France and Germany, I began keeping an eye out for them on prowlings through secondhand-book stores. Forester's vessel was evidently named the *Annie Marble,* for the books are called *The Voyage of the Annie Marble* and *The Annie Marble in Germany.* I found the second one first, in Tony Dixon's delightful Book Cabin in Cowes, England.

The discovery that the *Annie Marble* was a very ordinary-looking flat-bottomed skiff propelled by a noisy outboard motor (this was in the late Twenties) dampened my enthusiasm a bit, but I plunged in anyway—and was far from disappointed. The *Annie Marble in Germany* is a thoroughly delightful cruising book.

Forester describes an enchanted place for small-boat goings and comings, the Mecklenburg Lakes. The *Annie Marble* met up with some lovely sailing craft on those lakes. I like to think that one of them might have been the big cruising canoe *Nirwana,* designed by F. Rehfeldt. All I know about Herr Rehfeldt is that he was a German designer. But surely the creator of such a lovely craft must have had his country's consummate

small-boat cruising ground in mind for her headquarters.

The design of the *Nirwana* was published originally in *Die Yacht* for June 19, 1908. It is reproduced here from *The Yachting and Boating Monthly* for August of that year.

This boat would make a fine daysailer or short-range cruising boat for protected waters. And she can go where it is quite shallow, especially with a modification to the rudder.

The *Nirwana* is 20 feet long on deck, with a waterline length of 16 feet 7 inches, a beam of only 4 feet, and a draft of 5 inches when light. She displaces 787 pounds. Her sail area is 142 square feet, with 84 square feet in the mainsail, 31 in the mizzen, and 27 in the jib.

The boat would, of course, be quite sensitive to loading. If you didn't overload her, you couldn't ask for a hull that would be more easily driven. There is just nothing to her under water; the whole boat is one long, flat run. She really ought to fly, although she'd pound a bit in a short, steep head sea. This is a fault of any canoe that has to be rather flat in section to keep her draft very shoal.

The *Nirwana* is an extremely fine-lined boat, and would have to be handled sensitively. She would neither like—nor need—to be driven.

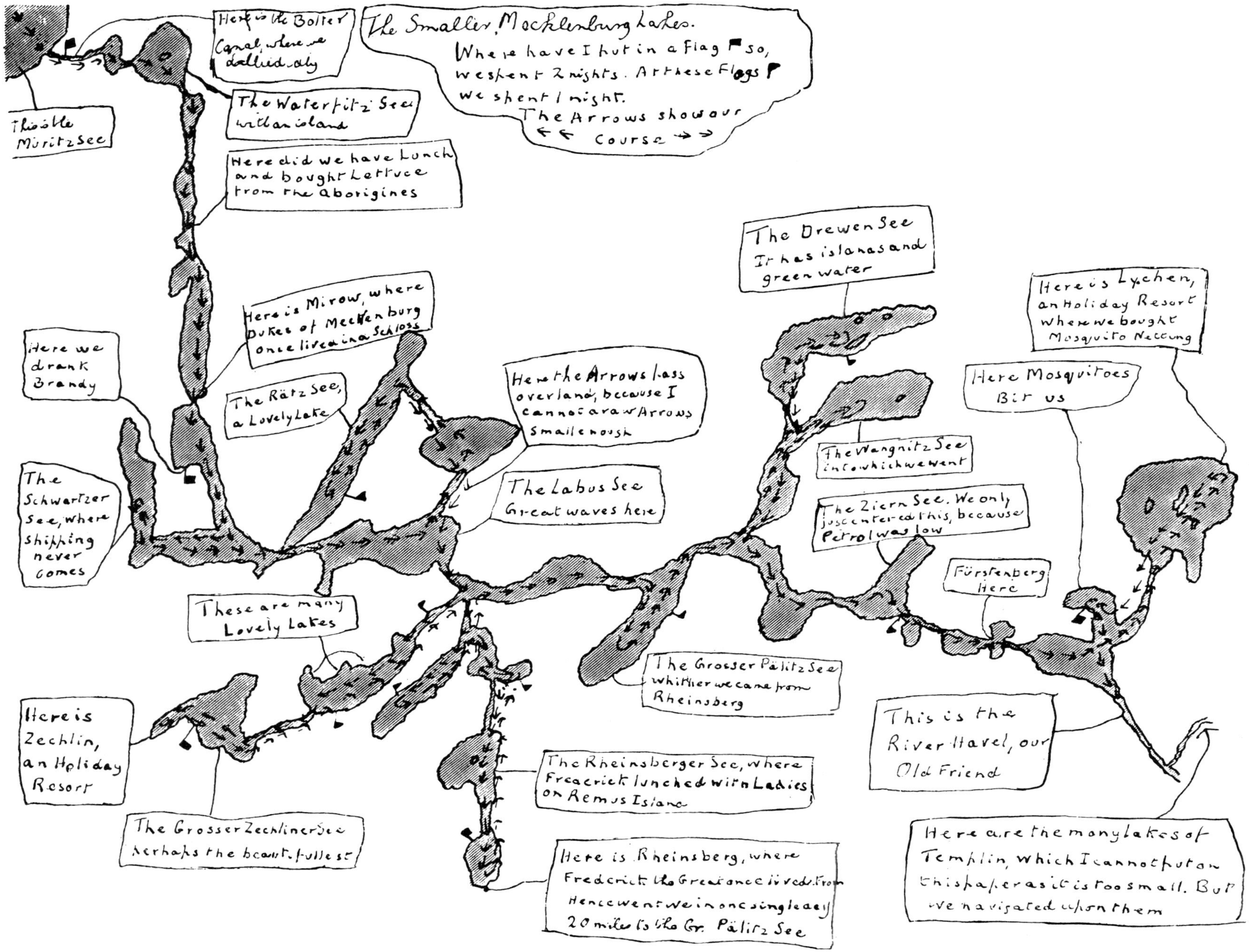
The Smaller Mecklenburg Lakes.
Where have I put in a Flag so, we spent 2 nights. At these Flags we spent 1 night.
The Arrows show our course
Here is the Bolter Canal, where we dallied idly
The Waterfitz See with an island
Thistle Müritz See
Here did we have Lunch and bought Lettuce from the aborigines
Here we drank Brandy
Here is Mirow, where Dukes of Mecklenburg once lived in a Schloss
The Rätz See, a Lovely Lake
Here the Arrows pass overland, because I cannot draw Arrows small enough
The Schwartzer See, where shipping never comes
The Labus See Great waves here
The Drewen See It has islands and green water
The Wangnitz See into which we went
The Ziern See. We only just entered this, because Petrol was low
Here is Lychen, an Holiday Resort where we bought Mosquito Netting
Here Mosquitoes Bit us
Fürstenberg Here
These are many Lovely Lakes
The Grosser Pälitz See whither we came from Rheinsberg
This is the River Havel, our Old Friend
Here is Zechlin, an Holiday Resort
The Rheinsberger See, where Frederick lunched with Ladies on Remus Island
The Grosser Zechliner See perhaps the beautifullest
Here is Rheinsberg, where Frederick the Great once lived. From Hence went we in one single day 20 miles to the Gr. Pälitz See
Here are the many lakes of Templin, which I cannot put on this paper as it is too small. But we navigated upon them

The Mecklenburg Lakes, *perhaps the inspiration for the design of this beautiful sailing canoe. This is C. S. Forester's sketch of the enchanted cruising ground; the notes refer to his cruise in the late Twenties in an outboard skiff.* (The Annie Marble in Germany *by C. S. Forester)*

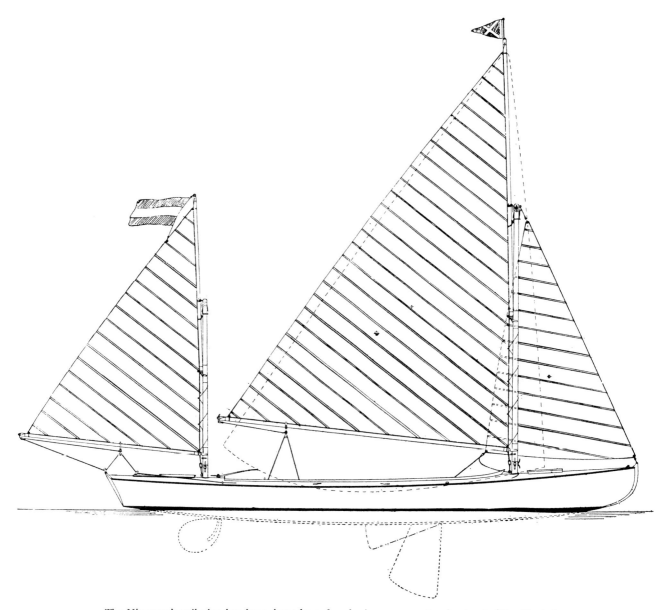

The Nirwana's *sail plan has been kept low, for she is a narrow, tender boat. (*The Yachting and Boating Monthly, *August, 1908)*

I visualize her as being carefully built of wood, and maybe finished off even quite fancy, with varnish work, polished brass, and fine rigging details. As a matter of fact, her whole hull could be finished bright in this day and age of tough, durable varnishes.

Her centerboard goes deep and has considerable area; she should hang on well going to windward. Is there enough bearing in the trunk with the board lowered to the position shown in the lines drawing?

She draws 3 feet 4 inches with the centerboard all the way down. The rudder draws 1 foot 6 inches. What about giving the rudder a trunk so it could be retracted when sailing in very shallow water (and then replaced by an oar over the lee quarter) or for beaching? This would mean that the rudder and trunk would have to be just off center to clear the mizzen mast.

Presumably both centerboard and rudder would be made of steel for ballast. If sailed light, this boat would probably like some inside ballast.

She has short outriggers for rowing and would move well with longish oars.

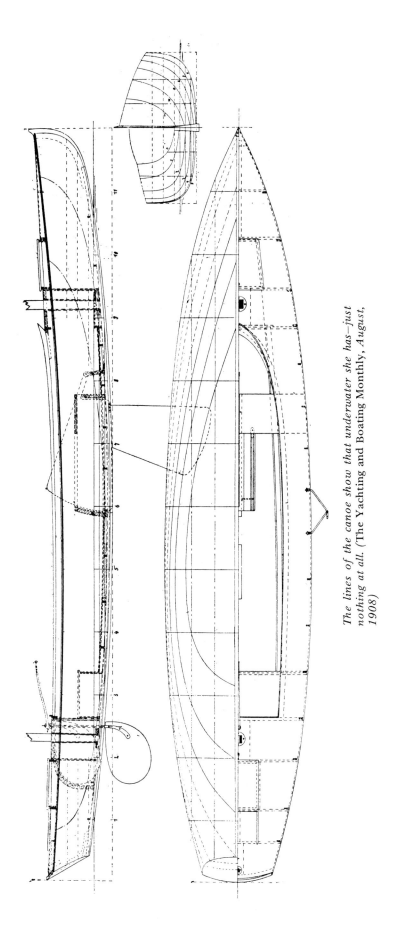

The lines of the canoe show that underwater she has—just nothing at all. (The Yachting and Boating Monthly, August, 1908)

There is considerable room for cruising gear under her side decks and in her ends, accessible through deck hatches.

A nice feature might be a spray hood folding over the forward end of the cockpit coaming with enough hoops to slide aft nearly to the tiller, the whole contraption being low enough so the boom would clear it. That way it could be pulled aft to keep the spray out of the cockpit when sailing on a blustery day.

When you stopped for the night, you'd want to rig a tent over the boom. And you'd want to be able to raise the boom to get headroom in your tent, which would mean fitting the gooseneck with a slide and downhaul.

For singlehanded work, you would probably want a longer tiller than that shown so you could center your weight more.

The *Nirwana*'s rig has been kept low, for she is not a stiff boat. The gunter rig allows exceptionally short masts. The mainmast stands a little less than ten feet above the deck, and the mizzen is just over six feet high. You'd want topping lifts and lazy jacks on both sails to keep the booms and yards under control when raising or lowering the sails.

The jib is shown set flying. A handy rig would be an outhaul for the tack, so the sail could be set or taken in without leaving the forward end of the cockpit.

The big canoe would sail under her mainsail alone in a fresh breeze. You might want to set up a preventer forestay when the jib was not set. I'd like to see a couple of deep reefs in the mainsail so it could be close-reefed to the heel of the yard.

In a strong breeze, the canoe could reach along under jib and mizzen. You might want a small storm jib cut with the foot up off the deck and a storm mizzen trysail setting to the masthead without a yard. With these two little sails on the ends of her, she could rush along safely in quite a breeze.

How do you like the big ballooner set flying from the main yard? Anybody dare pole it out like a spinnaker?

When at anchor in this canoe, you'd want to keep the mizzen set to stop her sailing around and to dampen what might otherwise be a quick, uncomfortable roll. But she'd be even happier with her bow nosed up on a beach at the head of a quiet cove.

This boat would be easy to carry over the road with her short spars tucked away inside her cockpit. She'd also be relatively easy to crate up and ship abroad.

It would be wonderful to take her to the Mecklenburg Lakes, but such a trip might not prove practical today, for the Lakes now lie in East Germany. Those who negotiated for the West after World War II made a big point of being sure to get a chunk of Berlin. If they wanted some pocket in East Germany, they might better have chosen Mecklenburg's lake district, but then, I suppose they hadn't read Forester's books on cruising in the *Annie Marble*.

The *Nirwana* may indeed be a well-named little vessel, for she may bring to one who has been through many levels of boating that highest state of bliss brought about by release from the cycle of owning one complex, costly boat after another.

36/ The *Aria*

Length on deck: 32 feet 3 inches
Length on waterline: 25 feet 4 inches
Beam: 8 feet 9 inches
Draft: 3 feet 1 inch
Displacement: 4-1/3 tons
Designer: Nathanael G. Herreshoff

Pop swapped the yawl *Brownie* for a Herreshoff Buzzards Bay 25-footer, the *Aria,* in the fall of 1948. As in the case of all even swaps, each party thought he had the best of the deal. The *Brownie* was described in *Good Boats* and the *Aria* is described right here, so you can judge for yourself.

In any event, Pop never got to capitalize on the arrangement; the following spring he got the new boat overboard but died before he could take her sailing the first time. So the *Aria* became my legacy, and I guess no 17-year-old whipper-snapper ever had better. I kept her ten years and never could get used to her speed. She is some boat.

She was designed by Nathanael Greene Herreshoff and built by the Herreshoff Manufacturing Company in 1914 for one C.R. Holmes at a contract price of $2,000.

She is Herreshoff hull number 738, and her original name was the *Whitecap.* She is one of a class of four D Class half-decked sloops designed for racing on Buzzards Bay and generally known as the Buzzards Bay 25-footers, from the length of the waterline. These boats are the *Mink,* No. 733; *Vitessa,* No. 734; *Bagetelle,* No. 736; and the *Whitecap.* All four were built in 1914.

The boats never became popular as a racing class, and the Herreshoff Company turned out no more of them. They supposedly gained a bad reputation when one of them filled and sank when she was left on her mooring with her mainsail set and sheeted flat and was struck broadside by a squall. They are certainly not tender boats. The only time that the *Aria*'s coaming went under while I had her was when she was struck by a heavy puff just after I had cast off the mooring and, without good steerageway, she was slow to luff.

The *Aria* is 32 feet 3 inches long on deck, with a waterline length of 25 feet 4 inches, a beam of 8 feet 9 inches, and a draft of 3 feet 1 inch. Her sail area is 490 square feet, and her displacement is just under 4½ tons.

The design is a modification of Captain Nat Herreshoff's third *Alerion,* hull No. 718, which he designed and built for his own use in 1912. The *Alerion* is smaller than the *Aria,* with a waterline length of 21 feet 9 inches. She has a bit more freeboard and somewhat shorter ends than the *Aria,* but the basic hull shape is the same. The *Alerion* is preserved in beautiful condition at the Mystic Seaport. A near sistership to the *Alerion* is the *Sadie,* hull No. 732, built in 1914, now also preserved in a museum, that at St. Michaels, Maryland.

Nathanael Greene Herreshoff. (Muriel Vaughn)

A further modification of this basic design resulted in the Newport 29 class of which three boats were built in 1914: the *Dolphin,* No. 727; *Mischief,* No. 728; and *Comet,* No. 737. These boats have the short ends and high freeboard of the *Alerion,* and they are keel boats without centerboards. They are 36 feet long on deck, with a waterline length of 29 feet, a beam of 10 feet 4 inches, and a draft of 5 feet.

Seven of these nine boats built by the Herreshoff Manufacturing Company in or before 1914 are going strong, and the other two may be also for all I know.

Of the three versions of this design of Captain Nat Herreshoff's, the *Alerion,* the Buzzards Bay 25-footers, and the Newport 29s, the Buzzards Bay 25s have the finest lines. The *Aria* was always a sweet and pretty boat to look at and to sail.

Her sections look deceptively easy and gentle, for her bilge is not hard, her draft is quite shoal, and her freeboard is low. Yet she was a powerful boat and could stand driving due to her considerable outside ballast, rather high ballast-to-displacement ratio, great flare in the topsides, and considerable beam. Her broad stern helps her stiffness by giving plenty of bearing aft.

She has about the prettiest bow I have ever seen on a boat. I think the stem profile is the most artistic one Captain Nat ever modelled. The entry is quite hollow, but above the waterline her bow has a lot of flare. The skipper of the only boat that ever beat her in a serious race told me that when the breeze lightened and we began to creep up on him, he was nearly mesmerized by the beauty of that approaching bow with its never-ending, delicately swept back bow wave.

That bow could pound on very rare occasions. When she was well heeled down, one sea in a whole afternoon might be shaped just wrong for her, and she would slap it like a beaver. One time in Gardiner's Bay we ran into a whole succession of such seas and she made such a commotion that I went below to see if she was cracking any frames up forward. The flexibility of her structure under attack was unbelievable. The give was very visible, but she wasn't even weeping.

But that bow loved to cope with 999 out of 1,000 head seas. It would spit 'em off to leeward and in the process seemed to wedge the boat to weather, so that instead of letting the seas knock her off, she seemed able to use them to shoulder her way to windward.

The bow and buttock lines are shallow for low resistance. She has a very long and flat run for such a small boat.

Her profile gives just the right compromise between steadiness on the helm—it was certainly no work at all to make her go straight—and maneuverability. She could do some fancy stepping and spinning for a 32-footer; we used to wriggle in and out of some narrow waters with glee, and, of course, no engine ever came anywhere near this boat.

The tiller is a small, skinny piece of locust that is beautifully shaped; it looks too small for her, but it isn't.

The *Aria* had a 6-meter rig in her when Pop got her. It suited her well, and the rig conversion had been carried out intelligently.

The mast was 47 feet long from keel to truck. The first time I hoisted it out, I simply cast off all the standing rigging, tied it off on the spar, slid the hook on my sheerpole fall a little way above what I thought would be the balance point, and hoisted away. Everything went fine until I began lowering the thing down to the horizontal, and then it about

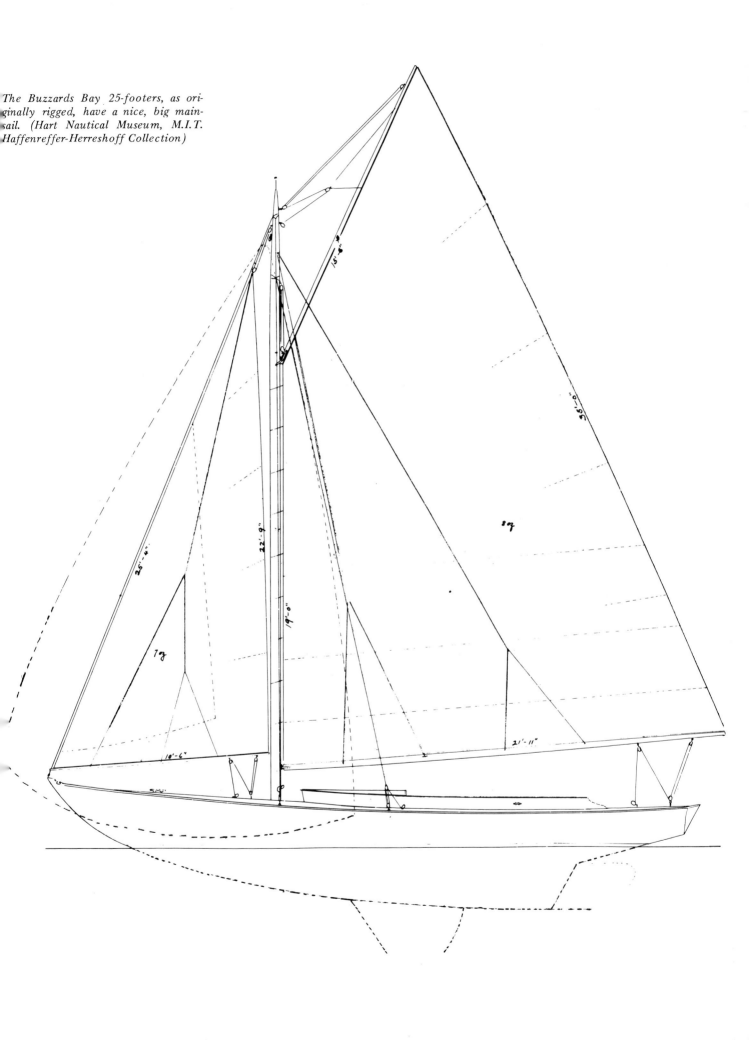

The Buzzards Bay 25-footers, as originally rigged, have a nice, big mainsail. (Hart Nautical Museum, M.I.T. Haffenreffer-Herreshoff Collection)

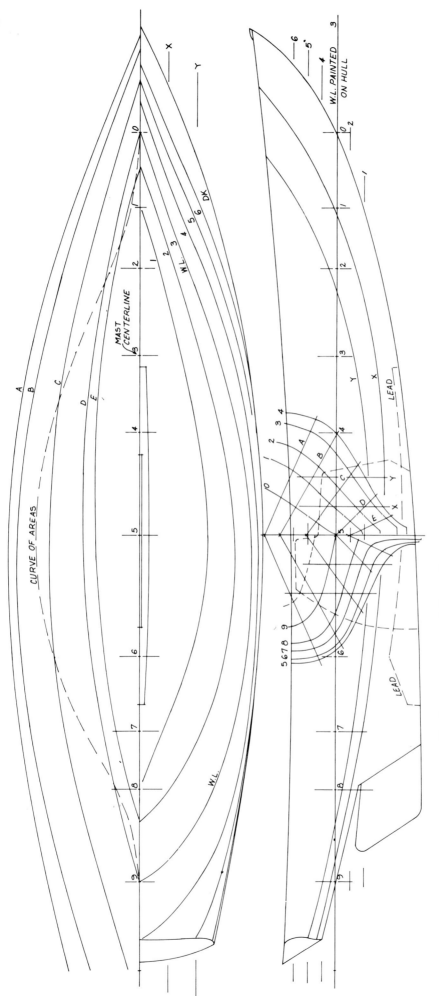

She has a sweet set of lines. The sections are deceptively gentle looking, for she is a powerful boat that will stand a bit of driving. (Edson A. Schock)

The Mischief, *a Newport 29, beating down Narragansett Bay under her original rig. That's the U.S. Naval War College over her bow. (David Cabot)*

bent double under its own weight and that of the rigging. I had no idea that spar was so limber, and figured I had just destroyed the mast. It held.

With a spar that limber, the standing rigging had to be set up pretty tight to keep the rig straight. There were plenty of wires to play with. She had three sets of spreaders, one set of jumper struts, five pairs of shrouds, one pair of jumper stays, double headstays, running backstays, and a permanent backstay. That made 17 pieces of wire with 15 turnbuckles to adjust it all.

Captain Nat hadn't designed the *Aria*'s hull to take the strain imposed by that tall rig with its taut standing rigging. Whoever put the rig into her had done the right thing by installing a steel strap from the sheer clamp in way of the chain plates down under the mast step and up to the opposite sheer clamp. Doubtless this helped hold things together, but after two seasons of sailing her fairly hard, I began to worry about the way the seams in way of the rigging were working. It just didn't seem fair to that delicate, 35-year-old hull to wrench away at it with such a tall, tightly stayed rig.

So, in 1951, another swap was engineered.

Most of the Aria *with some of her 6-meter rig showing. (Roberts Parsons)*

Sam Jones of Essex, Connecticut, had one of the *Aria*'s sisters, the *Mink,* and he still had her original gaff rig. He wasn't using it, and he figured a spare 6-meter rig would be a lot more valuable to him than a spare 1914 gaff rig. So we swapped rigs, and because of all that nice stainless steel wire and all those fancy stainless steel turnbuckles, I got enough money thrown into the bargain so I could buy an engagement ring for the most beautiful girl in the whole world. Slipping that ring on her finger late one night was about the only time I have ever surprised that girl, and putting the original gaff rig back into the *Aria* was one of the most useful things I have ever done, so Sam, wherever you are, thanks again for the trade.

The gaff rig has about the same sail area as had the 6-meter rig. The mast is 32 feet long, instead of 47 feet, and is hollow. I could just carry it on my shoulder once it was stripped of all the rigging, so you can see it was a nice, light spar. The mast position is the same with both rigs.

The gaff rig has one extra piece of running rigging, the peak halyard, but has only five pieces of standing rigging, a single shroud on each side, a headstay, and a pair of running backstays. So there are five pieces of wire instead of 17 and three turnbuckles instead of 15.

The sails that came with the gaff rig had been made at Herreshoff's, and the mainsail was the most beautifully setting gaff sail I ever saw. There was a club and traveler for the jib, but I had gotten used to the loose-footed jib of the 6-meter rig and so left the club and traveler off and set the new jib loose-footed. When the 6-meter rig had been put

in, a nice pair of Luders winches with folding handles had been mounted, one on each after corner of the cuddy roof, and these were so handy I kept them with the gaff rig.

The boat went just as well to windward with the gaff rig as she had with the 6-meter rig. She was never all that close-winded even with the tall, Marconi rig. Deep, narrow boats with tall rigs, like the Eastern Interclubs, could outpoint her with ease, but she had no trouble beating them badly to the windward mark because she footed so fast. The only time she didn't sail as well with the gaff rig as she had with the Marconi rig was in very light airs, when she missed that tall triangle of sail way up high where there is often a little more breeze stirring.

One of the things Pop did during the winter he was looking forward to sailing the *Aria* was to make her a yuloh. This is a Chinese sculling oar that Pop had come to know on China station in the Navy. It has been described in *The Mariner's Catalog,* Volume III, and it has been written up and drawn by real experts like George Worcester, so I won't go into it here. Suffice it to say that the yuloh worked just fine on the *Aria* on those evenings when we had overstayed our welcome in Fisher's Island Sound and were coming up the Pawcatuck River in a flat calm. You could shove her along at a knot or two depending on whether you were lazy or energetic.

The *Aria*'s dinghy has also come in for its share of mention in the *Mariner's Catalog.* The dinghy's name was the *Ano,* by which you can readily see that it had once been a canoe but had had each end

That's me misspending my youth in the Aria.

cut off. The *Ano* was at its best when stowed on the *Aria*'s deck, across the stern with the Marconi rig, and moved to the foredeck with the gaff rig so it wouldn't foul the mainsheet. If the *Ano* was light and docile on deck, she was crank and dangerous afloat. One night in Great Salt Pond, Block Island, a guest disregarded my strong suggestion that he not try to row ashore in the *Ano* against the usual southwest gale. He turned out to be an awfully good man in a small boat, for it took the *Ano* a full 30 minutes to return him on board, tired, wet, and frustrated through not having come anywhere near his destination.

The ground tackle in the *Aria* consisted of a 50-pound yachtsman's anchor that had been the *Brownie*'s best bower and a 15-pound yachtsman's anchor that Pop had calculated would be enough to hold her under most circumstances. They were just wrong. The 50-pounder was more than she ever needed; a 35-pounder would have been plenty

for a storm anchor. And the 15-pounder always left you worrying a bit; a 25-pounder would have been easy enough to handle and would have given more peace of mind.

The boat has plenty of deck space. There is a lot of room around the mast and her widely flaring bow makes a fine platform for handling headsails. The rather extreme flare to the topsides forward up near the rail makes a fine hand-hold when she's jumping a bit.

The *Aria* has a huge, deep cockpit, easily the most comfortable cockpit I have seen in any size of boat. The seats are about 9½ feet long, the coaming is slanted outboard just right for a backrest and is high enough to give you plenty of support and protection. The seats are high enough off the cockpit floor so that you have a really comfortable seat, and when the boat is heeled you have good foot braces in the centerboard trunk at the forward end of the cockpit and the opposite seat at the after end. In this cockpit, you feel as if you are sitting down in the boat, not perched up on her. Six people have plenty of room when sailing, and, of course, you can have quite a party on board at anchor.

Her coaming and seats are made of four beautiful pieces of mahogany. Behind the seats under the deck are long, open shelves that provide a great deal of handy stowage space.

The *Aria*'s big, deep cockpit is not, of course, watertight or self-bailing; rain or spray drains through narrow spaces between the cockpit floorboards directly into the bilge. She has a big tarp that goes over the boom and gaff, the peak halyard and lazy jacks being slacked away to the mast to accommodate it. The tarp covers the entire cockpit and provides a big sheltered area with considerable headroom for a rainy day. It also saves pumping out after a rain and protects considerable acreage of varnish work from the weather. At anchor, you can roll it forward to open up as much of the cockpit as you want to; we often used to set it close-reefed, forming just a nice windbreak over the cuddy and across the forward end of the cockpit.

One thing Pop put in during that last winter was a chart drawer on sail track and slides under the after deck. Sitting at the tiller, all you had to do was reach back through the opening into the lazarette, pull out the drawer, and there were the charts right handy.

The 6-meter rig did give her a tall beauty. This was standing out of Marion, Massachusetts, on Buzzards Bay. (Edward Cabot)

No hatch is needed in her cuddy roof, for the cockpit is deep enough so that you can easily stoop and walk into the cabin. Nice louvered mahogany doors can be slid out from under the forward ends of the cockpit seats, slipped onto their pintles, and used to shut off the cabin from the cockpit if desired.

One feature of the boat's construction that Pop said he particularly admired was a pair of strengthening members consisting of fairly wide, straight boards set on edge that ran from each side of the keel up and out to the sheer clamp along the forward face of the bulkhead separating the cuddy from the cockpit. These stiffen her up greatly right amidships without adding much weight to her structure.

In the cuddy there is a narrow seat on each side;

there is sitting headroom under the cuddy roof. She has a single pipe berth away forward.

Pop had put in a head at the forward end of the cabin, but I had little trouble rationalizing its early removal and replacement by a nicely varnished, brass-bound wooden bucket. I also got rid of a water tank way up in the eyes of her and another all the way aft in the lazarette, for I didn't think she needed that kind of weight way out in the ends of her—or that much civilization either, for that matter.

In the after starboard corner of the cabin are some shelves and lockers and a fold-down, single-burner alcohol stove. The centerboard trunk is half in the cabin and half in the cockpit, and the cabin half has a folding table leaf on each side.

The *Aria* was hauled and maintained on the

Running up into Buzzards Bay. We have just taken in the spinnaker, which she didn't really need. (Edward Cabot)

railway at Ram Point on the Pawcatuck River that Pop had built for the *Brownie.* Scraping, sanding, red-leading, puttying, and painting her hull, you got to know her shape pretty well, and every spring's work brought a renewed appreciation for the beauty and soundness of Captain Nat's model.

We'd get most of the work done during spring vacation from school, which meant getting her overboard usually about the third week in April. We'd leave her on the cradle a day or two so the lower seams in the centerboard trunk could swell up—aided by a little sawdust judiciously sprinkled down the slot.

I never made a long cruise in her, but did a lot of daysailing and cruised regularly to the eastward to Buzzards Bay and Vineyard Sound.

My first summer with her I sailed her single-handed to Buzzards Bay on a ten-day cruise. I made a couple of errors in judgment, both having to do with entering harbors, but the boat was so maneuverable and so well behaved that she got me out of both mistakes unscathed.

Since the *Aria* was obviously a fast boat, we

wanted to try her out against the competition, so we took her in three Off Soundings races. My regular and best racing crew consisted entirely of Cabots, Ed and Nelson, brothers who had been a major force to contend with in the Herreshoff 15-foot-waterline E class boats on Buzzards Bay and were old enough to remember when the 25-footers came out, and, of course, Ed's son and my very best friend, Dave. These able sailors always took a great interest in the boat and helped me a lot, not just with racing her, but also with her upkeep and general management.

In the three starts in Off Soundings, we took two firsts and a second in Class C, the racing class. The race in which we were beaten was, of course, by far the most interesting. The winning boat was the *Flying Scotchman,* a new—and at that time novel—light-displacement, fin-keeler, with very high freeboard, reverse sheer, and skimpy sail area. It blew quite hard on both days of the racing, and most of the sailing was to windward. Under these conditions, the *Flying Scotchman* had things a bit her own way, but we did notice that the one time

Beating up into Smith's Cove on Shelter Island Sound in a hard northwester under just a reefed mainsail. (Edward Cabot)

On the railway at Ram Point on the Pawcatuck River.

Soaking up. The original gaff rig has been put back into her.

it moderated, we came right up on her until it breezed on again. The boats would probably be a fairly even match for each other under a wide variety of sailing conditions.

I guess the *Aria*'s greatest day while I had her was in a race around Fisher's Island when she beat most of a fleet of far larger boats, including the 72-foot yawl *Bolero,* boat for boat. Granted, it was a flukey northwest day and we played in under the outside shore of Fisher's Island to the point of hitting the board on a couple of rocks so we could catch what few puffs were coming off the land while the bigger boats had to stay farther offshore becalmed. Still, it was all fair, and I have a nice big silver pitcher to help me remember the day.

After sailing her for four years, I went into the Navy, and Uncle Sam's operating schedules began to cut down on our sailing time.

For part of my first summer in a destroyer, though, the ship was actually in her home port of Newport, Rhode Island, and the recipient of the 6-meter diamond ring and I lived on board the *Aria* in Brenton's Cove. Early in the fall came a hurricane scare, and an embarrassed new ensign had to go to the exec to request permission to leave the ship in the face of impending danger. It was my fitness report versus Captain Nat's boat, and I figured there were 300 other guys who could look

after that tin can with her 60,000 horsepower. The exec was understanding, and I scooted back home, offered the bride a chance to get ashore dry while she could, and then proceeded to lay out one of the longest scopes of anchor rode ever seen in Newport harbor between Goat Island and Trinity Church. I also tied three reefs into the mainsail, one on top of the other, and generally put away and lashed down everything movable, including the tarp. All we got was much rain, so I spent most of the night pumping.

The *Aria* didn't get nearly the use she should have had in the next few busy years, and when we moved to Chesapeake Bay, I sold her.

Meanwhile, the *Bagetelle,* one of the other Buzzards Bay 25s, had been owned first by an uncle and then by Ed Cabot. Ed had rerigged her as a modern yawl. When Ed died, Dave took over his father's boat.

One time I crewed for Dave in the race around Fisher's Island. The *Aria* was then again owned locally, and she was in the race too. Five of us in the *Bagetelle* worked very hard on a day with changing conditions, shifting to different-sized Genoa jibs, setting and resetting the mizzen staysail, and fussing with spinnaker and spinnaker staysail. Two fellows in the *Aria* sailed her around the course with working jib and mainsail, never

Looking more like her original self. Ahhhh.

doing more than trim a sheet now and then. For all our efforts, we in the *Bagetelle* only beat the *Aria* by a couple of minutes, and the gaff-rigger saved her time on us. I never could figure out who to root for that day.

Whenever I look back on my experience sailing the *Aria*, the chief memory that comes up is her surprisingly great speed under all conditions. A couple of years ago I got to worrying that maybe she really hadn't been all that fast and that my remembrance of her fleetness was more nostalgic than accurate. Paul Bates, the *Aria*'s present owner in Noank, Connecticut, kindly gave me the opportunity to put the worry to the test. We took her out on a nice fresh southwest day, laid her off on a broad reach to Stonington Point, ran up into the harbor and back, and then stood back up Fisher's Island Sound just able to lay Noank, rail down, and going like smoke. It wasn't nostalgia. One more time the boat surprised me with how fast she could sail.

L. Francis Herreshoff once told me that the Buzzards Bay 25-footers were his favorite of his father's designs. That's a mighty powerful statement when you think about it. After ten years of surprises, plus a dividend, I have to agree. I just wish Pop could have sailed the *Aria*. He really would have loved her.

Epilogue — A Sail in the *Aria*

The throaty roar of a heavy diesel starting and the powerful, steady whisper of the exhaust came across the water, breaking the early morning stillness. "That must be the Gay Headers getting the *Babe* underway," I said sleepily to Dave, my longtime cruising mate in the *Aria* (and many another boat). We were anchored in the tiny harbor at the entrance to Menemsha Pond, at the west end of Martha's Vineyard.

I clambered out from under the tarpaulin we had put up to keep the night dampness out of the cockpit and stood on the after deck leaning on the boom to watch the *Babe* go out. The clew of the gaff mainsail was wet. Heavy dew.

I was giving the outhauls a little more slack as the tall Gay Header at the *Babe*'s wheel kicked her astern and swung the big dragger around ready to head out. While she was turning, he stepped aft and straightened out her docking lines, reaching down with long copper arms. Then he was back at the wheel, shoving her ahead and steadying her for the entrance. As she passed close astern, I got a good look at his face. It was the face of Melville's Tashtego. The *Babe* put to sea from Menemsha, going out with a fair tide.

Because the sou'wester was coming in again for the third straight day, I insisted on a double reef even though the breeze was light when we got underway. Around the Vineyard when a sou'wester has had two days to blow, it generally breezes right up on the third day, and we were bound offshore in an open boat. Dave was pretty disgusted about tying in a reef, though. As he fished the reefpoints through between the footrope and the boom, hauled taut and made his half-bow, he cast a scornful look or two in my direction.

We weighed anchor and stood for the narrow entrance to Menemsha Pond, where the tide was racing out between the jetties. With the helm alee as the current grabbed the sloop's bow, we eased out into the stream, and then turned to pour with it out into Vineyard Sound.

We worked to windward toward Gay Head. She was strapped right down with the working jib and double-reefed main set to a gentle breeze, at most. With the tide now against us, we weren't making much over the ground.

"Let's take a hitch inshore and get out of some of this tide," I suggested.

Dave got sulky the way you do when you're on a long, two-handed cruise in a small boat and the other fellow isn't sailing her the way you would.

"Why bother?" he wanted to know. He looked up at the shortened sail and down at our slow progress.

The wind wasn't coming. I had been wrong to reef so early. With an irritated look that was supposed to tell Dave, "Foolish one; it's going to be *blowing* here soon," I put the helm alee. Dave caught the look, and his eyes said, "Crazy old woman," as he automatically let go the jib and then sheeted it home on the new tack.

We passed Gay Head, but then instead of keeping her going to the westward on the port tack as we always had, we put her about again and steered about southeast. We wanted to go out and take a look at No Man's Land, the little, uninhabited island that stands as a sentinel outpost southwest of Martha's Vineyard. Dave and I hadn't talked much about going out to No Man's. We'd wanted a close look at the island for a long time, though, and here was a good chance.

No Man's Land didn't look very far offshore on the chart, and, in fact, it wasn't many miles. But as we sailed out, steering to pass close to leeward of the island, both of us were looking at a lot of open ocean over the bow, and it seemed as if we were in a far, desolate corner of the world.

The island, taken by itself, was no different, I suppose, than any other island southwest of Cape Cod. Behind the boulders on the beach rose a little grass-topped cliff, and back of that was a small, rolling meadow that could have been the "back forty" of some inland farm. But you couldn't think of the island by itself. The rocks and the blowing grass existed only in relation to the Atlantic Ocean. And the ground swell, heaving in from the east and breaking on the island, fetched from Portugal.

We saw we could fetch across the windward side of the island on the other tack and were glad enough to go about and stop heading for Africa. Then as we slanted by outside No Man's, we seemed pinned against the island by the ocean. The boat was footing well in the rising breeze, but I think we both had an unreasoning fear that No Man's somehow had us trapped. Certainly if a sea had dropped the sloop onto an off-lying rock, we would have swum ashore to a lonely haven.

But she made past the bouldery shore outside the breakers and gained an offing beyond the island. We started sheets and laid her off to the northward. On a broad reach, now, she raced down the building seas. The old girl's vast experience and the speed built into her by the "Wizard of Bristol" obviously revolted against our pranks. No Man's Land indeed. And in a rising sou'wester. She lifted her skirts and fast left No Man's Land behind her.

As we set a course to weather Sow and Pigs off Cuttyhunk, Dave grinned for the first time that day and said we were in for a dusting. It was still breezing up, and already she was twisting her way up on top of the seas and then falling off and shooting down in a welter of foam. It was hard steering. I was, at last, happy with my reef and tried to forget the hours we had spent shortened down too far.

Sometimes, as a big sea came up under her quarter and slewed her bow to windward (despite all the helm we could hold up without carrying away the light, locust tiller), her bow would dip down, and the crest would break across it as it rose again to meet the threat. Then the spray would shoot off the flare of her bow and blow halfway up the jib.

The seas that came in fairly square under her stern gave her a lift and then a tremendous, powerful push that sent her sleighriding down, pouring up a great bow wave. Then her bow would lift and she would slow as the sea passed under her, leaving her waiting for the next one.

In between the sets of big ones there would be a minute of fairly smooth water. Then she would tear along on a straighter course, cutting down the distance to the Sow and Pigs.

These rocks stand away off to the southwest of Cuttyhunk, last of the Elizabeth Islands that separate Vineyard Sound from Buzzards Bay. Off to windward of the rocks, the Vineyard light vessel would be pitching her stern into it, riding to the tide now turned westerly. We tried to made a good course that would take us well to leeward of the lightship, but to weather of the nun marking the outer end of the rocks.*

The purple hump of Cuttyhunk's hill could already be seen under the foot of the jib whenever the bow lifted. We took turns steering, pumping,

---

*This paragraph is not to be used for navigation. The Vineyard lightship has since been replaced by a mere tower.

and watching for the lightship. The *Aria* was old, and she made water when driven. It was not unpleasant though, to slide into the cuddy on the lee side, lift the floor board, get out the brass pump that came with her 40 years before, stuff the end of the hose in the centerboard trunk, and give the sloshing bilge 20 strokes or so. She had no power, so it was clean work.

We sighted the Vineyard lightship about where it should be, on the weather bow. A strong breeze had settled in for the afternoon. It seemed more than that when we had to sharpen up a little, bringing it right abeam. We had sighted the Sow and Pigs nun dead ahead and thought it best to haul a bit to weather, even though the tide was setting us up to windward.

It didn't take long to bring the nun close aboard. It was plunging and swaying in the big chop, and off to leeward the seas were breaking on the rocks it marked. Ahead, the Hen and Chickens lightship pounded her round stern into it.** We rounded the buoy and swung off dead before it, heading down for the west end of Cuttyhunk.

Now we had to steer by the hairs on the backs of our necks. As I took my turn at it, keeping her well off but not by the lee, trying to anticipate the seas made steep by the weather-going tide, I was both glad Pop wasn't there to glare when the boom lifted and quivered as she showed signs of jibing, and sorry he wasn't there to make sure she didn't slam over. Dave and I ran her off without jibing, though. She did roll some, but never tripped the boom.

Running down toward Penikese, the island which was once a leper colony, we seemed to be getting a little lee from Cuttyhunk, but we soon had to get her onto the other tack. We had the choice of jibing or bringing her up to the wind, tacking, and laying her off again. We decided not to push our luck and trimmed her up close-hauled. She dipped the lee rail well under, even with the double reef. Picking a smooth spot, we went about. The jib was a cannon; Dave took a turn with the new lee sheet, and, as her head fell off, the cannon stopped firing and was quiet again. Then off she tore as the mainsheet burned out around the cleat. We headed into the lee of Cuttyhunk and smooth water.

** It's no use looking for this one any more either.

The entrance to Cuttyhunk Pond, like that to Menemsha, is a narrow one between jetties. This time, there was little tide, but we couldn't quite lay the channel. We started in from the weather side with a good full and plenty of way. When she was almost ashore on the lee jetty we shot up dead to windward across the channel and then, as she lost way, filled away for another go. She made it handily, and we rounded up to an anchor in the Pond.

Then the jib came off and was spread out in the big cockpit to dry, the mainsail was shaken out and furled, and the tarpaulin went up over the forward end of the cockpit to keep out the wind. Out came the jar of wooden matches, wet outside but dry on the inside, and the single-burner alcohol stove was lighted. Pretty soon we had hot tea and pilot crackers, with enough of the latter to throw some to the geese that always come begging alongside in Cuttyhunk.

Thus fortified, we hove the light dinghy that was stowed on the foredeck overside and rowed ashore. It was almost sunset, so we hurried to climb the hill. First along the beach past the Coast Guard boathouse; then up the narrow, cement sidewalk past the little power station with its faithful diesel; on up alongside the "Poplars," where guests are always pitching horseshoes in the lee of the building; by the snug cottages, the store, and the always-closed library; and then to the final climb to the top. Once clear of the tiny village, it is hard—no, impossible—not to look back and down at the Pond to see how small the climb has made the boat. She is always smaller than you think she will be.

But on to the top to catch the sunset. Cuttyhunk always seems like a mountain, though it rises, I suppose, only some 150 feet above the water. Look southwest, to windward: the two lightships are on either bow of the island, escorting her through a quieting, reddening sea. Look north across Buzzards Bay: the mainland is a far-off purple line. Look east, to leeward: our island is leading a whole column of islands, splitting the water inside the Vineyard into the Bay inshore and the Sound offshore. And look to the south'ard, where we have sailed today: there are the last red rays of the sun on Gay Head. That could be the face of Tashtego, the Indian harpooner, outlined on the high, stony cliff. Is that speck the *Babe* returning?

I hope the Gay Headers got a good catch. Out beyond, where No Man's Land lies, we can see only the darkening Atlantic.

"Well," said Dave as we started back down the hill, "that was a good sail out there, but I don't know why you had to reef her down this morning."

"Well," said I, falling into step, "I guess I was a little cautious. Next time, let's not pick a busting sou'wester to go to No Man's. Anyway, we both forgot to set the riding light, down aboard."

Index